major hazard control

A practical manual

major hazard control
A practical manual

An ILO contribution to the
International Programme on Chemical Safety of UNEP,
ILO, WHO (IPCS)

International Labour Office   Geneva

ISBN 92-2-106432-8

First published 1988

Second impression 1990

The documents on pages 129 to 252 are British Crown copyright. Reproduced by permission of the Controller of Her Britannic Majesty's Stationery Office.

ILO publications can be obtained through major booksellers or ILO local offices in many countries, or direct from ILO Publications, International Labour Office, CH-1211 Geneva 22, Switzerland. A catalogue or list of new publications will be sent free of charge from the above address.

Preface

Fires, explosions and the release of toxic gases can cause deaths and injuries to workers and the public, result in the evacuation of communities and adversely affect the environment as a whole. Disasters that have come to be known as "Basel", "Bhopal", "Flixborough", "Mexico City" and "Seveso" gave rise to the terms "major hazards" and "major hazard control"; the prevention and control of major hazards have subsequently become a pressing issue in all parts of the world. This manual on major hazard control is a response to the public discussion on how to prevent major accidents. Its preparation was recommended by a tripartite ad hoc meeting of special consultants convened by the International Labour Office in 1985, after the major accident in Bhopal.

The potential for major accidents caused by the increasing production, storage and use of dangerous substances implies that a well-defined and systematic approach is required if major disasters are to be avoided. This manual is therefore designed to deal with the safety aspects of siting, planning, design, construction and operation of plants. It explains how to identify major hazard installations and describes all the components of a major hazard control system. Because of the potential adverse effects of major accidents on both workers and the community, extensive information is provided on planning for emergencies, both on site and in the surrounding neighbourhood.

The day-to-day application of safety and health practices is part of normal plant operation and is therefore not covered in this manual. Also not taken into account are hazards associated with nuclear industrial activities and national and international transport of dangerous goods, because the management and legislative control of these activities are generally treated separately.

The manual aims at assisting all countries which are considering major hazard control. The system described is applicable to countries where certain aspects of major hazard control are already in operation and to those which intend, for the first time, to develop a programme for controlling major hazards. In particular, factory inspectorates, managements of major hazard installations, trade unions and local authorities, as well as the police, fire stations, hospitals and emergency units, will find this manual indispensable.

This book is the result of a collaborative effort on the part of the ILO and several experts. The Office wishes to thank the consultants, Dr.-Ing. D. Hesel, TÜV Rheinland, Federal Republic of Germany; Dr. C. A. W. A. Husmann, Directorate General of Labour, Ministry of Social Affairs and Employment, the Netherlands; and Dr. A. F. Ellis, United Kingdom, in his capacity as an ILO expert in the field of major hazard control.

G. R. Kliesch,

Director,
Working Conditions and Environment Department

Scope

This manual identifies and discusses the various components of a major hazard control system. It is written particularly for those countries which are considering such controls for the first time. However, it should be useful for many other countries with major hazard works that have some degree of major hazard control already in operation, although not yet representing the comprehensive package which is now part of the legislation adopted by the member States of the European Communities (EC).

The manual recognises that the achievement of major hazard control is usually the result of a step-by-step approach, and priorities for progress are identified consistent with this policy.

These priorities will involve government authorities and factory inspectorates both centrally and locally, works managements and trade unions, in addition to the various organisations which may be involved with emergency planning – police, fire authorities, hospitals, and so on.

Contents

Figures

Tables

1. Introduction

The rapid growth in the use of hazardous chemicals in industry and trade has brought about a very significant increase in the number of people, both workers and members of the general public, whose life could be endangered at any one time by an accident involving these chemicals. The rapid pace of progress in modern technology allows less opportunity for learning by trial and error, making it increasingly necessary to get design and operating procedures right the first time. However, safeguards in the chemical industry are not limited to the factory floor alone. Public concern at multiple injuries and deaths from spectacular events such as a major explosion invariably leads to calls for additional controls at national and international levels. It is therefore important, particularly for projects involving the storage and use of hazardous chemicals, to address both on-site and off-site safety when deciding on the safety measures to be applied.

This chapter discusses the definition of major industrial hazards, their types and consequences and the components of their control systems. Mention is made of the types of industrial activities that are excluded from the scope of this manual.

1.1. Major industrial hazards

Sixty thousand inhabitants were evacuated as a result of fire involving ammonium nitrate in France in October 1987. Fire involving methane caused four fatalities and one injury in Italy in April 1987. In Bulgaria a vinyl chloride explosion resulted in 17 deaths and 19 injuries in November 1986. An explosion involving fireworks killed 11 and injured eight in the Philippines in April 1986. In February 1986 a chlorine leak in the United States injured 76 persons. These cases are but a sample of recent reported events.

More disastrous events may also be cited. These include the release of the chemical methyl isocyanate in Bhopal, India, in 1984, resulting in over 2,000 fatalities and 200,000 injuries. Two weeks earlier was the explosion of liquefied petroleum gas (LPG) in Mexico City, resulting in 650 deaths and several thousand injuries. An explosion of propane gas in Ortuella, Spain, also resulted in 51 fatalities and many injuries in 1980. In 1976, 30 people were injured and 220,000 persons

evacuated from local villages when a process malfunction resulted in a small release of the chemical dioxin in Seveso, Italy. A cyclohexane explosion at Flixborough in the United Kingdom in 1974 killed 28, and injured 89, persons. The economic damage resulting from all these events and many others is huge.

Although these cases may have differed in the way they happened and the chemicals that were involved, they shared a common feature: they were uncontrolled events involving fires, explosions or releases of toxic substances that either resulted in the death and injury of a large number of people inside and outside the plant or caused extensive property and environmental damage, or both. The storage and use of flammable, explosive or toxic chemicals having the potential to cause such disasters are generally referred to as major hazards. This potential, therefore, is a function both of the inherent nature of the chemical and the quantity that is present on site.

In recent years much effort has been devoted to the development of legislation controlling major hazards. Most notable is that of the Council of the European Communities (EC) which in 1982 issued a Directive on major accident hazards of certain industrial activities. This defined the term "major accident" as "an occurrence such as a major emission, fire or explosion resulting from uncontrolled developments in the course of an industrial activity, leading to a serious danger to man, immediate or delayed, inside or outside the establishment, and to the environment, and involving one or more dangerous substances".

1.2. Types and consequences of major industrial hazards

Major industrial hazards are generally associated with the potential for fire, explosion or dispersion of toxic chemicals and usually involve the release of material from containment followed, in the case of volatile materials, by its vaporisation and dispersion. Accidents involving major hazards could include:

- leakage of flammable material, mixing of the material with air, formation of a flammable vapour cloud and drifting of the cloud to a source of ignition, leading to a fire or an explosion affecting the site and possibly populated areas;

— leakage of toxic material, formation of a toxic vapour cloud and drifting of the cloud, affecting directly the site and possibly populated areas.

In the case of the release of flammable materials, the greatest danger arises from the sudden massive escape of volatile liquids, or gases, producing a large cloud of flammable and possibly explosive vapour (United Kingdom Health and Safety Commission, 1976). If this cloud were ignited, the effects of combustion would depend on many factors, including wind speed and the extent to which the cloud was diluted with air. Such hazards could lead to large numbers of casualties and wholesale damage on site and beyond its boundaries. Nevertheless, even for severe accidents the effect is generally limited to a few hundred metres from the site.

The sudden release of very large quantities of toxic materials has the potential to cause deaths and severe injuries at a much greater distance. In theory, such a release could, in certain weather conditions, produce lethal concentrations at several kilometres from the point of release, but the actual number of casualties would depend on the population density in the path of the cloud and the effectiveness of the emergency arrangements, which might include evacuation.

Some installations or groups of installations pose both types of threat. Moreover, blast and missiles from an explosion can affect the integrity of other plants containing flammable and toxic materials, thereby causing an escalation of the disaster, which is sometimes referred to as the "domino effect". This situation may exist where industry is situated in groups because of the attraction of power, water or a pool of suitable labour. Such grouping can facilitate the transfer of supplies and products from one site to another. Indeed, it is not uncommon to find three or more separate but contiguous installations presenting a combination of explosion and toxic hazards along a river bank or an estuary or near housing developments.

The release of flammable or toxic materials to the atmosphere may therefore lead to an explosion, a fire or the formation of a toxic cloud, which are now considered in more detail.

1.2.1. Explosions

Explosions are characterised by a shock-wave which can be heard as a bang and which can cause damage to buildings, breaking windows and ejecting missiles over distances of several hundred metres. The injuries and damage are in the first place caused by the shock-wave of the explosion itself. People are blown over or knocked down and buried under collapsed buildings or injured by flying glass. Although the effects of over-pressure can directly result in deaths, this would be likely to involve only those working in the direct vicinity of the explosion. The history of industrial explosions shows that the indirect effects of collapsing buildings, flying glass and debris cause far more loss of life and severe injuries.

The effects of the shock-wave vary depending on the characteristics of the material, the quantity involved and the degree of confinement of the vapour cloud. The peak pressures in an explosion therefore vary between a slight over-pressure and a few hundred kilopascals (kPa). Direct injury to people occurs at pressures of 5-10 kPa (with loss of life generally occurring at a greater over-pressure), whereas dwellings are demolished and windows and doors broken at pressures of as low as 3-10 kPa. The pressure of the shock-wave decreases rapidly with the increase in distance from the source of the explosion. As an example, the explosion of a tank containing 50 tonnes of propane results in a pressure of 14 kPa at 250 metres and a pressure of 5 kPa at 500 metres from the tank.

1.2.1.1. Deflagration and detonation

Explosions can occur either in the form of a deflagration or a detonation, depending on the burning velocity during the explosion. Deflagration occurs when the burning velocity or the flame speed is relatively slow, of the order of 1 m/sec. In a detonation the flame speed is extremely high. The flame front travels as a shock-wave, with a typical velocity of 2,000-3,000 m/sec. A detonation generates greater pressures and is far more destructive than a deflagration. The peak pressure caused by a deflagration in a closed atmospheric vessel reaches about 70-80 kPa, whereas a detonation can easily reach a pressure of 200 kPa. Whether a deflagration or a detonation takes place depends on the material involved as well as the conditions under which the explosion occurs. It is generally accepted that a vapour phase explosion requires some degree of confinement for a detonation to take place.

1.2.1.2. Gas and dust explosions

The distinction between gas and dust explosions can be made on the basis of the material involved. Generally catastrophic gas explosions happen when considerable quantities of flammable material are released and dispersed with air to form an explosive vapour cloud before ignition takes place. Dust explosions occur when flammable solid materials are intensively mixed with air. The dispersed solid material is in the form of powder with very small particle sizes. The explosion occurs following an initiating event such as a fire or a small explosion that causes powder that has settled on surfaces to become airborne. Upon mixing with air the result is a secondary explosion which in turn can create a tertiary explosion, and so on. In the past, these subsequent series of explosions have led to catastrophes and the destruction of complete factories. Because grain, milk powder and flour are flammable, dust explosions have been more common in the agricultural industry. However, the history of dust explosions, particularly those in recent years, has shown that the damaging effects are generally confined to the workplace rather than to those living outside the plant.

1.2.1.3. Confined and unconfined vapour-cloud explosions

Confined explosions are those which occur within some sort of containment such as a vessel or pipe-work. Explosions in buildings also come under this category. Explosions which occur in the open air are referred to as unconfined explosions and produce peak pressures of only a few kPa. The peak pressures of confined explosions are generally higher and may reach hundreds of kPa. A list of some industrial explosions appears in table 1. All the examples given are vapour-cloud explosions which, in some cases, led to detonation due to the confinement of the gas cloud.

1.2.2. Fires

The effects of fire on people take the form of skin burns due to exposure to thermal radiation. The severity of the burns depends on the intensity of the heat and the exposure time. Heat radiation is inversely proportional to the square of the distance

Table 1. Examples of industrial explosions

Chemical involved	Consequences		Place and date
	Deaths	Injuries	
Dimethylether	245	3 800	Ludwigshafen, Federal Republic of Germany, 1948
Kerosene	32	16	Bitburg, Federal Republic of Germany, 1954
Isobutane	7	13	Lake Charles, Louisiana, United States, 1967
Oil slops	2	85	Pernis, Netherlands, 1968
Propylene	–	230	East St. Louis, Illinois, United States, 1972
Propane	7	152	Decatur, Illinois, United States, 1974
Cyclohexane	28	89	Flixborough, United Kingdom, 1974
Propylene	14	107	Beek, Netherlands, 1975

from the source. In general terms the skin withstands a heat energy of 10 kW/m^2 for approximately 5 seconds and that of 30 kW/m^2 for only 0.4 seconds before pain is felt.

Fires occur in industry more frequently than explosions and toxic releases, although the consequences in terms of loss of life are generally less. Therefore, fire might be considered as having less major hazard potential than explosions and toxic releases. However, if the ignition of escaping flammable material is delayed, an unconfined vapour cloud of flammable material may be formed. Such an occurrence was considered in subsection 1.2.1.

Fires can take several different forms, including jet fires, pool fires, flash fires and boiling liquid expanding vapour explosions (BLEVEs). A jet fire would appear as a long narrow flame produced, for example, from an ignited gas pipeline leak. A pool fire would be produced, for example, if a release of crude oil from a storage tank into a bund ignited. A flash fire could occur if an escape of gas reached a source of ignition and rapidly burnt back to the source of the release. The BLEVE is generally far more serious than the other fires and is described below in greater detail.

Another lethal effect that must be considered in case of fire is the depletion of oxygen in the atmosphere due to the consumption of oxygen in the combustion process – generally this is limited to the immediate vicinity of the fire. Of importance also are the health effects arising from exposure to the fumes generated as a result of fire. These fumes may include toxic gases, such as sulphur dioxide from the combustion of carbon disulphide and nitrous oxides from a fire involving ammonium nitrate.

1.2.2.1. Boiling liquid expanding vapour explosion (BLEVE)

Sometimes referred to as a fireball, a BLEVE is a combination of fire and explosion with an intense radiant heat emission within a relatively short time interval. As implied by the term, the phenomenon can occur within a vessel or tank in which a liquefied gas is kept above its atmospheric boiling-point. If a pressure-vessel fails as a result of a weakening of its structure, the contents are instantaneously released from the vessel as a turbulent mixture of liquid and gas, expanding rapidly and dispersing in air as a cloud. When this cloud is ignited, a fireball occurs, causing an enormous heat-radiation intensity within a few seconds. This heat intensity is sufficient to cause severe skin burns and deaths at several hundred metres from the vessel, depending on the quantity of the gas involved. A BLEVE can therefore be caused by a physical impact on a vessel or tank which is already overstressed or damaged, for example from a traffic accident with a tank-car or a derailment of a tank-wagon, or it can be caused by fire impinging upon or engulfing a vessel and thus weakening its structure. A BLEVE involving a 50-tonne propane tank can cause third-degree injuries at distances of approximately 200 metres and blisters at approximately 400 metres.

A list of some major fires is given in table 2.

Sometimes it is difficult to make a distinction

Table 2. Examples of major fires

Chemical involved	Consequences		Place and date
	Deaths	Injuries	
Methane	136	77	Cleveland, Ohio, United States, 1944
LPG [1] (BLEVE)	18	90	Feyzin, France, 1966
LNG [2]	40	–	Staten Island, New York, United States, 1973
Methane	52	–	Santa Cruz, Mexico, 1978
LPG (BLEVE)	650	2 500	Mexico City, Mexico, 1985

[1] Liquefied petroleum gas.   [2] Liquefied natural gas.

between a fire and an explosion. Quite often an explosion is followed by a fire, and the casualties are caused by both phenomena.

1.2.3. Toxic releases

There are large numbers of chemicals with which particular care needs to be taken to prevent them from having harmful effects on workers. The major discipline of occupational hygiene exists to develop the methods necessary to control exposure to these chemicals, possibly over as long a period as the working lifetime of a plant operator. This is of fundamental importance to workers' safety. The effects of toxic chemicals when considering major hazards, on the other hand, are quite different and are concerned with acute exposure during and soon after a major accident rather than with long-term chronic exposure. In other words, this manual considers the storage and use of toxic chemicals, often in very large quantities which, if released, would disperse with the wind and have the potential to kill or injure people living many hundreds of metres away from the plant, and being unable to escape or find shelter.

The toxicity of chemicals is commonly determined by using four major methods. These are incident studies, epidemiological studies, animal experiments and micro-organism tests. Despite their obvious value, these methods all suffer from weaknesses which are outside the scope of this manual, but which mean that caution should be exercised in the interpretation of results. Other factors also affect the toxicity of chemicals – for instance age, sex, genetic background, ethnic grouping, nutrition, fatigue, diseases, exposure to other substances with synergistic effects, and hours and patterns of work.

Although toxicity data are not abundant, the toxicity of certain chemicals has been established. Chlorine, for example, is known to be dangerous to human health at concentrations of 10-20 parts per million (ppm) for an exposure of 30 minutes. The gas becomes fatal at concentrations of 100-150 ppm with exposure durations of 5-10 minutes. Exposure to chlorine for shorter periods can be fatal at concentrations of 1,000 ppm. As far as the consequences of a chlorine release are concerned, it is known that an instantaneous release of 10 tonnes of this chemical may produce a maximum concentration of 140 ppm at a distance of 2 km downwind from the source and of 15 ppm at a distance of 5 km in D5 weather conditions (normal non-inversion weather).

Table 3 lists some major industrial accidents involving toxic releases of different chemicals, some of which caused fatalities. Chlorine and ammonia are the toxic chemicals most commonly used in major hazard quantities and both have a history of major accidents. None the less, other chemicals, such as methyl isocyanate and dioxin, must be used with particular care in view of their higher toxicity, even though they may be handled in lesser quantities. For this reason, a number of these very toxic chemicals have been included in the so-called "Seveso Directive" of the EC (see Appendix 1).

Table 3. Examples of major toxic releases

Chemical involved	Consequences		Place and date
	Deaths	Injuries	
Phosgene	10	–	Poza Rica, Mexico, 1950
Chlorine	7	–	Wilsum, Federal Republic of Germany, 1952
Dioxin/TCDD	–	–	Seveso, Italy, 1976
Ammonia	30	25	Cartagena, Colombia, 1977
Sulphur dioxide	–	100	Baltimore, Maryland, United States, 1978
Hydrogen sulphide	8	29	Chicago, Illinois, United States, 1978
Methyl isocyanate	2 000	200 000	Bhopal, India, 1984

1.3. Components of a major hazard control system

Section 1.2 has described the variety of major accidents that can take place, leading to the concept of a "major hazard" as an industrial activity requiring controls over and above those applied in normal factory operations, in order to protect both workers and people living and working outside. These controls form an integrated package – a major hazard control system – which aims not only at preventing accidents but also, and most importantly, at mitigating the consequences of any accidents which do take place.

Because of the complexity of the industrial activities concerned, major hazard control needs to be based on a systematic approach.

The basic components of this system are:

(a) *Identification of major hazard installations.* It is necessary to identify the installations which, according to the definition, may fall within the criteria set for the classification of major hazard installations. Governmental authorities and management should institute the identification of major hazard installations on a priority basis. Identification may be done in accordance with the guidance set out in Chapter 2, which also provides a shortlist of 20 priority substances for this purpose.

(b) *Information about the installation.* Once the major hazard installations have been identified, additional information needs to be collected about their design and operation. In addition, such information must also describe all other hazards specific to the installation. Because of the likely complexity of the installation, the information should be gathered and arranged systematically, and should be accessible to all parties concerned within the industry, such as management and workers, and outside the industry, such as the governmental bodies which may require it for licensing and inspection purposes. In order to achieve a complete description of the hazards, it may be necessary to carry out safety studies and hazard assessments to discover possible process failures and to set priorities during the process of hazard assessment. Rapid ranking methods may be used to select the units which require a more thorough assessment. In section 3.5 and Appendix 6 the contents of such a study are described in the form of a safety report. An example of a rapid ranking method to classify units according to their hazard appears in Appendix 2.

(c) *Action inside the industrial activity.* In addition to preparing a report, management has the primary responsibility of operating and maintaining a safe plant. A sound safety policy is required. Technical inspection, maintenance, plant modification, training and selection of suitable personnel must be carried out according to sound procedures. In addition to the preparation of the safety report, accidents should be investigated and reports submitted to the authorities. Lessons should be learnt from accidents and near misses. For further details concerning the role of management, reference should be made to sections 3.1 to 3.5.

(d) *Actions by the governmental authorities.* Assessment of the hazards for the purposes of licensing, where appropriate, inspection and enforcement of legislation are the responsibility of government in the control of major hazards. Land-use planning can appreciably reduce the potential for a disaster and will probably come under government control. The training of factory inspectors, including chemical inspectors, is also an important government role. More on the role of the authorities appears in Chapter 4.

(e) *Emergency planning.* All previous elements focus on the prevention of the occurrence of major accidents. Emergency planning aims at the reduction of the consequences of major accidents, and assumes that absolute safety cannot be guaranteed. In setting up emergency planning, a distinction is made between on-site and off-site planning. A well-structured and clear plan is one which is based on a well-prepared safety report and which can be quickly and effectively employed when a major accident occurs. More details on emergency planning are provided in Chapter 6.

1.4. Exclusions

Although certain parts will be applicable to a wider range of industrial activities, this manual considers the control of industrial major hazards as described in section 1.1. The controls necessary for the transport of hazardous chemicals are excluded, since their control and management are quite different from those of static sites.

Also excluded from the scope of this manual are nuclear hazards and those of a strictly military nature, both of which are likely to have existing comprehensive controls of their own.

2. Identification of major hazard installations

Any major hazard control system is concerned with priorities which may reasonably differ from one country to another. Resources are always likely to be limited both within the various authorities and within industry, and therefore the special attention that is demanded for major hazard control should be directed at the priority areas.

It is clearly inappropriate to consider all possible industrial processes which could result in injury or death and to call them all major hazards. The final list would be enormous and unmanageable in any country (developed or developing).

Major hazards usually need to be defined by means of a list of hazardous substances with associated trigger quantities, in such a way that the industrial installations brought within the scope of the definition as major hazard works are recognised as those requiring priority attention, i.e. they have the potential for causing a very serious incident which is likely to affect people both on and off site.

2.1. Identification: Purpose and procedures

Identification of major hazards is the starting-point for a system of control and, once such works have been identified, the agenda is set for implementing the various components of the system. Identification will show which hazardous materials are most commonly available in major hazard quantities, therefore requiring priority attention by the group of experts (subsection 7.3.1). Where licences are being sought for new major hazards, the authorities (the factory inspectorate) may require sufficient additional information (section 3.5) to enable the application to be properly considered. A start can be made on the other components described in later chapters (e.g. emergency planning).

Although a substance/quantity definition of major hazards is likely to be the method of defining a major hazard in most if not all countries, the identification of works from this definition will depend on local circumstances and is discussed in section 7.2. Making it a statutory requirement for the major hazard works management to notify the authorities of the activity is likely to be the method

most commonly chosen, but alternatives – based, for example, on factory inspectorate records – may be appropriate.

The definition of a major hazard for any country may need to be amended as experience and knowledge are accumulated on both existing and new hazards and on the history of major accidents since the substance/quantity definition was established.

2.2. Major hazard installations under the EC Directive

Following serious incidents in the chemical industry in Europe in the last two decades, specific legislation covering major hazard activities was developed in various countries in Western Europe. A key feature in the legislation was the obligation of the employer of a major hazard industrial activity to submit information about the activity and its hazards based on the results of systematic safety studies. After the accident in Seveso (Italy) in 1976, the major hazard regulations in the various countries were put together and integrated in an EC Directive. This Directive, on the major accident hazards of certain industrial activities, has been in force since 1984 and is often referred to as the Seveso Directive.

For the purpose of identifying major hazard installations, the EC Directive uses certain criteria. These criteria are based on the toxic, flammable and explosive properties of the chemicals, as described in table 4.

For the selection of specific major hazard industrial activities, a list of substances and threshold limits is provided. This list appears in Appendix 1. An industrial activity is defined by the Directive as the aggregate of all installations within a distance of 500 metres of each other and belonging to the same factory/plant. When the quantity of the substances present exceeds the given threshold limit appearing in the list, the activity is referred to as a major hazard installation. The list of substances consists of 180 chemicals, whereas the threshold limits vary between 1 kg for extremely toxic substances to 50,000 tonnes for highly flammable liquids. For isolated storage of substances, a separate list of a few substances is given.

Table 4. EC Directive criteria for major hazard installations

Toxic substances (very toxic and toxic):

Substances showing the following values of acute toxicity and having physical and chemical properties capable of entailing major accident hazards:

	LD50 oral, rat mg/kg	LD50 cut, rat/rab mg/kg	LC50, ihl, 4hr, rat mg/l
1.	LD50 < 5	LD < 1	LC50 < 0.10
2.	5 < LD50 < 25	10 < LD50 < 50	0.1 < LC50 < 0.5
3.	25 < LD50 < 200	50 < LD50 < 400	0.5 < LC50 < 2

Flammable substances:

1. Flammable gases: substances which in the gaseous state at normal pressure and mixed with air become flammable and the boiling-point of which at normal pressure is 20° C or below.

2. Highly flammable liquids: substances which have a flash-point lower than 21° C and the boiling-point of which at normal pressure is above 20° C.

3. Flammable liquids: substances which have a flash-point lower than 55° C and which remain liquid under pressure, where particular processing conditions, such as high pressure and high temperature, may create major accident hazards.

Explosive substances:

Substances which may explode under the effect of flame or which are more sensitive to shocks or friction than dinitrobenzene.

In addition to flammable gases, liquids and explosives, the list contains chemicals such as ammonia, chlorine, sulphur dioxide and acrylonitrile.

2.3. Scope for priorities

For a major hazard control system to achieve its objectives, it must be capable of being applied. In order to facilitate the application of the system and to encourage the authorities and management to apply it, it must be priority-oriented, with attention being focused on the more hazardous installations.

Setting of priorities can be achieved by various methods and techniques. One way to do this is by concentrating on fewer chemicals than are currently in the EC definition. The list of chemicals appearing in Appendix 1 can therefore be shortened so as to give prominence to the more hazardous chemical sites. A suggested list of priorities is given in table 5.

With the chemicals shown in table 5 acting as a guide, a list of installations can be identified. If the list is still too big to be coped with by the

authorities, new priorities can be set by means of setting new quantity thresholds. Priority setting can also be used inside the factory to identify the more hazardous parts using rapid ranking methods, for example.

These are based on a short survey of the industrial activity as a whole or in part. This establishes numerical factors which are incorporated in the calculation of a "safety index" giving an indication of the magnitude of the major hazard. This method is described in Appendix 2. It is somewhat laborious and great care should be taken in its interpretation.

2.4. Typical major hazard installations

In view of the diversity and complexity of industry in general, it is not possible to restrict major hazard installations to certain sectors of industrial activity. Experience, however, indicates

Table 5. Priority chemicals used in identifying major hazard installations

Name of substance	Quantity (>)	EC list serial number
General flammable substances:		
Flammable gases	200 t	124
Highly flammable liquids	50 000 t	125
Specific flammable substances:		
Hydrogen	50 t	24
Ethylene oxide	50 t	25
Specific explosives:		
Ammonium nitrate	2 500 t	146 b
Nitroglycerine	10 t	132
Trinitrotoluene	50 t	145
Specific toxic substances:		
Acrylonitrile	200 t	18
Ammonia	500 t	22
Chlorine	25 t	16
Sulphur dioxide	250 t	148
Hydrogen sulphide	50 t	17
Hydrogen cyanide	20 t	19
Carbon disulphide	200 t	20
Hydrogen fluoride	50 t	94
Hydrogen chloride	250 t	149
Sulphur trioxide	75 t	180
Specific very toxic substances:		
Methyl isocyanate	150 kg	36
Phosgene	750 kg	15

that major hazard installations are most commonly associated with the following activities:

(a) petrochemical works and refineries;

(b) chemical works and chemical production plants;

(c) LPG storage and terminals;

(d) stores and distribution centres for chemicals;

(e) large fertiliser stores;

(f) explosives factories; and

(g) works in which chlorine is used in bulk quantities.

3. The role of management

Major hazard installations have to be operated to a very high standard of safety. This is the duty of management. In addition, management holds a key role in the organisation and implementation of a major hazard control system. In particular, management has the responsibility to –

(a) provide the information required to identify major hazard installations;

(b) carry out the hazard assessment;

(c) report to the authorities on the results of the hazard assessment;

(d) set up an emergency plan;

(e) take measures to improve plant safety.

Figure 1 summarises the duties a manufacturer has to fulfil in the major hazard control system.

First and foremost, the management of an installation which can cause a major accident has a duty to control this major hazard. To do this, it must be aware of the nature of the hazard, of the events that cause accidents and of the potential consequences of such accidents. This means that, in order to control a major hazard successfully,

management must have answers to the following questions:

(a) Do toxic, explosive or flammable substances in our facility constitute a major hazard?

(b) Which failures or errors can cause abnormal conditions leading to a major accident?

(c) If a major accident occurs, what are the consequences of a fire, an explosion or a toxic release for the employees, people living outside the factory, the plant or the environment?

(d) What can management do to prevent these accidents happening?

(e) What can be done to mitigate the consequences of an accident?

3.1. Assessment of hazards

The most appropriate way of answering these questions is to carry out a hazard assessment, the purpose of which is to understand why accidents occur and how they can be avoided or at least mitigated.

A properly conducted assessment will therefore

Figure 1. The role of management in major hazard control systems

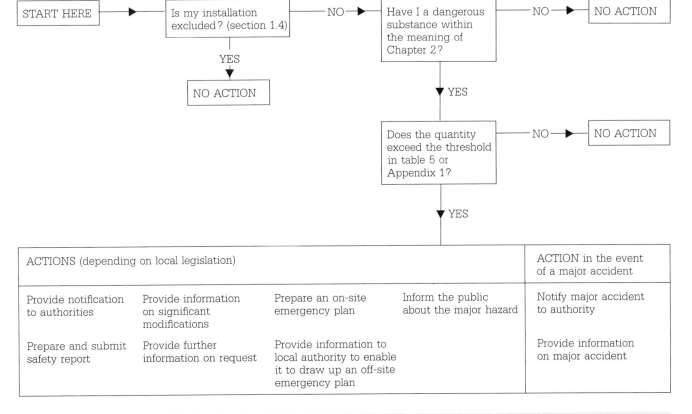

(a) analyse the existing safety concept or develop a new one;

(b) identify the remaining hazards; and

(c) develop optimum measures for technical and organisational protection in the event of abnormal plant operation.

Methods which can be used for an assessment, and their application, are described below.

3.1.1. Methods of hazard assessment

To achieve the aims of a hazard assessment, it is necessary to follow certain procedures or use certain aids. A number of working methods have been developed for this purpose. These are summarised in table 6.

Of the methods listed in table 6, a detailed discussion is given on two which are complementary to one another. These are:

– preliminary hazard analysis (PHA); and

– hazard and operability study (HAZOP).

A brief account will follow of two other methods used to determine the frequency of occurrence of an accident. These are the "fault tree analysis" and the "accident sequence analysis". Their application in a hazard assessment should be limited to a small number of special cases.

This section concludes with a discussion of the "accident consequence analysis", which is used in describing the damage that would result if an accident occurred.

3.1.1.1. Preliminary hazard analysis (PHA)

The PHA is performed as the first step in a hazard assessment. It starts with the type of accident involving toxic, flammable and explosive materials. The procedure specifies the system elements (plant components such as storage tanks, reaction vessels) or event (overloading of a tank, runaway reaction) that can lead to a hazardous condition.

Once the hazardous systems have been identified, the events that may lead to the accident must be specified. Events such as "the formation of an explosive atmosphere outside or inside a storage vessel" or "the release of a toxic gas" will need to be examined so as to identify the components of the plant that can cause the accident. The components, which include storage tanks, reaction vessels, pipes, pumps, stirrers, relief valves or other systems, will then be singled out for a more detailed examination by other evaluation methods such as the HAZOP.

The results of the PHA are recorded on a form as shown in table 7.

Since the PHA is fast and cost-effective, and since it identifies key problems, hazard evaluation should always start with this method.

Its results indicate which systems or procedures require further analysis and which systems are of less interest from a major hazard point of view. In this way it is possible to limit the evaluation to key problems, thus avoiding unnecessary effort.

Table 6. Working methods for hazard assessment

Method	Purpose	Aim	Working principle
1. Preliminary hazard analysis 2. Matrix diagrams of interactions 3. Use of check-lists	1. Identification of hazards	1. Completeness of safety concept	1. Use of "thinking aids"
4. Failure effect analysis 5. Hazard and operability study			2. Use of "searching aids" and schematic documentation
6. Accident sequence analysis (inductive) 7. Fault tree analysis (deductive)	2. Assessment of hazards according to their occurrence frequency	2. Optimisation of reliability and availability of safety systems	3. Graphic description of failure sequences and mathematical calculation of probabilities
8. Accident consequence analysis	3. Assessment of accident consequences	3. Mitigation of con-sequences and development of optimum emergency plans	4. Mathematical modelling of physical and chemical processes

Table 7. Preliminary hazard analysis in an LPG storage plant

Accident	System	Hazard	Safety-relevant component
Vapour explosion	Storage vessel	Formation of an explosive atmosphere outside storage vessel due to:	
		– faulty safety valve	Safety valve
		– corroded vessel	Vessel, corrosion protection
		– overpressure	Pressure gauge, temperature gauge, sprinkler system, safety valve

3.1.1.2. Hazard and operability study (HAZOP)

Once a PHA has established the systems or events that could cause a major hazard, it is necessary to consider which deviations from normal operation in these systems, or which operational malfunctions, could lead to such hazardous events. In order to do this, a closer look into the details of the system and its mode of operation becomes essential. The hazard and operability study enables us to do this. This method is described in detail in Appendix 3.

(a) *Basic concept*

The HAZOP examines fully the process, or at least those parts of the process, that have been classified as "relevant" in the PHA. It systematically questions every part of the process in order to discover how deviations from the intention of the design can occur and decides whether these deviations can give rise to hazardous conditions.

The examination is focused on every part of the design in turn. Each part is subjected to a number of questions formulated around a series of guide words derived from method study techniques. In essence, the guide words are used to ensure that the questions, which are posed to test the integrity of each part of the design, will explore every conceivable way in which that design could deviate from the design intention. This usually produces a number of theoretical deviations and each deviation is then considered to decide how it could be caused and what would be the consequences.

Some of the causes may be unrealistic and so the derived consequences will be rejected as not meaningful. Some of the consequences may be trivial and would not be considered any further. However, there may be some deviations with both causes that are conceivable and consequences that are potentially serious. These are then noted for remedial action.

Having examined one part of the design and recorded any potential hazards associated with it, the study progresses to focus on the next part of the design. The examination is repeated until the whole plant has been studied.

The purpose of the examination is to identify all possible deviations from the way the design is intended to work and all the hazards associated with these deviations. In addition, some of the hazards can be resolved if the solution is obvious and is not likely to cause adverse effects on other parts of the design, a decision may be taken for the design to be modified on the spot. This, however, is not always possible, particularly where, for example, it may be necessary to obtain further information. Thus the output from examinations normally consists of a mixture of decisions and questions for answering at subsequent meetings.

(b) *A simple example*

To illustrate the principles of the examination procedure, consider a plant in which chemicals A and B react together to form a product C, and assume that the chemistry of the process is such that the concentration of raw material B must never exceed that of A, otherwise an explosion may occur.

Referring to figure 2, let us start, say, with the pipeline extending from the suction side of the pump which delivers raw material A to where it enters the reaction vessel (see Appendix 3 for an explanation of the guide words).

The intention defines how the part is expected to operate. This can take a number of forms and can be either descriptive or diagrammatic. In many cases it will be a flowsheet or line diagram. In our example, the intention is partly described by the flowsheet and partly by the process control requirements to transfer A at some specified rate. The first deviation is that obtained by applying the guide words NOT, DON'T or NO to the intention. This is combined with the intention to give

DON'T TRANSFER A.

Figure 2.   An example of a simple flowsheet

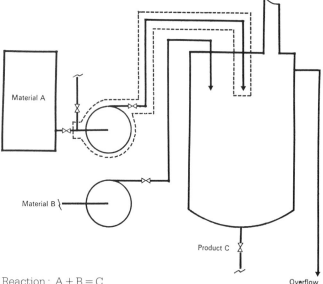

Reaction: A + B = C
Component B must not exceed Component A to avoid an explosion
The part of the plant examined is outlined thus - - - - - - - -

The flowsheet is then examined to establish the causes which might produce a complete cessation of flow of A. These causes could be –

(a) supply tank is empty;

(b) pump fails to turn:

- mechanical failure;

- electrical failure;

- pump is switched off, etc.;

(c) pipeline is fractured;

(d) isolation valve is closed.

Clearly at least some of these causes are conceivable and so this is a meaningful deviation.

Next we consider the consequences. A complete cessation of flow of A would very soon lead to an excess of B over A in the reaction vessel and consequently to a risk of explosion. A hazard is therefore discovered in the design and this is noted for further consideration.

The next guide word to apply is MORE. The deviation is:

MORE A IS PASSED INTO THE
REACTION VESSEL.

The cause would be that the characteristics of the pump may, under some circumstances, produce an excessive flow rate. If this cause is

accepted as realistic, the consequences are then considered:

(a) the reaction produces C contaminated with an excess of A which goes on into the next stage of the process;

(b) the excess flow into the reaction vessel means that some will leave the vessel by the overflow.

Further information will have to be obtained to decide whether these consequences would constitute a hazard.

In the same way, further guide words are applied until the pipeline which introduces raw material A has been examined. The examination then progresses to the next design part and is repeated for every part of the design.

3.1.1.3. Other methods of assessment

Methods of assessment which allow quantification of the likelihood of an accident and the risk associated with plant operation are based on the graphic description of accident sequences. This, for example, can be in the form of fault tree or event tree analysis, which is used to carry out a mathematical analysis of the accident sequences (Lambert, 1973; Fussell, 1976; Henley and Kumamoto, 1981).

These methods have been used to determine the reliability of electronic systems. They are also widely used in the nuclear industry, but they are not suitable for the general assessment of major hazards because of the substantial effort required for their use.

Should their application become necessary for certain parts of the process control, the publications cited above are recommended for details.

3.1.1.4. Accident consequence analysis

A hazard assessment is complete only if the consequences of a possible accident are known. For this reason, the last step of a hazard assessment is to analyse the consequences that a potential major accident could have on the plant itself, on the employees, on the neighbourhood and on the environment. The results of the analysis are used to determine which protective measures, such as fire-fighting systems, alarm systems or pressure-relief systems, have to be installed.

An accident consequence analysis should contain the following:

(a) a description of the accident (tank rupture, rupture of a pipe, failure of a safety valve, fire);

(b) an estimate of the quantity of material released (toxic, flammable, explosive);

(c) a calculation of the dispersion of the material released (gas or evaporating liquid);

(d) an estimate of the effects (toxic, heat radiation, blast wave).

While requirements (a) and (b) can be fulfilled using the results of the hazard assessment, models have to be applied to determine (c) and (d) (see Appendix 4).

3.2. Causes of major industrial accidents

The hazard assessment described in section 3.1 eventually leads to the identification of a number of potential hardware and software failures in and around the plant. Once these have been identified, the manufacturer has to determine whether or not something must be done about them.

To help the manufacturer in this procedure, the following sections give examples of typical failures followed by suitable control measures.

3.2.1. Component failure

The fundamental precondition for safe operation is that components can withstand the operational loads and thus enclose any potentially hazardous substances. Causes of failure include –

(a) inappropriate design against internal pressure, external forces, corrosive media and temperature;

(b) mechanical failure of vessels and pipe-work due to corrosion or external impact;

(c) failure of components such as pumps, compressors, blowers and stirrers;

(d) failure of control systems (pressure and temperature sensors, level controllers, flow-meters, control units, process computers);

(e) failure of safety systems (safety valves, bursting discs, pressure-relief systems, neutralisation systems, flare towers);

(f) failure of welds and flanges.

Each of these causes can lead to a major accident. If a hazard assessment has been carried out in the planning phase of the plant, management must decide which failures require additional safeguards and where the design must be changed or improved.

3.2.2. Deviations from normal operating conditions

While component failures can be avoided by careful design or maintenance, deviations from normal operating conditions require in-depth examination of operational procedures.

The following failures can occur, leading to deviations from normal operating conditions:

(a) failure in the monitoring of crucial process parameters (pressure, temperature, flow, quantity, mixing ratios) and in the processing of these parameters;

(b) failure in the manual supply of chemical components;

(c) failures in the utilities, such as:

   (i) insufficient coolant for exothermal reactions;

   (ii) insufficient steam or heating medium;

   (iii) no electricity;

   (iv) no nitrogen;

   (v) no compressed air (instrument air);

(d) failures in the shut-down or start-up procedures, which could lead to an explosive atmosphere within the plant;

(e) formation of side products, residues or impurities which could cause side reactions (polymerisation).

The consequences of these failures can be understood only after examination of the behaviour of the entire system in the event of such a failure. Counter-measures can be provided by reliable process control (automatic or manual), good operating procedures and a proper inspection and testing programme.

3.2.3. Human and organisational errors

Human ability to run a major hazard installation is of fundamental importance, not only for plants which require a lot of manual operation but also for highly automated plants requiring human intervention only in the case of an emergency.

Errors made by operating personnel, however, can be as diverse as their tasks in running the plant. Some of the most common errors are listed below:

(a) operator error (wrong button, wrong valve);

(b) disconnected safety systems because of frequent false alarms;

(c) mix-up of hazardous substances (material identification check);

(d) communication errors;

(e) incorrect repair or maintenance work;

(f) unauthorised welding.

These human errors occur because —

(a) the operating personnel are not aware of the hazards;

(b) the operating personnel are insufficiently trained for the job; or

(c) too much is expected from operating personnel.

To reduce human and organisational errors, careful selection of personnel and regular training in conjunction with clear operating instructions represent essential features in the management of personnel on major hazard sites.

3.2.4. Outside accidental interferences

A major accident in an installation can be caused not only by operational failures but also by external events which can influence the plant. These include accidents involving –

(a) road and rail transport (especially dangerous goods);

(b) ship traffic;

(c) loading stations for flammable/explosive substances;

(d) air traffic;

(e) neighbouring plants, especially those handling flammable/explosive substances; and

(f) mechanical impact such as that caused by a falling crane.

These accidents cannot always be avoided. They should, however, be considered when siting

the plant or when designing very sensitive parts of it.

3.2.5. Natural forces

Other external impacts may be caused by natural forces. The following are of importance:

(a) wind;

(b) flooding;

(c) earthquakes;

(d) settlement as the result of mining activities;

(e) extreme frost;

(f) extreme sun;

(g) lightning.

If such hazards are known to occur in the natural environment of the installation, precautions should be taken against them.

3.2.6. Acts of mischief or sabotage

Every major hazard installation can be a target for mischief or sabotage by plant personnel or from outside. Protection is difficult and will never be perfect. It should, however, be considered in the design.

3.2.7. Additional failures

Further information is available in the form of check-lists concerning additional failures which may cause accidents (American Institute of Chemical Engineers, 1985).

3.3. Safe operation of major hazard installations

Having discussed the evaluation of hazards and the causes of major accidents, it is necessary to give an idea of how the hazards should be controlled. This section therefore summarises the most important control systems and organisational measures which are widely used to control major hazards. A fuller description of the state of the art in the safety of LPG, anhydrous ammonia storage and bulk chlorine installations is provided in Appendix 5.

3.3.1. Plant component design

In view of the accidents that can occur as a result of improper component design, the following facts should be kept in mind. A component has to withstand the following:

(a) static loads;

(b) dynamic loads;

(c) internal and external pressure;

(d) corrosion;

(e) loads due to large differences in temperature;

(f) loads due to external impacts (wind, snow, earthquakes, settlement).

These loads may, but need not necessarily, be included in the approved design standards. Design standards are therefore a minimum requirement as far as major hazard installations are concerned. This is of particular importance for pressurised systems containing flammable, explosive or toxic gases or liquids above their boiling-points.

3.3.2. Operation and control

When an installation is designed to withstand all loads that can occur during normal or foreseen abnormal operating conditions, it is the task of a process control system to keep the plant safely within these limits. To achieve this, use may be made of systems such as –

– manual control;

– automatic control;

– automatic shut-down systems;

– safety devices;

– alarm systems.

The basic idea of an operational safety concept is to keep the plant or the process in a safe condition. Figure 3 shows how a control system keeps a process variable within safe limits when it leaves its normal range.

The controlled process variable could be temperature, pressure, flow rate, the mixing ratio of certain components, the rate of temperature rise or an increase or decrease in pressure. The three control or protection systems act as follows:

First system

As soon as the process variable exceeds the set limit value, this is signalled by the monitoring device and a control action (mostly manual) must be taken. If this action fails and the process is such that the process variable does not cause a hazardous condition, a further system is not necessary.

Second system

When the variable exceeds the limit value, the control system initiates an automatic action to bring the process variable back into its normal range. If the system fails to do so, the variable can reach a value which causes a hazardous condition.

If this is a possibility, other protection devices become necessary, e.g. rupture discs and safety valves acting as pressure-relief systems, overflow basins and cooling devices.

Figure 3. Sketch of the operation of safety devices

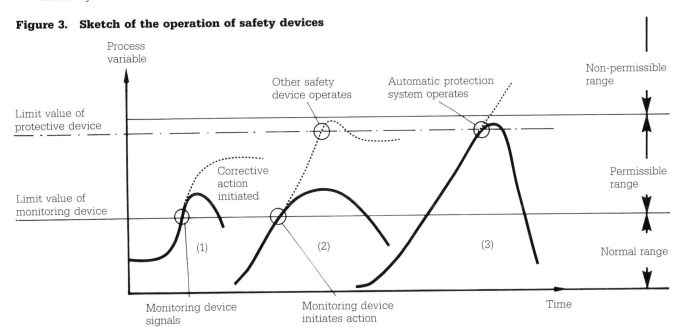

Third system

If no safety features such as those mentioned above are available or if hazardous conditions of the process variable can lead to a major accident, it becomes necessary to install an independent protective system which takes automatic action when the hazardous condition is approached.

One example of this is temperature measurement in the case of a chemical process that can lead to a runaway reaction. As soon as the hazardous temperature is reached, the system initiates additional cooling of the process and adds a reaction stopper to the mixture.

In order to operate such control systems, it is necessary to monitor the process variables and active parts of the plant, e.g. pumps, compressors and blowers, with regard to operation and to dangerous conditions such as excessive pressure.

To ensure that the operating personnel do not have to rely solely on the functioning of automatic systems, these systems should be combined with acoustic or optical alarms. Moreover, the operating personnel should be well trained to be aware of the mode of operation and the importance of the control systems.

It is most important to realise that any control system will have problems in rare operating conditions such as start-up and shut-down phases. Special attention must be paid to these phases of operation.

3.3.3. Safety systems

Any major hazard installation will require some form of safety system. The form and design of the system depend on the hazards present in the plant. The following gives a survey of available safety systems and their purposes.

3.3.3.1. Systems preventing deviation from permissible operating conditions

(a) *Pressure-relief systems*

Rupture discs and safety valves can release material into the atmosphere. If the material released forms an explosive mixture with air, care must be taken that this mixture does not come into contact with an ignition source before the lower explosive limit is reached. If the material released is toxic, it should be led into a secondary system such

as a blowdown system, a scrubber or a flare tower, and not directly into the atmosphere.

(b) *Temperature/pressure/flow sensors*

Temperature/pressure/flow sensors in the process initiate actions such as emergency cooling, the input of a reaction stopper or the opening of a bypass.

(c) *Systems preventing overflow*

Level controls prevent vessels from being overfilled; they cut off the flow of material or divert it.

(d) *Safety shut-down systems, emergency shut-off systems*

These are systems which shut down the plant (i.e. cut off pumps and compressors and close or open quick-acting valves) in order to bring the plant into a safe condition. These systems can be initiated automatically or manually.

3.3.3.2. Systems preventing failure of safety-related components

Safety-related components may need to be specially equipped for additional reliability, depending on their importance in the safety system. The plant can have different systems which take over the function of these components (diversity), or there can be a second component for the same purpose, e.g. a second coolant pump (redundancy).

3.3.3.3. Utilities

Safety-related utility supplies, such as electricity supply to control systems, compressed air for instruments or nitrogen supply as an inert gas, might need a second source, e.g. batteries, a buffer-storage tank or an extra set of pressure gas cylinders in case of a failure in the primary system.

3.3.3.4. Alarm systems

These are systems which, on the basis of sensors, allow the operator to determine the causes of a malfunction as soon as it has occurred. Such alarm systems are available for –

(a) monitoring of process parameters (temperature, pressure, flow rate, quantity, level, mixing ratio, O_2 content);

(b) detection of failures of safety-related components (pumps, compressors, stirrers, blowers);

(c) detection of leaks (gas detectors, explosimeters);

(d) detection of fire or smoke;

(e) detection of failure of safety devices (closed-circuit current principle).

3.3.3.5. Technical protective measures

Over and above the safety systems which help to keep the plant in a safe condition, protective measures can be taken to limit the consequences of an accident. Such measures are –

(a) gas detectors;

(b) water spray systems (to cool tanks or to extinguish a fire);

(c) water jets;

(d) steam spray systems;

(e) collecting tanks and bunds.

3.3.3.6. Mitigating measures

To mitigate the consequences of an accident, it is important to plan and to take adequate organisational measures. These are described in section 3.4.

3.3.3.7. Prevention of human and organisational errors

As shown in subsection 3.2.3, human errors can be a source of major accidents. For this reason, their prevention needs to be addressed as one of the key safety measures. The following preventive measures can be taken:

(a) use of differently sized connections in loading stations for tank-cars to prevent mixing of reactive substances (e.g. sulphuric acid and nitric acid);

(b) prevention of material mix-ups by means of proper labelling, packaging, receiving inspection and analysis;

(c) interlocking of safety-related valves and switches which may not operate simultaneously;

(d) clear marking of switches, knobs and displays on control panels;

(e) proper communication devices for the plant personnel;

(f) safeguarding against inadvertent switching actions;

(g) training of personnel.

3.3.4. Maintenance and monitoring

The safety of a plant and the function of safety-related systems can only be as good as the maintenance and monitoring of these systems. For this reason, it is of great importance to establish a plant maintenance and monitoring schedule which includes the following tasks:

(a) checking of safety-related operating conditions both in the control room and on site;

(b) checking of safety-related parts of the plant on site, e.g. by visual inspection or by remote monitoring;

(c) monitoring of safety-related utilities (electricity, steam, coolant, compressed air, etc.);

(d) preparation of a maintenance plan and documentation of maintenance work specifying the different maintenance intervals and the type of work to be performed.

In addition, the maintenance and monitoring schedule must specify the qualifications and experience required by the personnel to perform their tasks.

3.3.5. Inspection and repair

It is necessary to establish a plan for on-site inspections which should include a schedule and the operating conditions to be adhered to during inspection work.

Repair work can be a major source of accidents. For this reason, strict procedures must be specified for carrying out repair work (e.g. welding of components containing flammable substances). These procedures should cover repair work requiring shut-down of the plant and cleaning of tanks, the qualifications required by personnel, quality requirements of the work to be performed and requirements for the supervision of repair work. Because of the importance of this, many manufacturers establish their own standards for repair work over and above what national standards may require.

3.3.6. Training

While technical measures are essential for the safety of the plant, no plant can be designed so that it will operate without human intervention. As people can have a negative as well as a positive influence on plant safety, it is important to reduce the negative influence and support the positive one. Both goals can be achieved by proper selection and training of the personnel, which should include information on –

(a) the hazards of the process/the substances used;

(b) possible operating conditions, including start-up and shut-down procedures;

(c) behaviour in the case of malfunctions or accidents;

(d) experience in similar plants elsewhere, including accidents and near misses.

3.4. Mitigation of consequences

No major hazard installation can ever be absolutely safe. Even if a hazard assessment has been carried out, if the hazards have been detected and appropriate measures have been taken, the possibility of an accident cannot be completely ruled out.

For this reason, it must be part of the safety concept to plan and provide measures which can mitigate the consequences of an accident. Measures involving the plan have already been considered in subsection 3.3.3.

Other measures for mitigating the consequences of an accident deal mainly with the response to a release of a hazardous substance. In order to be able to initiate counter-measures in the event of an accident, the manufacturer may need to –

(a) set up and train a fire brigade, professional or voluntary;

(b) provide alarm systems with a direct line to the fire brigade or to public emergency forces;

(c) draw up an emergency plan containing –

(i) the system of organisation used to fight the emergency;

(ii) the alarm and communication routes;

(iii) guide-lines for fighting the emergency;

(iv) information about hazardous substances;

(v) examples of possible accident sequences (Chapter 6 gives a detailed description of the content of an on-site emergency plan);

(d) reach an agreement with the authorities regarding co-ordination with their contingency plan;

(e) notify the authorities of the nature and scope of the hazard in the event of an accident;

(f) provide antidotes in the event of a release of toxic substances (although this is more likely to be carried out, if required, by the local medical services).

All of these measures have to be consistent with the hazards identified in the assessment. Furthermore, they must be accompanied by proper training of plant personnel, the emergency forces and responsible representatives from public services. Only training and rehearsals of accident situations can make emergency plans realistic enough for them to work in a real emergency.

3.5. Reporting to authorities

Depending on local arrangements in different countries, the management of a major hazard installation is likely to be required to report to the authorities. Reporting may be carried out in three steps. These are –

(a) identification/notification of a major hazard installation;

(b) preparation of a safety report;

(c) immediate reporting of accidents.

The following subsections describe the various components of a comprehensive reporting system. Each country will need to decide on the amount of information it requires to fulfil the role outlined in Chapter 4.

3.5.1. Purpose of reporting

Whether or not an installation is classified as a major hazard depends on the types and quantities of substances used, produced, stored or handled. Notification to the authorities of the existence on site of hazardous chemicals above the "trigger" quantities is necessary in order to identify major hazards coming within the scope of the additional controls described in this manual.

The purpose of the second step, the preparation of a safety report, is to present the entire safety system. This gives the authorities the opportunity (a) to check adherence to safety standards as part of any licensing decisions, (b) to carry out specific inspection in order to learn about hazards arising from these installations, (c) to take proper siting decisions for new plants, and (d) to establish contingency plans.

Finally, if an accident occurs, this may need to be reported at once to the authorities. This is in addition to informing the authorities involved in handling the emergency off site, where immediate contact will be essential.

3.5.2. Contents of reports to the authorities

3.5.2.1. Identification

The following information is necessary to identify a plant as a major hazard installation:

(a) information about the manufacturer;

(b) general information about the plant;

(c) information about available licences;

(d) information about the hazardous substances, their names, quantities and physical condition.

3.5.2.2. The safety report

If a plant is identified as a major hazard installation according to the criteria specified in Chapter 2, a safety report may have to be prepared. This is to inform the authorities about the installation and its hazards, and has the following objectives:

(a) to identify the nature and scale of the use of hazardous substances in the installation;

(b) to give an account of the arrangements for safe operation of the installation, for control of serious deviations that could lead to a major accident and for emergency procedures at the site;

(c) to identify the type, relative likelihood and consequences of major accidents that might occur; and

(d) to demonstrate that the manufacturer has identified the major hazard potential of his

activities and has provided appropriate measures.

These objectives will assist both management and authorities in the evaluation of plant safety.

In order to fulfil these objectives, a safety report has two basic tasks. Firstly, it gives factual information about the site, the processes and the surroundings. Secondly, it performs a hazard assessment allowing judgement of the nature, likelihood and scale of potential major accidents and of the means for controlling such hazards.

The safety report, an example of which appears in Appendix 6, should therefore contain the following information:

A. *Description of the installation and the processes*

(1) *Description of the installation*

(a) site –
(i) site plans;
(ii) surroundings (factories, traffic routes, buildings, hospitals, schools, etc.);

(b) constructive design –
(i) materials (only those related to safety);
(ii) design data (pressure, temperature, volume);
(iii) foundations (stability);

(c) protection zones (explosion protection, separation distances);

(d) accessibility of plant –
(i) escape routes;
(ii) routes for emergency services.

(2) *Description of the processes*

(a) technical purpose of the installation;

(b) basic principles of the technological process –
(i) basic operations;
(ii) physical and chemical reactions;
(iii) operational storage;
(iv) discharge, retention, recycling or disposal of waste;
(v) discharge or treatment of off-gases;

(c) process conditions: description of the process and safety-related data (pressure, temperature) for the individual process stages;

(d) process description: this description is best given by appropriate flow diagrams (PI diagrams). They should contain information on –

   (i) components used in the process;

   (ii) utility supplies;

   (iii) characteristic operating conditions;

   (iv) size of vessels and pipe-work containing hazardous substances;

   (v) press control systems;

(e) utility supply: all safety-related types of utilities (electricity, steam, coolant, compressed air, inert gas) and, if available, the emergency supplies should be described.

B. *Description of the hazardous substances*

  (1) *Substances*

   (a) the process stage in which the substances are or may be involved;

   (b) quantities of substances;

   (c) substance data (physical and chemical);

   (d) safety-related data (explosive limits, flash-point, thermal stability);

   (e) toxicological data (toxicity, effects, odour level);

   (f) threshold values (TLV, lethal concentrations).

  (2) *Form of substances*: the form in which the substances may occur or into which they may be transformed in the event of abnormal conditions.

C. *Preliminary hazard analysis (PHA)*

On the basis of the process description and the description of the hazardous substances, it is possible to identify the hazards and to determine which components, safety measures or human interventions may be of importance. This can be done according to the procedure described in subsection 3.1.1.1.

The result of this PHA is a list of those components, equipment, safety features and operations that might be linked to the occurrence of a major accident. These are called "safety-relevant units".

D. *Description of safety-relevant units*

The safety-relevant parts identified in the PHA need to be described in greater detail in order to perform the hazard assessment. The following data are required:

(a) function;

(b) type and extent of loads;

(c) importance for safety;

(d) special design criteria;

(e) controls and alarms;

(f) pressure-relief systems;

(g) quick-acting valves;

(h) collecting tanks/dump tanks;

(i) sprinkler systems;

(j) fire protection.

E. *Hazard assessment*

On the basis of the hazards identified in the PHA and all the information available about the installation, namely the descriptive sections of the safety report, the next step is to perform the hazard assessment. To enable the reader to carry out such an assessment, this manual contains the following aids:

(a) the methods used for hazard assessment, shown in subsection 3.1.1;

(b) the causes of the hazards to be considered, listed in section 3.2; and

(c) the major hazard control instrumentation, given in subsection 3.3.3.

As additional information, the hazard assessment should include the known accident history both of the plant in question and of similar plants elsewhere.

It is recommended that the HAZOP method should be followed in the safety-relevant units and that documentation on the HAZOP analysis may be included in the safety report. For reference, an example of HAZOP appears in Appendix 3.

In cases where the assessment leads to the identification of particularly sensitive features (safety devices, control instruments or actions by operating personnel), it is necessary to consider the reliability of these features. This consideration will show whether sufficient precautions have been taken to avoid major accidents. If this is not the case, the identified sensitive features of the plant will have to be improved.

F. *Organisation*

Organisational systems used for the safe operation of a plant are important factors to consider in the overall assessment of plant safety. This should include information on the following:

(a) maintenance and inspection schedules;

(b) guide-lines for the training of personnel;

(c) allocation and delegation of responsibility for plant safety;

(d) implementation of safety procedures.

G. *Assessment of the consequences of major accidents*

While sections A to E of the safety report deal with technical and operational safety measures, this section should provide information on possible accidents. The following information should be given:

(a) assessment of the possible releases of hazardous substances or of energy;

(b) possible dispersion of released substances;

(c) assessment of the effects of the releases (size of affected area, health effects, property damage).

Some physical models are available to assist with these assessments. Several references exist that give more details on these models (Havens and Spicer, 1984; Netherlands, Directorate General of Labour, 1979). Further details appear in Appendix 4.

H. *Information on the mitigation of major accidents*

While in-plant safety measures are solely within the manufacturer's responsibility, the mitigation of major accidents may affect the authorities as well. For this reason, it is of great importance that the mitigating measures listed in section 3.4 of this manual are described in detail and are consistent with the measures taken by the authorities. This applies mainly to:

(a) warning systems;

(b) emergency plans; and

(c) emergency services.

3.5.2.3. Reporting of accidents

If a major accident occurs on a site, the manufacturer should immediately notify the authorities of this accident. This notification should contain the following information:

(a) the circumstances of the accident;

(b) the hazardous substances involved;

(c) data available for assessing the effects of the accident on persons and the environment;

(d) the emergency measures taken.

Furthermore, the notification should state the steps envisaged:

(a) to mitigate medium- or long-term effects of the accident; and

(b) to prevent the recurrence of such an accident.

In notifying the accident, use may be made of forms such as that of the European Communities, shown in Appendix 7.

3.5.3. Updating of reports

The safety reports may need to be updated in the event of:

(a) major changes in the plant or process;

(b) relevant new information about the hazardous substances; or

(c) substantial improvements available in safety engineering.

In general, reports should be updated regularly every three to five years.

4. The role of the authorities

The prevention of major accidents as described in this manual is basically a task that the manufacturer operating a major hazard installation has to cope with. Within the framework of a major hazard control system, this task must be supported and reviewed by the authorities. In order to meet these responsibilities, the authorities will need to perform the following activities.

4.1. Establishment of an inventory of major hazard installations

This manual deals with a number of potentially hazardous industrial activities and substances. The competent authorities will need to identify these major hazard installations in order to draw up an inventory. The procedures for identification are described in Chapter 2. Depending on the number of identified installations in relation to the resources that are available, it will be necessary to set priorities for the review of safety reports and the implementation of off-site emergency plans. This must be carried out on the basis of the following criteria:

– type and quantities of hazardous substances handled; and

– location of the installations in relation to populated areas.

Furthermore, it may be of help to consider how many accidents have occurred in the past with these substances. Literature on accident statistics is available (Lees, 1980). International data bases (e.g. MHIDAS in the United Kingdom) also enable this information to be rapidly obtained.

4.2. Receipt and review of the safety reports

According to the priorities deduced from the inventory of major hazard installations, the authorities will need to set a deadline for the preparation of safety reports. They should allow sufficient time (i.e. one or two years) for the preparation of these reports by existing works. When the reports are reviewed, the authorities will need to check:

– whether the requirements listed in Chapter 3 of the manual have been fulfilled; and

– whether the information given is correct.

The review should involve a detailed examination of the written statements, in particular of the hazard assessment. Furthermore, it must include an on-site inspection of those components or processes identified in the safety report as being "safety-relevant".

As part of the safety report should describe the on-site emergency plan, the authorities must review this to make sure that it is consistent with the off-site emergency plan. Details about on-site and off-site emergency plans are given in Chapter 6 of this manual.

4.3. Mitigation of consequences

The off-site emergency plans are likely to be prepared by the local authorities. They should be drawn up in consultation with the manufacturer and organisations such as the fire brigade, police, ambulance service, hospitals, water authorities, public transport, and so on.

The off-site emergency plan must be maintained in a state of readiness; provision must be made for training and exercises, the details of which appear in section 6.3.

In addition to helping manufacturers deal with the immediate effects of accidents on site, the emergency services should be prepared to cope with possible consequential effects in the surrounding area. Off-site effects usually take longer to develop and therefore allow some time for contingency action to be taken. Equally they may continue for a period of several hours or possibly longer and require considerable mobilisation of resources to cope with possible evacuation, restriction of access, movement of foodstuffs and control of water supplies.

4.4. Other roles

4.4.1. Siting

The authorities need to decide whether certain major hazard installations should be separated from the population living and working outside the installation. This is described in detail in Appendix 8.

4.4.2. Introduction of an inspection programme

As soon as priorities have been determined, based on the inventory and location of major hazard installations, a system will be required to enforce control measures additional to those already in operation covering health and safety in the workplace.

Depending on the experience of major hazards on the part of the authorities, they may need to:

(a) acquire sufficient expertise by establishing a group of experts;

(b) prepare check-lists to evaluate works safety measures;

(c) develop inspection systems and programmes for use by factory inspectorates.

All these tasks are described in more detail in Chapter 7.

5. The role of workers and workers' organisations

Workers have the essential role of operating major hazard plants in a safe and responsible manner. Irrespective of the best efforts of designers and constructors of chemical plant, safe operation will depend on workers consistently being aware of the hazardous nature of the materials being processed and stored, and on their accepting responsibility for the safety of the plant.

5.1. The role of workers

Workers should co-operate with and participate in the implementation of the organisational and other measures related to the major hazard control system in operation. They can play an active role in constantly watching over the safety of their workplaces and the equipment that they use, and in applying all safety and health instructions pertaining to their work. Workers should always make proper use of all safeguards and safety devices and other appliances made available for their protection or the protection of others.

It should be made clear that no worker, unless authorised, should interfere with, remove, alter or displace any safety device or other appliance made available for his or her protection or the protection of others, or interfere with any method or process adopted with a view to avoiding accidents and injuries to health. Furthermore, workers should not tamper with equipment such as controls, machines, valves, piping, electrical conductors and appliances that they have not been authorised to operate, maintain or use.

Any defects found in the course of work should be reported without delay to a competent supervisor. When workers, through their job experience, have reason to believe that there would be high risk to life or health if a task assigned to them or to their fellow workers were carried out, they should report the fears immediately to their supervisors, to workers' safety representatives and

to the competent safety and health officers in the plant. Workers' co-operation in dealing with such imminent dangers is essential in the prevention of major hazards.

Each worker should be fully informed in an adequate manner of the major accident hazard involved in his or her work. This should include safety and health information on planning or altering work processes or the organisation of work.

5.2. The role of workers' organisations

At the national and enterprise levels, workers' organisations can contribute significantly to the establishment and implementation of a major hazard control system. Given adequate information, they can participate actively in examining factors related to major accident risks and proposing measures to counteract such risks. Workers' organisations should continue to develop and promote awareness and expertise among their members in matters concerning the safety of major hazard installations and hazardous chemicals.

Training activities organised by workers' organisations are especially important. Such training should promote an awareness of the basic principles of major hazard control, with emphasis on specific aspects of a major hazard control system at the workplace. The development of trade union specialists knowledgeable about major hazard control should be encouraged. Also important are the preparation and use of training and information materials directed at workers and their organisations.

There should be regular consultations between the organisations of workers and of employers concerning the development and operation of the major hazard control system.

6. Emergency planning

6.1. Introduction

6.1.1. Definition

A major emergency in a works is one which has the potential to cause serious injury or loss of life. It may cause extensive damage to property and serious disruption both inside and outside the works. It would normally require the assistance of outside emergency services to handle it effectively. Although the emergency may be caused by a number of different factors, e.g. plant failure, human error, earthquake, vehicle crash or sabotage, it will normally manifest itself in three basic forms: fire, explosion or toxic release.

6.1.2. Scope

Much of the earlier part of this manual has been concerned with preventing accidents through good design, operation, maintenance and inspection. Achieving all this will reduce the risk of an accident, but it will not eliminate it altogether – absolute safety is not achievable, and an essential part of major hazard control is concerned with mitigating the effects of a major accident.

An important element of mitigation is emergency planning, i.e. recognising that accidents are possible, assessing the consequences of such accidents and deciding on the emergency procedures, both on site and off site, that would need to be implemented in the event of an emergency.

Emergency planning is just one aspect of safety and cannot be considered in isolation. In particular, it is not a substitute for maintaining good standards inside the works. Before starting to prepare the plan, works managements should ensure that the necessary standards, appropriate to their safety legislation, are in place.

Emergency plans are likely to be separate for on-site and off-site matters, but they must be consistent with each other, i.e. they must be related to the same assessed emergency conditions. While an on-site plan will always be the responsibility of the works management, different legislations may place the responsibility for the off-site plan elsewhere: for example, the EC Seveso Directive requires the local authority to prepare the off-site plan.

6.1.3. Objectives

The overall objectives of an emergency plan are:

(a) to localise the emergency and, if possible, eliminate it; and

(b) to minimise the effects of the accident on people and property.

Elimination will require prompt action by operators and works emergency staff using, for example, fire-fighting equipment, emergency shut-off valves and water sprays.

Minimising the effects may include rescue, first aid, evacuation, rehabilitation and giving information promptly to people living nearby.

6.1.4. Identification and assessment of hazards

This stage is crucial to both on-site and off-site emergency planning and requires works managements systematically to identify what emergencies could arise in their plants. These should range from small events which can be dealt with by works personnel without outside help to the largest event for which it is practical to have a plan. Experience has shown that for every occasion that the full potential of an accident is realised, there are many occasions when some lesser event occurs or when a developing incident is made safe before reaching full potential.

Most major hazard accidents come within the following categories:

(1) *Events involving flammable materials*

    (a) major fires with no danger of explosion; hazards from prolonged high levels of thermal radiation and smoke;

    (b) fire threatening items of plant containing hazardous substances; hazards from spread of fire, explosion or release of toxic substances;

    (c) explosion with little or no warning; hazards from blast wave, flying debris and high levels of thermal radiation.

(2) *Events involving toxic materials*

    (a) slow or intermittent release of toxic substances, e.g. from a leaking valve;

(b) items of plant threatened by fire (Chemical Industries Association, 1976); hazards from potential loss of containment;

(c) rapid release of limited duration, due to plant failure, e.g. fracture of pipe; hazards from toxic cloud, limited in size, which may quickly disperse;

(d) massive release of toxic substance, due to failure of large storage or process vessel or uncontrollable chemical reaction and failure of safety systems; the exposure hazard would affect a wide area.

The assessment of possible incidents should produce a report indicating –

(a) the worst events considered;

(b) the route to those worst events;

(c) the time-scale to lesser events along the way;

(d) the size of lesser events if their development is halted;

(e) the relative likelihood of events;

(f) the consequences of each event.

This report may be part of the hazard assessment report (Chapter 3) or may be a separate exercise produced specifically for the purposes of emergency planning.

Incidents should be assessed in terms of the quantity of hazardous materials which could be released, the rate of release and the effects of that release – e.g. as thermal radiation from a fire or fireball or as a toxic gas cloud – as a function of distance from the plant. The calculation of consequences is discussed in Chapter 1 and the techniques for hazard assessment are explained in Chapter 3.

The effects of blast over-pressure on structures are given in table 8, the effects of thermal radiation on unprotected skin in table 9 and the effects on people of gas concentration (with times) for chlorine, the most common toxic gas, are given in table 10. Equivalent data for other toxic gases, where used, are an essential element of any emergency plan. **Guidance on the dangers of hazardous substances should be obtained from the suppliers of those substances.**

This overall assessment of the major hazard provides the framework for both emergency plans to be drawn up.

Techniques for the more formal identification and assessment of hazards have been developed and are used routinely in many countries,

Table 8. Effects of blast over-pressure on structures

Structural element	Failure	Approximate peak side-on over-pressure psi [1]	kPa [1]
Window panes	5% broken	0.1-0.15	0.7-1
	50% broken	0.2-0.4	1.4-3
	90% broken	0.5-0.9	3-6
Houses	Tiles displaced	0.4-0.7	3-5
	Doors and window frames broken in	0.8-1.3	6-9
	Inhabitable after repair – some damage to ceilings, windows and tiling	0.2-0.4	1.4-3
	Minor structural damage, partitions and joinery wrenched from fixings	0.5-0.9	3-6
	Uninhabitable: partial or total collapse of roof, partial demolition of one or two external walls, severe damage to load-bearing partitions	2-4	14-28
	50-75% external brickwork destroyed or rendered unsafe	5-12	35-80
	Almost complete demolition	11-37	80-260
Telegraph poles	Destroyed	10-25	70-170
Large trees	Destroyed	24-55	170-380
Rail freight wagons	Limit of derailment	12-27	80-190

[1] 1 bar = 100 kPa = 14.7 psi.

Table 9. Effects of thermal radiation on unprotected skin

Radiation level (kW/m²)	Duration period, seconds before: Pain is felt	Blistering starts
22	2	3
18	2.5	4.3
11	5	8.5
8	8	13.5
5	16	25
2.5	40	65
Below 2.5	Prolonged exposure can be tolerated	

Table 10. Effects of chlorine gas concentrations (ppm) on people (1 ppm = 3 mg/m³)

Concentration (ppm)	Time	Effect
3-6	–	Causes stinging or burning sensation but tolerated without undue ill effect for up to 1 hour
10	1 min	Coughing
10-20	30 mins	Dangerous – immediate irritation of nose, throat and eyes with cough and lachrymation
100-150	5-10 mins	More vulnerable people might suffer fatality
300-400	30 mins	Predicted average lethal concentration for 50% of active healthy people
1 000	Brief (a few breaths)	Likely to be fatal

particularly during the consideration of a new project. These techniques, known as hazard and operability studies, or HAZOPs for short, require the systematic consideration of adverse process variables at each stage of the process and each area of plant. Fuller details of this are given in Appendix 3.

6.2. On-site emergency planning

6.2.1. Formulation of the plan and of emergency services

The assessment of the risks and hazards in a major hazard works leads either to improvements being made to the plant, in the form, for example, of additional safeguards or better procedures, or to the decision being taken that the risk is sufficiently small to be accepted.

The on-site emergency plan must be related to the final assessment and it is the responsibility of the works management to formulate it. The plan must therefore be specific to the site. On very simple sites, the emergency plan may consist merely of putting key personnel on stand-by and calling in the emergency services. On large multi-process sites, the plan may well be a substantial document including the following elements:

(a) assessment of the size and nature of the events foreseen and the probability of their occurrence;

(b) formulation of the plan and liaison with outside authorities, including the emergency services;

(c) procedures:

(i) raising the alarm;

(ii) communications both within and outside the works;

(d) appointment of key personnel and their duties and responsibilities:

(i) works incident controller;

(ii) works main controller;

(e) emergency control centre;

(f) action on site;

(g) action off site.

The plan should set out the way in which designated people at the site of the incident can initiate supplementary action both inside or outside the works at an appropriate time. An essential element of the plan must be the provision for attempting to make safe the affected unit, for example by shutting it down. On a complex site, the plan should contain the full sequence of key personnel to be called in from other sections or from off site.

It is particularly important that the requirements of the plan for emergency resources, both personnel and equipment, are reasonable and can be quickly assembled in the event of an emergency. Management should consider whether sufficient resources exist at their works to carry out the plan for the various assessed incidents in conjunction with the emergency services. Is there, for example, sufficient water for cooling and, if this water is applied via hoses, are there sufficient people to operate them? Has the time-scale been assessed correctly? The time element is of great significance but is often overlooked. For example, if a period of 15 minutes has elapsed between the start of the incident and the arrival of the fire brigade, and if a further period of 15 minutes is needed for the firefighters and equipment to be deployed, will the works resources be able to contain the incident in the meanwhile? Although a large vessel may leak for a long period, a 1-tonne chlorine vessel releasing liquid at full flow through an open valve will be empty in about 10 minutes, and a cylinder in far less time. If the possibility of such a release is identified, the remedial action must be appropriately quick if it is to be worth taking.

The plan needs to take account of absences due to sickness and holidays, and of shut-down periods, for example when only security personnel may be present: in other words, it must be applicable to all the variations in manning, and so on, that could occur while the hazard exists.

6.2.2. Alarm and communication mechanism

Communication is a crucial factor in handling an emergency. It is the practice at many works that any employee can raise an emergency alarm, so allowing the earliest possible action to be taken to control the situation.

Alarm systems vary and will depend on the size of the works. There should be an adequate number of points from which the alarm can be raised either directly, by activating an audible warning, or indirectly, via a signal or message to a permanently manned location. The alarm should alert the incident controller (subsection 6.2.3), who should assess the situation and implement appropriate emergency procedures. In areas where there is a high level of noise, it may be necessary to install more than one audible alarm transmitter or flashing lights. Automatic alarms may be appropriate on some sites.

There should be a reliable system for informing the emergency services as soon as the alarm is raised on site. The details of the communication arrangements should be agreed locally; in some cases it may be advisable to have a direct line to the fire brigade. Predetermined code words to indicate the scale and type of the emergency may be valuable.

6.2.3. Appointment of personnel and definition of duties

Effective emergency plans require that, in the event of an accident, nominated individuals are given specific responsibilities, often separate from their day-to-day activities. The two principal people are the site incident controller and the site main controller.

The site incident controller will take control of handling the incident. He or she will often be the person in charge of the plant at the time of the incident and should provide 24-hour cover when shift operation applies. The site incident controller may have to take decisions involving neighbouring plant liable, perhaps, to be involved in an escalating emergency if it is not shut down.

The responsibilities of the site incident controller include the following:

(a) to assess the scale of the incident (both for internal and external emergency services);

(b) to initiate the emergency procedures to secure the safety of employees, minimise damage to plant and property and minimise loss of material;

(c) to direct rescue and fire-fighting operations until (if necessary) the fire brigade arrives;

(d) to search for casualties;

(e) to arrange evacuation of non-essential workers to assembly areas;

(f) to set up a communications point with the emergency control centre (subsection 6.2.4);

(g) to assume the responsibilities of the site main controller pending his or her arrival;

(h) to provide advice and information as requested to the emergency services.

It is important that the site incident controller is readily recognisable at the scene of the incident. This is usually achieved by the wearing of a distinctive safety helmet and jacket, which is known to all concerned. It should contrast with equipment worn by the emergency services.

The site main controller is often chosen from the senior management of the works and has the general responsibility of directing operations from the emergency control centre after relieving the site incident controller of the responsibility for overall control.

The specific responsibilities of the site main controller include:

(a) to decide (if not decided already) whether a major emergency exists or is likely, requiring the emergency services and the off-site emergency plan (section 6.3);

(b) to exercise direct operational control of the works outside the affected area;

(c) continually to review and assess possible developments to determine the most probable course of events;

(d) to direct the shutting down of plants and their evacuation, in consultation with the site incident controller and key personnel;

(e) to ensure that casualties are receiving adequate attention;

(f) to liaise with chief officers of the fire and police services and with the factory inspectorate;

(g) to control traffic movement within the works;

(h) to arrange for a log of the emergency to be maintained;

(i) to issue authorised statements to the news media;

(j) to control rehabilitation of affected areas after the emergency.

Apart from the two site controllers, other works personnel will have key roles to play in the implementation of the emergency plan. These will include senior managers of plants not directly involved in the emergency, first aiders, atmospheric monitoring staff, casualty reception staff and public relations staff to liaise with the media. All need to be aware at the emergency pre-planning stage of the precise nature of their roles.

6.2.4. Emergency control centres

The emergency control centre is the place from which the operations to handle the emergency are directed and co-ordinated. It will be attended by the site main controller, key personnel and the senior officers of the fire and police services.

For a small works it may be a designated office which converts to a control centre in the event of an emergency. For large works, a purpose-built facility is advisable. In all cases, however, the centre should be equipped to receive and transmit information and directions from and to the incident controller and other areas of the works, as well as outside.

Emergency control centres should therefore contain the following (as applicable):

(a) an adequate number of external telephones; if possible, one should accept outgoing calls only, in order to bypass jammed switchboards during an emergency;

(b) an adequate number of internal telephones;

(c) radio equipment;

(d) a plan of the works, to show:

  (i) areas where there are large inventories of hazardous materials;

  (ii) sources of safety equipment;

  (iii) the fire-fighting system and additional sources of water;

  (iv) site entrances and roadways, including up-to-date information on roadworks;

  (v) assembly points;

  (vi) the location of the works in relation to the surrounding community;

  (vii) lorry parks and rail sidings;

   (additional works plans should be available to show affected areas, etc., during an emergency;)

(e) notepads, pens and pencils;

(f) a nominal roll of employees;

(g) a list of key personnel, with addresses, telephone numbers, etc.

The emergency control centre should be sited in an area of minimum risk. For large sites, or where toxic releases might be anticipated, consideration should be given to setting up two control centres to ensure, as far as possible, that one will always be available for use should the other be put out of action.

6.2.5. Action on site

The primary purpose of the on-site emergency plan is to control and contain the incident and so to prevent it from spreading to nearby plant. It is not possible to cover every eventuality in the plan and the successful handling of the emergency will depend on appropriate action and decisions being taken on the spot. Other important aspects needing to be considered include the following:

(a) *Evacuation.* Non-essential personnel will usually be evacuated from the incident area and also from adjacent areas. Evacuation should be to a predetermined assembly point in a safe part of the works. In some cases, particularly where toxic releases are being considered, alternative assembly points need to be arranged to allow

for the effects of wind direction. Assembly points need to be clearly marked. The plan should designate someone to record all personnel arriving at the assembly point so that the information can be passed to the emergency control centre.

(b) *Accounting for personnel.* It is important to be able to account for personnel during an emergency, but it can be particularly difficult. Because of visitors, contractors, shift changes, holidays and sickness absence, it is normally not practical to maintain a detailed roll of personnel on site at any one time. Nominal rolls, which can be updated during the early stage of an emergency, are usually kept. Detailed lists of contractors on site should be maintained, with a similar list for visitors.

At the emergency control centre, a nominated person should collate the lists of personnel arriving at the assembly points with those involved in the incident. These should then be checked against the nominal roll of those believed to be on site, updated with known changes for that day. Where it is possible that missing people might have been in the area of the emergency, the incident controller should be informed and arrangements made to organise a further search.

(c) *Access to records.* This will be necessary in order that relatives of any casualties can be quickly informed. It is suggested that lists of names and addresses of works personnel should be kept in the emergency control centre. These will need to be regularly updated to take account of changes in personnel, address, next of kin, and so on.

(d) *Public relations.* Any incident will attract the interest of the media, and a major accident is likely to involve widespread radio and television coverage. Unless appropriate arrangements are made, this can divert personnel from the task of handling the emergency. It is essential to make arrangements for the authoritative release of information during any emergency of significant length, and a senior manager or member of the staff should be appointed as the *sole* source of this information. Inquiries made to other employees should be directed to this appointed person.

(e) *Rehabilitation.* The emergency will continue until all fires have been extinguished with no risk of reignition or, for a gas release, when the escape has been stopped and the gas cloud safely dispersed. Even then, care is required when re-entering the incident area. The local factory inspectorate may wish to initiate an inquiry and should be consulted regarding the collection of evidence before it is disturbed.

6.2.6. Planning shut-down procedures

For single plant sites, shut-down procedures may be comparatively simple, with no knock-on effects elsewhere on site. With complex sites, such as large petrochemical works or refineries, plant operations are often interlinked and the shut-down of any key plant on site (e.g. a power station) may have significant implications for other plant. Emergency plans will need to take account of this so that ordered and phased shut-downs can take place when necessary, depending on the type of incident occurring.

6.2.7. Rehearsing emergency procedures

Once the emergency plan is finalised, it should be made known to all personnel so that each knows his or her role in the event of an emergency. It is essential that the plan is regularly tested because it is only through such rehearsals that defects become apparent. The plan can be tested in a number of different ways. Communication is a key component of handling an emergency and a rehearsal of the communications system, including contingency action if part of the system (e.g. telephones) becomes inoperative, should be undertaken. Evacuation rehearsals should be regularly carried out and should cause minimum disruption to the normal activities. More elaborate exercises, involving the emergency services where they are part of the emergency plan, will also need to take place.

Many organisations use table-top exercises to test their emergency plans. These are very cost-effective because they do not interrupt the day-to-day running of the plant and because the organiser of the exercise can "arrange" for a variety of difficulties to arise which will need on-the-spot decisions to be taken. Full-scale exercises, providing a realistic rehearsal setting, will still be needed to complement the table-top exercises.

6.2.8. Plan appraisal and updating

Emergency planning rehearsals and exercises should be monitored by observers not involved in the exercise, and preferably independent of the site, e.g. senior officers from the emergency services or factory inspectorate. After each exercise, the plan should be thoroughly reviewed to take account of omissions or shortcomings. Emergency plans, particularly for complex sites, are the subject of continual refinement and updating, but it is important that any changes of substance are made known to those likely to be involved in that part of the plan when used for a real emergency.

6.3. Off-site emergency planning

6.3.1. Introduction

The off-site emergency plan is an integral part of any major hazard control system. It should be based on those accidents identified by the works management which could affect people and the environment outside the works. Thus, the off-site plan follows logically from the analysis that took place to provide the basis for the on-site plan and the two plans should therefore complement each other. The off-site plan in detail should be based on those events which are most likely to occur, but other less likely events which would have severe consequences should also be considered. Incidents which would have very severe consequences yet have a small probability of occurrence will be in this category, although there will be certain events which are so improbable that it would not be sensible to consider them in detail in the plan. These events might include aircraft crashes on to the installation. However, the key feature of a good off-site emergency plan is flexibility in its application to emergencies other than those specifically included in the formation of the plan.

The roles of the various parties who may be involved in the implementation of an off-site plan are described below. Depending on local arrangements in different countries, the responsibility for the off-site plan will be likely to rest either with the works management or, as is the case under European Community legislation, with the local authority. Either way, the plan must identify an emergency co-ordinating officer (subsection 6.3.3) who would take overall command

of the off-site activities. As with the on-site plan, an emergency control centre will be required within which the emergency co-ordinating officer can operate.

An early decision will be required in many cases on the advice to be given to people living "within range" of the accident – in particular whether they should be evacuated or told to go indoors. In the latter case, the decision can regularly be reviewed in the event of an escalation of the incident. Consideration of evacuation may include the following factors:

(a) in the case of a major fire but without explosion risk (e.g. an oil storage tank), only houses close to the fire are likely to need evacuation, although a severe smoke hazard may require this to be reviewed periodically;

(b) if a fire is escalating and in turn threatening a store of hazardous material, it might be necessary to evacuate people nearby, but only if there is time; if insufficient time exists, people should be advised to stay indoors and shield themselves from the fire. This latter case particularly applies if the installation at risk could produce a fireball with very severe thermal radiation effects (e.g. LPG storage);

(c) for releases or potential releases of toxic materials, limited evacuation may be appropriate down wind if there is time. The decision would depend partly on the type of housing "at risk". Conventional housing of solid construction with windows closed offers substantial protection from the effects of a toxic cloud, while shanty houses which can exist close to factories, particularly in developing countries, offer little or no protection.

The major difference between releases of toxic and flammable materials is that toxic clouds are generally hazardous down to much lower concentrations, and therefore hazardous over greater distances. Also, a toxic cloud drifting at, say, 300 metres per minute covers a large area of land very quickly. Any consideration of evacuation must take this into account.

Although a plan should have sufficient flexibility built in to cover the consequences of the range of accidents identified for the on-site plan, it is suggested that it should cover in some detail the handling of the emergency to a particular distance from each major hazard works. This distance may be judged to be similar to the separation zone distance (Appendix 8) or the information-to-the-public distance (subsection 7.3.11).

6.3.2. Aspects to be included in an off-site emergency plan

Guidance from the United Kingdom Health and Safety Executive has been given on some of the aspects to be included in off-site emergency plans.

Organisation

Details of command structure, warning systems, implementation procedures, emergency control centres.
Names and appointments of incident controller, site main controller, their deputies and other key personnel.

Communications

Identification of personnel involved, communication centre, call signs, network, lists of telephone numbers.

Specialised emergency equipment

Details of availability and location of heavy lifting gear, bulldozers, specified fire-fighting equipment, fire boats.

Specialised knowledge

Details of specialist bodies, firms and people upon whom it may be necessary to call, e.g. those with specialised chemical knowledge, laboratories.

Voluntary organisations

Details of organisers, telephone numbers, resources, etc.

Chemical information

Details of the hazardous substances stored or processed on each site and a summary of the risks associated with them.

Meteorological information

Arrangements for obtaining details of weather conditions prevailing at the time and weather forecasts.

Humanitarian arrangements

Transport, evacuation centres, emergency feeding, treatment of injured, first aid, ambulances, temporary mortuaries.

Public information

Arrangements for: *(a)* dealing with the media – press office; *(b)* informing relatives, etc.

Assessment

Arrangements for: *(a)* collecting information on the causes of the emergency; *(b)* reviewing the efficiency and effectiveness of all aspects of the emergency plan.

6.3.3. Role of the emergency co-ordinating officer

The various emergency services will be co-ordinated by an emergency co-ordinating officer (ECO) who is likely to be a senior police officer but, depending on the circumstances, could be a senior fire officer. The ECO will liaise closely with the site main controller. Again depending on local arrangements, for very severe incidents with major or prolonged off-site consequences, the external control may pass to a senior local authority administrator or even an administrator appointed by the central or state government.

6.3.4. Role of major hazard works managements

This will vary depending on the local circumstances in different countries. Where the local authority (subsection 6.3.5) has the organisation to formulate the plan, the role of works managements in off-site emergency planning will be to establish liaison with those preparing the plans and to provide information appropriate to such plans. This will include a description of possible on-site accidents with potential for off-site harm, together with their consequences and an indication of the relative likelihood of the accidents.

Advice should be provided by works managements to all the outside organisations which may become involved in handling the emergency off site and which will need previously to have familiarised themselves with some of the technical aspects of the works activities, e.g. emergency services, medical departments and also water authorities (if water contamination could be a consequence of an accident).

6.3.5. Role of the local authority

In many countries the duty to prepare the off-site plan lies with the local authorities. They may have appointed an emergency planning officer (EPO) to carry out this duty as part of the EPO's role in preparing for a whole range of different emergencies within the local authority area. The EPO will need to liaise with the works to obtain the information to provide the basis for the plan. This liaison will need to be maintained to ensure that the plan is continually kept up to date.

It will be the responsibility of the EPO to ensure that all those organisations which will be involved off site in handling the emergency know of their role and are able to accept it by having, for example, sufficient staff and appropriate equipment to cover their particular responsibilities.

Rehearsals for off-site plans are important for the same reasons as on-site plans (section 6.2) and will need to be organised by the EPO.

6.3.6. Role of the police

The overall control of an emergency is normally assumed by the police, with a senior officer designated as emergency co-ordinating officer (subsection 6.3.3).

Formal duties of the police during an emergency include protecting life and property and controlling traffic movements.

Their functions include controlling bystanders, evacuating the public, identifying the dead and dealing with casualties, and informing relatives of death or injury.

6.3.7. Role of the fire authorities

The control of a fire is normally the responsibility of the senior fire brigade officer who would take over the handling of the fire from the site incident controller on arrival at the site. The senior fire brigade officer may also have a similar responsibility for other events, such as explosions and toxic releases. Fire authorities having major hazard works in their area should have familiarised themselves with the location on site of all stores of flammable materials, water and foam supply points, and fire-fighting equipment. They may well have been involved in on-site emergency rehearsals both as participants and, on occasion, as observers of exercises involving only site personnel.

6.3.8. Role of the health authorities

Health authorities, including doctors, surgeons, hospitals, ambulances, and so on, have a vital part to play following a major accident, and they should form an integral part of any emergency plan.

For major fires, injuries will be the result of the effects of thermal radiation to a varying degree, and the knowledge and experience to handle this in all but extreme cases may be generally available in most hospitals. For major toxic releases, the effects vary according to the chemical in question, and it is important for health authorities who might be involved in dealing with the aftermath of a toxic release to be familiar with the treatment appropriate to such casualties.

Major off-site incidents are likely to require medical equipment and facilities additional to those available locally, and a medical "mutual aid" scheme should exist to enable the assistance of neighbouring authorities to be obtained in the event of an emergency.

6.3.9. Role of the government safety authority

This will be the factory inspectorate in most countries. Inspectors are likely to want to satisfy themselves that the organisation responsible for producing the off-site plan has made adequate arrangements for handling emergencies of all types, including major emergencies. They may wish to see well-documented procedures and evidence of exercises undertaken to test the plan.

In the event of an accident, local arrangements regarding the role of the factory inspector will apply. These may vary from keeping a watching brief to a close involvement in advising on operations. In cases where toxic gases may have been released, the factory inspectorate may be the only external agency with equipment and resources to carry out tests.

In the aftermath, factory inspectors may wish to ensure that the affected areas are rehabilitated safely. In addition, they may require items of plant and equipment essential for any subsequent investigation to be impounded for expert analysis, and may also want to interview witnesses as soon as practicable.

6.4. Rehearsals and exercises in off-site emergency planning

Extensive experience in the chemical industry with on-site emergency planning has proved the need and value of rehearsals of emergency procedures.

The organisation responsible for producing the off-site plan should test its arrangements in conjunction with on-site exercises. Table-top rehearsals have proved extremely useful in such cases, although needing close control to maintain a sufficient element of realism in the exercises.

An essential component of any trial is that of testing fully the various communication links necessary to gather the information needed for overall co-ordination, e.g. between works and emergency services, and between the works emergency control centre and the incident.

Managements of major hazard works are well placed to advise on the setting up of rehearsals, and particularly to advise on the scope for an escalation in the degree of emergency.

7. Implementation of major hazard control systems

7.1. Introduction

Although the storage and use of large quantities of hazardous materials is widespread across many, perhaps most, countries of the world, the present systems for their control will differ substantially from one country to another. These will range from sophisticated inspection and enforcement regimes, on the one hand, requiring the co-ordinated attention of many different authorities at local and national level, to very limited inspection programmes, on the other, often concentrating on the structural integrity of buildings and excluding the major hazard aspects of the operations.

This wide variability of control means that the speed of implementation of a major hazard control system will depend on the facilities already existing in each country, particularly with regard to trained and experienced factory inspectors, together with the resources available locally and nationally for the different components of the control system described in this manual.

For all countries, however, implementation will require the setting of priorities for a stage-by-stage programme. It is most important that, where existing control arrangements are few, the planned programme should not attempt too much too soon. Experience has shown that this leads easily to a slippage in the planned time for meeting targets, with a subsequent general loss of morale.

7.2. Identification of major hazards

This is the essential starting-point for any major hazard control system – the definition of what actually constitutes a major hazard. Any list needs to be clear and unambiguous in order that all the organisations involved in implementing the various components of a system can establish quickly which works come within the definition and which do not.

Although definitions exist in some countries and particularly in the EC, a particular country's definition of a major hazard should reflect local priorities and practices and, in particular, the industrial pattern in that country. It would be particularly unhelpful, for example, to bring within scope far more works than the control authority could allocate resources for.

Any definition for identifying major hazards is likely to involve a list of hazardous materials, either specifically named or in general categories, together with an inventory for each, such that any works storing or using in excess any of these quantities is by definition a major hazard works.

Once the definition has been finalised, the next stage is to identify where the major hazard works exist for any particular region or country. If the definition has been established in legislation, works coming within its scope may have been required to notify their activity to the control authority.

Where, however, a country wishes to identify major hazard works before the necessary legislation is in place, considerable progress can be achieved informally, particularly where the co-operation of industry is available. Existing sources such as factory inspectorate records, information from industrial bodies, and so on, may enable a provisional list to be obtained which, apart from allowing early inspection priorities to be allocated, will enable an assessment to be made of the resources required for different parts of the control system. These provisional arrangements would need to be confirmed legally as soon as practicable.

7.3. Setting priorities

7.3.1. Establishment of a group of experts

For countries considering establishing a major hazard control system for the first time, an important first stage is likely to be setting up a group of experts as a special unit at government level. The unit should consist mainly of trained engineers (particularly chemical engineers), chemists and physicists, and should have the task of advising government, industry management, trade unions, local authorities, factory inspectorates, and so on, on all aspects of establishing a control system. Where the expertise is not readily available, it may be necessary to consider seconding experts from industry, universities or consultancies, possibly part time, to assist in this important work.

Where resources available for new major hazard works are very limited, it is important not to dilute this effort by moving experts away from a central base to work in areas on their own. The resources are generally better kept together as an expert unit in which members can develop as a team and pool their individual experiences.

The group will have to set priorities in deciding on its early work programme. Where definitions of major hazards have already been decided and the works identified, these can be collated for the whole country, with early priorities being directed at the most commonly occurring major hazards (likely to be chlorine ammonia and LPG).

The group may be required to train factory inspectors in the techniques of major hazard inspection, including operational standards for such works. They will need to be familiar with the methods for major hazard assessment (e.g. hazard and operability studies) and to be able to advise government, industry and local authorities when they are considering new or modified projects and drawing up emergency plans.

They should also be able to provide advice about the siting of new major hazards and the use of land nearby, e.g. for residential development.

They will need to establish contacts in other countries in order to keep up to date with major hazard developments, including new technologies and legislative changes.

7.3.2. Emergency planning on site

A fuller description of on-site emergency planning is given in section 6.2. On-site emergency planning should not be confined to major hazard works but is fully appropriate to a whole range of activities storing hazardous materials in smaller quantities. It is likely to have been recognised already by the managements of major hazards as requiring priority attention. Existing legislation may well have required emergency plans to have been drawn up as part of the general duty of safe operation. Where this is not the case, it should be remedied urgently.

Emergency plans require that the works be assessed for the range of accidents that could take place, together with how they would be tackled in practice. The handling of these potential accidents will require both staff and equipment, and a check should be made to ensure that both are available in sufficient numbers.

Once the plan has been drawn up, early rehearsals are essential to identify its weaknesses (particularly in the chain of communication) and to rectify them.

7.3.3. Emergency planning off site

A fuller description of off-site emergency planning is given in section 6.3. This is an area which has received less attention than on-site emergency planning, and many countries will be faced with considering this for the first time.

Advice can be obtained from the countries of the EC, which has a requirement for off-site planning for all the largest major hazard works. Here, the duty is placed on the local authority to draw up the plan based on information about assessed accidents and their consequences obtained from the works.

It may well be the case in some countries that this duty is more appropriate for the works than for the local authority, for it is at works management level that the technical expertise lies, often with the support of a multinational organisation.

The off-site emergency plan will have to link the possible accidents identified by the works, their expected likelihood of occurrence and the proximity of people living and working nearby. It must have addressed the need for evacuation and how it might be achieved – bearing in mind that conventional housing of solid construction offers substantial protection from toxic gas clouds whereas a shanty-type house is vulnerable to such accidents, and also remembering that sufficient time is often unavailable to allow widespread evacuation.

Finally, the emergency plan must identify organisations whose help will be required in the event of an emergency and must ensure that they know what role is expected of them: hospitals and medical staff should, for example, have decided how they would handle large numbers of casualties and in particular what treatment they would give to them. This is particularly important for accidents involving the lesser-known toxic gases.

The off-site emergency plan will need to be rehearsed; fuller details are given in section 6.3.

7.3.4. Siting

The basis for needing a siting policy for major hazard works is straightforward: since absolute safety cannot be guaranteed, major hazard works should be separated from people living and working outside the factory. The implementation of the policy is more difficult – possibly the hardest of the components of a control system to achieve.

Appendix 8 discusses this aspect in more detail, together with suggested separation distances for some typical hazardous inventories. Advice from the group of experts (subsection 7.3.1) is likely to be crucial in making progress in this area.

As a first priority, it may be appropriate to concentrate efforts on proposed new major hazards and to try and prevent the encroachment of housing, particularly shanty houses, which are a common feature in many countries.

This is likely to be an area requiring specific legislation, although consideration is being given in some countries to the developers of new works being required to buy additional land equivalent to the separation distance in order that they can maintain control of this land and prevent encroachment. This is an area of policy which will be dependent on local circumstances and practices.

It is particularly important to remember that if the recommended separation distances cannot be achieved in practice, substantial protection may be achieved by applying somewhat smaller distances, although clearly with less protection than by meeting the full distances.

7.3.5. Training of factory inspectors

The role of the factory inspectors is likely to be central in many countries in implementing a major hazard control system. They may have licensed the works before operations began and subsequently these works will have to be inspected. Factory inspectors will have the knowledge that will enable early identification of major hazards to take place (section 7.2).

Where they have specialist inspectors to call upon, factory inspectors will be assisted in the often highly technical aspects of major hazard inspection. In many countries, however, specialist inspectors are few and inspectors having academic qualifications that are not directly relevant to this work will be required to carry out complex inspections. The degree of success that they achieve will determine to a large extent the success of major hazard control in their country.

Inspectors will need appropriate training to aid them in this work. Fellowships to visit and work with more experienced factory inspectors in other countries have proved very successful, but this can be expensive although generally cost-effective.

The group of experts (subsection 7.3.1) will have an important part to play in organising training courses for inspectors, either centrally or regionally. As an interim measure, the group could draw up inspection check-lists for the more commonly encountered hazardous materials for use by inspectors as part of their enforcement duties.

Industry itself is likely to be the largest source of technical expertise within many countries, and may be able to provide assistance in factory inspectorate training – for example, in conjunction with its own internal training programmes.

7.3.6. Preparation of check-lists

A check-list is one of the more useful tools in hazard identification. Like a code of practice, it is a means of passing on hard-won experience to less experienced users. Check-lists are applicable to management systems in general and to a project throughout all its stages, starting with check-lists of the properties and process features of basic materials, continuing with check-lists for detailed design, and finishing with operations audit check-lists.

A check-list should be used as a final check that nothing has been neglected (like the one a pilot uses just before take-off).

Although not generally produced for this purpose, check-lists can be used by factory inspectors who are gaining experience in new technologies (subsection 7.3.5), but this should be done with caution.

For check-lists to be effective, they must be used and kept up to date. At the two extremes, there is a risk either of leaving them on the shelf to gather dust or else blindly adhering to a check-list which has been overtaken by a developing technology. Both tendencies should be firmly avoided.

Detailed references are available for a range of check-lists, including management systems, plant siting, plant layout, physical and chemical properties, process design, fire precautions, training and incident investigations (Lees, 1980).

7.3.7. Inspection of works by factory inspectors

This section describes aspects to be considered by inspectors at major hazard works. Necessarily, it concentrates on the techniques of identifying and inspecting items of plant which, in the event of a failure, would give rise to a serious risk to the safety of personnel both on and off site.

The work of a generalist factory inspector will depend on whether he or she has specialist inspectors (subsection 7.3.8) in support. Here it is assumed that this is the case. Where it is not, this section and the next dealing with the work of specialist inspectors should be read together.

The majority of serious incidents arise from the loss of containment of a hazardous substance. Therefore, it is necessary in the first instance to identify those items of plant which contain hazardous materials in sufficient quantity to cause a serious incident.

The responsibilities arising from major hazard works fall on the works managements, and it is they who should provide the expertise and resources to evaluate the risk of their own operations – and to take precautions accordingly. The role of the factory inspector as the enforcing authority is to make sufficient checks on what management has done to be satisfied of its competence to operate the plant safely and to maintain control in the event of an incident.

Factory inspectorates normally do not have the resources fully to inspect every item of plant and every operational procedure at a major hazard works. These need to be sampled, and the setting of priorities will be necessary, particularly at the largest plants, in order that the appropriate sample selection is made. Sampling here means the selection of a plant component (e.g. a pressure vessel) as representing a number of similar components, and then inspecting this sample in depth. A factory inspector faced with the inspection of a large site must estimate the resources available to achieve this and then plan

the time carefully. It is likely that at each visit a different sample will be selected for inspection, leading over time to a full coverage of the site. With this in mind, and with inspectors changing over the years, it is important to keep accurate records of what was inspected and the actions which arose from that inspection. If the inspector then moves job, his or her successor can look at the file and maintain continuity with the overall strategy for that works.

A key part of the inspection will be to check that operators are familiar with the safety aspects of the plant, both hardware and software, and have clear operating instructions covering, for example, their required action in the event of process deviation. Works inspection, testing and maintenance schedules will need to be examined for the sample of plant selected. The inspector would also need to check the emergency procedures for that plant and their integration into the overall on-site emergency plan.

7.3.8. Inspection of works by specialists

Specialist inspectors will include electrical, mechanical, civil and chemical engineers. Their role is likely to be to provide specialist support to the generalist factory inspectors, including advice on the selection of samples for inspection, and then to apply their specialist skills in the subsequent inspection.

Their work will include such procedures as:

(a) inspecting pressure vessels for design, operation and maintenance to approved standards;

(b) checking computer-controlled chemical plant for software integrity;

(c) checking the layout of liquefied gas installations together with the associated fire precautions;

(d) checking the procedures for plant modifications to maintain the initial integrity of the plant after modification;

(e) checking the design and maintenance procedures for pipelines carrying hazardous materials.

Specialist inspectors should be aware of the world-wide experience of accidents involving their particular discipline and be able to advise factory inspectors and works management on that basis.

Above all, specialist inspectors, particularly those chemically based, would be likely to have first-hand experience of some of the major hazard substances. Their advice may be crucial when factory inspectors are faced with licence applications to start a new major hazard works, particularly in relation to conditions which may need to be applied, and to a consideration of the potential off-site impact.

7.3.9. Evaluation of major hazards

This should be carried out by specialists, if possible, according to guide-lines drawn up, for example, by the group of experts (subsection 7.3.1) or by specialist inspectors or general factory inspectors, possibly with assistance from the works management. Evaluation involves a systematic study for major accident hazard potential, including knock-on effects, missiles, and so on. It will be a similar exercise, although in much less detail, to that carried out by the works management in producing its safety report for the factory inspectorate and in establishing an on-site emergency plan.

Evaluation will include a study of all handling operations of hazardous materials, including transport, because it is in this general category that major hazard accidents are most frequent.

An examination of the consequences of process instability or major changes in the process variables will be included. The works management should have looked at this in detail during the hazard and operability study at the design stage, but an independent examination, albeit again in much less detail, is well worth while.

The evaluation should also look at the positioning of one hazardous material in relation to another, e.g. are potentially explosive substances too close to pressurised toxic gases?

The consequences of common mode failure will also need to be assessed, e.g. what would be the consequences of a total and sudden loss of power feeding both plant and safety features?

The evaluation will consider the consequences of the identified major accidents in relation to off-site populations, which may determine whether the process or plant can be put into operation.

Evaluation, then, involves examining the plant and asking such questions as "What if . . .?", "How likely . . .?" and "Could it happen?", and deciding on actions leading from that assessment.

7.3.10. Actions arising from evaluation

Evaluation in conjunction with the factory safety report provides a basis for:

(a) deciding if a new process can be licensed;

(b) deciding on the layout of a new plant or process;

(c) deciding on hardware and software control requirements, e.g. automatic shut-off valves;

(d) formulating an on-site emergency plan and providing information for an off-site emergency plan;

(e) deciding on the separation required between the works and the neighbourhood;

(f) deciding the extent to which the public in the neighbourhood should be informed about the major hazard (subsection 7.3.11).

7.3.11. Information to the public

Experience of major accidents, particularly those involving toxic gas releases, has shown the importance of the public nearby having prior warning of: *(a)* how to recognise that an emergency is occurring; *(b)* what action they should take; *(c)* what remedial medical treatment would be appropriate for anyone being affected by the gas. EC legislation now requires those living near to the largest major hazard sites to be given information, particularly covering their action in the event of an emergency. For inhabitants of conventional housing of solid construction, the advice in the event of an emergency usually is to go indoors and close all doors and windows, switch off all ventilation or air conditioning, and switch on the local radio for further instructions.

Where large numbers of shanty-dwellers live close to a works, this advice would be inappropriate because, for example, of the low protection from gas clouds that such housing offers, and large-scale evacuation might be necessary. The difficulties of this are discussed in section 6.3. In these cases, film shows are considered a useful medium for passing advice to local people, particularly where a proportion of them may be unable to read.

The distance from a major hazard works within which people should be informed will come from the assessment of the major hazard, and is a subject on which advice from the group of experts (subsection 7.3.1) may be obtainable. As a first approximation, the separation distance (Appendix 8) may be found to be appropriate.

8. Prerequisites for a major hazard control system

8.1. Manpower requirements

A fully developed major hazard control system similar to that now operating within the EC requires a wide variety of specialised manpower.

Apart from industrial staff concerned either directly or indirectly with the safe operation of the major hazard plant, resources are required for general factory inspectors, specialist inspectors, risk assessors, emergency planners, local authority land planners, police, medical facilities, river authorities, and so on, in addition to legislators to promulgate new legislation and regulations for major hazard control.

Although this list might appear daunting to countries which are considering starting a control system from scratch, it should be remembered that it has taken other countries some 20 years to complete a comprehensive control package.

In most countries, manpower resources for this work are likely to be limited and the setting of realistic priorities is essential.

The installation of a system is likely to be based on the existing factory inspectorate for that particular country. With assistance from the group of experts (subsection 7.3.1), and particularly if some specialist support is available, a lot can be achieved at relatively small cost.

Major hazards can be defined, works identified and the key components of plant inspected. Works management can prepare on-site emergency plans. Training courses can be arranged for general factory inspectors in the techniques of major hazard inspection. To achieve all this would represent substantial progress. The objective should be to move forward one step at a time: if too much is attempted at one go, there is a strong likelihood, particularly with inexperienced staff, that they will feel overwhelmed and hence will fail to achieve their potential.

8.2. Equipment

A feature of establishing a major hazard control system is that much can be achieved with very little equipment. Factory inspectors will not need much in addition to their existing safety equipment. What will be required is the acquisition of technical experience and knowledge (section 8.3) and the means to relay this from the group of experts, say, to regional labour institutes, factory inspectorates and industry. Additional training aids and facilities may be necessary, depending on existing arrangements.

One type of equipment which will be very beneficial, although not essential, is the micro-computer. Access to computers will enable data bases to be established of major hazard works in the country and will assist in setting priorities, particularly for the group of experts. In addition, data bases can be obtained from other countries with information on hazardous substances and accidents (e.g. via the ILO International Occupational Safety and Health Information Centre (CIS)). In this respect, the computer will act as an information storage system.

Computers will also be invaluable in assessing the consequences of potential accidents in relation to nearby populations. In this respect, the computer will act as a high-powered calculator.

8.3. Sources of information

A key element in establishing a major hazard control system is obtaining state-of-the-art information, if necessary from overseas, and quickly passing this information on to all those who will need it for their safety work.

Useful sources of information are likely to include:

(a) industry experts and researchers;

(b) consultants;

(c) universities and colleges;

(d) professional institutions, e.g. the Institution of Chemical Engineers in the United Kingdom;

(e) national standards institutes;

(f) research institutes and corporations, e.g. the Netherlands Organisation for Applied Scientific Research – TNO (Netherlands), Batelle Institute (United States and the Federal Republic of Germany), Lawrence Livermore Laboratory (United States), Harwell (United Kingdom), Safety and Reliability Directorate – SRD (United Kingdom);

(g) published reports of major hazard assessments;

(h) reports of accidents, e.g. as described in *Loss Prevention Bulletin* by the Institution of Chemical Engineers in the United Kingdom;

(i) technical papers and conference proceedings;

(j) textbooks, particularly F. P. Lees: *Loss prevention in the process industries* (Lees, 1980);

(k) factory inspectorate reports.

The volume of literature covering the various aspects of major hazards work is now considerable and, used selectively, this would provide an important source of information to the group of experts.

Bibliography

American Institute of Chemical Engineers. 1985. *Guide-lines for hazard evaluation procedures.* New York.

Chemical Industries Association. 1984. *Guide-lines for chemical sites on off-site aspects of emergency procedures.* London.

——. 1976. *Recommended procedures for handling major emergencies.* London.

European Communities Council. 1982. Directive of 24 June 1982 on the major accident hazards of certain industrial activities. Publication No. L 230/1.

Fussell, J. 1976. *Fault tree analysis – Concepts and techniques in generic techniques in reliability assessment.* Leyden, Netherlands, Nordhoff Publishing Company.

Havens, J. A.; Spicer, T. O. 1984. *Development of a heavier-than-air dispersion model for the US Coast Guard hazard assessment computer system.* Symposium on Heavy Gas and Risk Assessment III. Bonn.

Henley, H. J.; Kumamoto, H. 1981. *Reliability engineering and risk assessment.* New Jersey, Prentice-Hall.

ILO. 1985. *Control of major hazards in India.* Geneva.

Lambert, H. E. 1973. *Systems safety analysis and fault tree analysis.* UCID-16238.

Lees, F. P. 1980. *Loss control in the process industry.* Vol. 1. London, Butterworth.

Netherlands, Directorate-General of Labour. 1979. *Methods for the calculation of physical effects of the escape of dangerous materials.*

——. 1982. *Occupational safety report regulation.*

Otway, H; Peltu, M. 1985. *Regulating industrial risks.* London, Butterworth.

United Kingdom Health and Safety Commission. 1976. *First report of the Advisory Committee on Major Hazards.* London.

United Kingdom Health and Safety Executive. 1985. *The control of industrial major accidents hazards regulations.* London, HMSO.

Appendix 1

List of dangerous substances and threshold quantities

(derived from Annex III to EC Directive (82/501/EEC))

List of substances for the application of Article 5

The quantities set out below relate to each installation or group of installations belonging to the same manufacturer where the distance between the installations is not sufficient to avoid, in foreseeable circumstances, any aggravation of major-accident hazards. These quantities apply in any case to each group of installations belonging to the same manufacturer where the distance between the installations is less than approximately 500 m.

Name	Quantity (≥)	CAS No.	EEC No.
1. 4-Aminodiphenyl	1 kg	92-67-1	
2. Benzidine	1 kg	92-87-5	612-042-00-2
3. Benzidine salts	1 kg		
4. Dimethylnitrosamine	1 kg	62-75-9	
5. 2-Napthylamine	1 kg	91-59-8	612-022-00-3
6. Beryllium (powders, compounds)	10 kg		
7. Bis(chloromethyl)ether	1 kg	542-88-1	603-046-00-5
8. 1,3-Propanesultone	1 kg	1120-71-4	
9. 2,3,7,8-Tetrachlorodibenzo-p-dioxin (TCDD)	1 kg	1746-01-6	
10. Arsenic pentoxide, Arsenic (V) acid and salts	500 kg		
11. Arsenic trioxide, Arsenious (III) acids and salts	100 kg		
12. Arsenic hydride (Arsine)	10 kg	7784-42-1	
13. Dimethylcarbamoyl chloride	1 kg	79-44-7	
14. 4-(Chloroformyl) morpholine	1 kg	15159-40-7	
15. Carbonyl chloride (Phosgene)	750 kg	75-44-5	006-002-00-8
16. Chlorine	25 t	7782-50-5	017-001-00-7
17. Hydrogen sulphide	50 t	7783-06-04	016-001-00-4
18. Acrylonitrile	200 t	107-13-1	608-003-00-4
19. Hydrogen cyanide	20 t	74-90-8	006-006-00-X
20. Carbon disulphide	200 t	75-15-0	006-003-00-3
21. Bromine	500 t	7726-95-6	035-001-00-5
22. Ammonia	500 t	7664-41-7	007-001-00-5
23. Acetylene (Ethyne)	50 t	74-86-2	601-015-00-0
24. Hydrogen	50 t	1333-74-0	001-001-00-9
25. Ethylene oxide	50 t	75-21-8	603-023-00-X
26. Propylene oxide	50 t	75-56-9	603-055-00-4
27. 2-Cyanopropan-2-ol (Acetone cyanohydrin)	200 t	75-86-5	608-004-00-X
28. 2-Propenal (Acrolein)	200 t	107-02-8	605-008-00-3
29. 2-Propen-1-ol (Allyl alcohol)	200 t	107-18-6	603-015-00-6
30. Allylamine	200 t	107-11-9	612-046-00-4
31. Antimony hydride (Stibine)	100 kg	7803-52-3	
32. Ethyleneimine	50 t	151-56-4	613-001-00-1
33. Formaldehyde (concentration ≥ 90%)	50 t	50-00-0	605-001-01-2
34. Hydrogen phosphide (Phosphine)	100 kg	7803-51-2	
35. Bromomethane (Methyl bromide)	200 t	74-83-9	602-002-00-3
36. Methyl isocyanate	150 kg	624-83-9	615-001-00-7
37. Nitrogen oxides	50 t	11104-93-1	
38. Sodium selenite	100 kg	10102-18-8	
39. Bis(2-chloroethyl)sulphide	1 kg	505-60-2	
40. Phosacetim	100 kg	4104-14-7	015-092-00-8
41. Tetraethyl lead	50 t	78-00-2	
42. Tetramethyl lead	50 t	75-74-1	
43. Promurit (1-(3,4-Dichlorophenyl)-3-triazenethio-carboxamide	100 kg	5836-73-7	
44. Chlorfenvinphos	100 kg	470-90-6	015-071-00-3
45. Crimidine	100 kg	535-89-7	613-004-00-8
46. Chloromethyl methyl ether	1 kg	107-30-2	
47. Dimethyl phosphoramidocyanidic acid	1 t	63917-41-9	
48. Carbophenothion	100 kg	786-19-6	015-044-00-6
49. Dialifos	100 kg	10311-84-9	015-088-00-6
50. Cyanthoate	100 kg	3734-95-0	015-070-00-8
51. Amiton	1 kg	78-53-5	
52. Oxydisulfoton	100 kg	2497-07-6	015-096-00-X
53. 00-Diethyl S-ethylsulphinylmethyl phosphorothioate	100 kg	2588-05-8	
54. 00-Diethyl S-ethylsulphonylmethyl phosphorothioate	100 kg	2588-06-9	
55. Disulfoton	100 kg	298-04-4	015-060-00-3
56. Demeton	100 kg	8065-48-3	
57. Phorate	100 kg	298-02-2	015-033-00-6
58. 00-Diethyl S-ethylthiomethyl phosphorothioate	100 kg	2600-69-3	
59. 00-Diethyl S-isopropylthiomethyl phosphorodithioate	100 kg	78-52-4	
60. Pyrazoxon	100 kg	108-34-9	015-023-00-1
61. Pensulfothion	100 kg	115-90-2	015-090-00-7
62. Paraoxon (Diethyl 4-nitrophenyl phosphate)	100 kg	311-45-5	
63. Parathion	100 kg	56-38-2	015-034-00-1
64. Azinphos-ethyl	100 kg	2642-71-9	015-056-00-1
65. 00-Diethyl S-propylthiomethyl phosphorodithioate	100 kg	3309-68-0	
66. Thionazin	100 kg	297-97-2	
67. Carbofuran	100 kg	1563-66-2	006-026-00-9
68. Phosphamidon	100 kg	13171-21-6	015-022-00-6
69. Tirpate'2,4-Dimethyl-1,3-dithiolane-2-carboxaldehyde 0-methylcarbamoyloxime	100 kg	26419-73-8	
70. Mevinphos	100 kg	7786-34-7	015-020-00-5
71. Parathion-methyl	100 kg	298-00-0	015-035-00-7
72. Azinphos-methyl	100 kg	86-50-0	015-039-00-9
73. Cycloheximide	100 kg	66-81-9	
74. Diphacinone	100 kg	82-66-6	
75. Tetramethylenedisulphotetramine	1 kg	80-12-6	
76. EPN	100 kg	2104-64-5	015-036-00-2
77. 4-Fluorobutyric acid	1 kg	462-23-7	
78. 4-Fluorobutyric acid, salts	1 kg		
79. 4-Fluorobutyric acid, esters	1 kg		
80. 4-Fluorobutyric acid, amides	1 kg		
81. 4-Fluorocrotonic acid	1 kg	37759-72-1	
82. 4-Fluorocrotonic acid, salts	1 kg		
83. 4-Fluorocrotonic acid, esters	1 kg		
84. 4-Fluorocrotonic acid, amides	1 kg		
85. Fluoroacetic acid	1 kg	144-49-0	607-081-00-7
86. Fluoroacetic acid, salts	1 kg		
87. Fluoroacetic acid, esters	1 kg		
88. Fluoroacetic acid, amides	1 kg		
89. Fluenetil	100 kg	4301-50-2	607-078-00-0
90. 4-Fluoro-2-hydroxybutyric acid	1 kg		
91. 4-Fluoro-2-hydroxybutyric acid, salts	1 kg		
92. 4-Fluoro-2-hydroxybutyric acid, esters	1 kg		
93. 4-Fluoro-2-hydroxybutyric acid, amides	1 kg		

Name	Quantity (≥)	CAS No.	EEC No.
94. Hydrogen fluoride	50 t	7664-39-3	009-002-00-6
95. Hydroxyacetonitrile (Glycolonitrile)	100 kg	107-16-4	
96. 1,2,3,7,8,9-Hexachlorodibenzo-p-dioxin	100 kg	19408-74-3	
97. Isodrin	100 kg	465-73-6	602-050-00-4
98. Hexamethylphosphoramide	1 kg	680-31-9	
99. Juglone (5-Hydroxynaphthalene-1,4-dione)	100 kg	481-39-0	
100. Warfarin	100 kg	81-81-2	607-056-00-0
101. 4,4'-Methylenebis(2-chloroaniline)	10 kg	101-14-4	
102. Ethion	100 kg	563-12-2	015-047-00-2
103. Aldicarb	100 kg	116-06-3	006-017-00-X
104. Nickel tetracarbonyl	10 kg	13463-39-3	028-001-00-1
105. Isobenzan	100 kg	297-78-9	602-053-00-0
106. Pentaborane	100 kg	19624-22-7	
107. 1-Propen-2-chloro-1,3-diol-diacetate	10 kg	10118-72-6	
108. Propyleneimine	50 t	75-55-8	
109. Oxygen difluoride	10 kg	7783-41-7	
110. Sulphur dichloride	1 t	10545-99-0	016-013-00-X
111. Selenium hexafluoride	10 kg	7783-79-1	
112. Hydrogen selenide	10 kg	7783-07-5	
113. TEPP	100 kg	107-49-3	015-025-00-2
114. Sulfotep	100 kg	3689-24-5	015-027-00-3
115. Dimefox	100 kg	115-26-4	015-061-00-9
116. 1-Tri(cyclohexyl)stannyl-1H-1,2,4-triazole	100 kg	41083-11-8	
117. Triethylenemelamine	10 kg	51-18-3	
118. Cobalt (metal, oxides, carbonates, sulphides as powders)	1 t		
119. Nickel (metal, oxides, carbonates, sulphides as powders)	1 t		
120. Anabasine	100 kg	494-52-0	
121. Tellurium hexafluoride	100 kg	7783-80-4	
122. Trichloromethanesulphenyl chloride	100 kg	594-42-3	
123. 1,2-Dibromoethane (Ethylene dibromide)	50 t	106-93-4	602-010-00-6
124. Flammable substances as defined in Annex IV(c)(i)	200 t		
125. Flammable substances as defined in Annex IV(c)(ii)	50 000 t		
126. Diazodinitrophenol	10 t	7008-81-3	
127. Diethylene glycol dinitrate	10 t	693-21-0	603-033-00-4
128. Dinitrophenol, salts	50 t		609-017-00-3
129. 1-Guanyl-4-nitrosaminoguanyl-1-tetrazene	10 t	109-27-3	
130. Bis(2,4,6-trinitrophenyl)amine	50 t	131-73-7	612-018-00-1
131. Hydrazine nitrate	50 t	13464-97-6	
132. Nitroglycerine	10 t	55-63-0	603-034-00-X
133. Pentaerythritol tetranitrate	50 t	78-11-5	603-035-00-5
134. Cyclotrimethylene trinitramine	50 t	121-82-4	
135. Trinitroaniline	50 t	29652-12-1	
136. 2,4,6-Trinitroanisole	50 t	606-35-9	609-011-00-0
137. Trinitrobenzene	50 t	25377-32-6	609-005-00-8
138. Trinitrobenzoic acid	50 t	(35860-50-5 (129-66-8	
139. Chlorotrinitrobenzene	50 t	28260-61-9	610-004-00-X
140. N-Methyl-N,2,4,6-N-tetranitroaniline	50 t	479-45-8	612-017-00-6
141. 2,4,6-Trinitrophenol (Picric acid)	50 t	88-89-1	609-009-00-X
142. Trinitrocresol	50 t	28905-71-7	609-012-00-6
143. 2,4,6-Trinitrophenetole	50 t	4732-14-3	
144. 2,4,6-Trinitroresorcinol (Styphnic acid)	50 t	72-71-3	609-018-00-9
145. 2,4,6-Trinitrotoluene	50 t	118-96-7	609-008-00-4
146. (a) Ammonium nitrates[1]	2 500 t	(6484-52-2	
(b) Ammonium nitrates in the form of fertilisers[2]	5 000 t	(	
147. Cellulose nitrate (containing > 12.6% nitrogen)	100 t	9004-70-0	603-037-00-6
148. Sulphur dioxide	250 t	7446-09-5	016-011-00-9
149. Hydrogen chloride (liquefied gas)	250 t	7647-01-0	017-002-00-2
150. Flammable substances as defined in Annex IV(c)(iii)	200 t		
151. Sodium chlorate	250 t	7775-09-9	017-005-00-9
152. tert-Butyl peroxyacetate (concentration ≥ 70%)	50 t	107-71-1	
153. tert-Butyl peroxyisobutyrate (concentration ≥ 80%)	50 t	109-13-7	
154. tert-Butyl peroxymaleate (concentration ≥ 80%)	50 t	1931-62-0	
155. tert-Butyl peroxy isopropyl carbonate (concentration ≥ 80%)	50 t	2372-21-6	
156. Dibenzyl peroxydicarbonate (concentration ≥ 90%)	50 t	2144-45-8	
157. 2,2-Bis(tert-butylperoxy)butane (concentration ≥ 70%)	50 t	2167-23-9	
158. 1,1-Bis(tert-butylperoxy)cyclohexane (concentration ≥ 80%)	50 t	3006-86-8	
159. Di-sec-butyl peroxydicarbonate (concentration ≥ 80%)	50 t	19910-65-7	
160. 2,2-Dihydroperoxypropane (concentration ≥ 30%)	50 t	2614-76-8	
161. Di-n-propyl peroxydicarbonate (concentration ≥ 80%)	50 t	16066-38-9	
162. 3,3,6,6,9,9-Hexamethyl-1,2,4,5-tetroxacyclononane (concentration ≥ 75%)	50 t	22397-33-7	
163. Methyl ethyl ketone peroxide (concentration ≥ 60%)	50 t	1338-23-4	
164. Methyl isobutyl ketone peroxide (concentration ≥ 60%)	50 t	37206-20-5	
165. Peracetic acid (concentration ≥ 60%)	50 t	79-21-0	607-094-00-8
166. Lead azide	50 t	13424-46-9	082-003-00-7
167. Lead 2,4,6-trinitroresorcinoxide (Lead styphnate)	50 t	15245-44-0	609-019-00-4
168. Mercury fulminate	10 t	(20820-45-5 (628-86-4	(080-005-00-2 (
169. Cyclotetramethylenetetranitramine	50 t	2691-41-0	
170. 2,2',4,4',6,6'-Hexanitrostilbene	50 t	20062-22-0	
171. 1,3,5-Triamino-2,4,6-trinitrobenzene	50 t	3058-38-6	
172. Ethylene glycol dinitrate	10 t	628-96-6	603-032-00-9
173. Ethyl nitrate	50 t	625-58-1	007-007-00-8
174. Sodium picramate	50 t	831-52-7	
175. Barium azide	50 t	18810-58-7	
176. Di-isobutyryl peroxide (concentration ≥ 50%)	50 t	3437-84-1	
177. Diethyl peroxydicarbonate (concentration ≥ 30%)	50 t	14666-78-5	
178. tert-Butyl peroxypivalate (concentration ≥ 77%)	50 t	927-07-1	
179. Liquid oxygen	2 000 t	7782-44-7	008-001-00-8
180. Sulphur trioxide	75 t	7446-11-9	

[1] This applies to ammonium nitrate and mixtures of ammonium nitrate where the nitrogen content derived from the ammonium nitrate is greater than 28 per cent by weight and aqueous solutions of ammonium nitrate where the concentration of ammonium nitrate is greater than 90 per cent by weight.

[2] This applies to straight ammonium nitrate fertilisers which comply with Directive 80/876/EEC and to compound fertilisers where the nitrogen content derived from the ammonium nitrate is greater than 28 per cent by weight (a compound fertiliser contains ammonium nitrate together with phosphate and/or potash).

N.B.: The EEC numbers correspond to those in Directive 67/548/EEC and its amendments.

Appendix 2

Example of a rapid ranking method for the classification of units/plant elements

(reproduced from the section on "Description of foreseeable hazards and of preventive provisions to control such hazards", in *Operational safety report: Guideline for the compilation*, Draft manual, Netherlands, Directorate-General of Labour, Labour Inspectorate.)

This shows how a rapid ranking system can be used in order to classify separate elements of plant within an industrial complex. It is a simplified version of the method established by the Dow Chemical Company. Besides this rapid ranking method, other methods are available. Generally, the more laborious the method, the more reliable are the results as an indication of the hazards.

1. Subdivision of the installation

Before hazard indexing can be applied, the installation in question should be subdivided into logical, independent elements or units. In general, a unit can logically be characterised by the nature of the process that takes place in it. In some cases, the unit may consist of a plant element separated from the other elements by space or by protective walls.

A plant element may also be an apparatus, instrument, section or system that can cause a specific hazard.

Examples of logical, independent units are given below:

- feed section;
- heating section/cooling section;
- reaction section;
- compression section;
- distillation section;
- wash section;
- collection system;
- filtration section;
- buffer tanks;
- prill tower;
- destruction section;
- flare system;
- blow-down system;
- recovery section;
- quench section, etc.

In the case of storage installations, each tank, bunker and silo is regarded as a separate unit.

In the case of storage of dangerous substances in packaging units (bags, bottles, drums, etc.), the total of packaging units stored in one location is regarded as one plant element.

2. Determination of fire and explosion index F and toxicity index T

For each separate plant element which contains flammable or toxic substances, a fire and explosion index F and/or a toxicity index T may be determined in a manner derived from the method for determining a fire and explosion index developed by the Dow Chemical Company (United States).[1]

The fire and explosion index F is calculated from:

$$F = MF \times (1 + GPH_{tot}) \times (1 + SPH_{tot}),$$

in which:

MF = *material factor* = a measure for the potential energy of the dangerous substances present (according to National Fire Protection Association (NFPA) data: see section 3);

GPH_{tot} = *general process hazards* = a measure for the hazards inherent in the process (from the nature and characteristics of the process: see section 4);

SPH_{tot} = *special process hazards* = a measure for the hazards originating from the specific installation (process conditions, nature and size of the installation: see section 5).

The toxicity index T is calculated from:

$$T = \frac{T_h + T_s}{100} (1 + GPH_{tot} + BPG_{tot}),$$

in which:

T_h = *toxicity factor* (obtained from NFPA data (see section 6);

T_s = *supplement* for MAC-value (see section 6).

For GPH_{tot} and SPH_{tot} the same values apply as for the determination of the fire and explosion index.

For the determination of F and T, a form may be used which is inserted in table 2.1.

Where more than one dangerous substance occurs in one plant element, a fire and explosion index F and/or a toxicity index T must be determined – when desired with the help of the form – for each substance.

When determining the hazard category of the plant element, the highest values found for F or T respectively are applied.

Substances which occur in a concentration of less than 5 per cent (weight percentage for liquids and solids, volume percentage for gases) need not be considered here.

3. Determination of the material factor MF

The starting-point for the calculation of the fire and explosion index is the material factor. This factor is a measure of the energy potential of the most hazardous material, or mixture of materials, present. The material factor is denoted by a number from 0 to 40, with the higher numbers indicating greater energy available.

The material factor is determined using only two properties – flammability [2] and reactivity – characterised by instability and water reactivity of

Table 2.1 Determination of the fire and explosion index F and of the toxicity index T

			Penalty	Penalty used**
LOCATION	NAME			DATE
PLANT	Unit	Job number		
MATERIALS AND PROCESS*		Charge		
MATERIALS	Solvents			
MATERIAL FACTOR MF (see table 1 or Appendix 2) 3	⟶			
GENERAL PROCESS HAZARDS (GPH)	4	Penalty	Penalty used**	
Exothermic reactions	4.1			
Endothermic reactions	4.2	0.20		
Material handling and transfer	4.3			
Process units within a building	4.4			
Add: GPH_{tot}	⟶			
$(1 + GPH_{tot})$ x material factor MF = sub-factor	⟶			
SPECIAL PROCESS HAZARDS (SPH)	5			
Process temperature (use highest penalty only)	5.1			
– Above flashpoint		0.25		
– Above boiling point		0.60		
– Above auto ignition		0.75		
Low pressure (atmospheric/sub-atmospheric)	5.2			
– Hazard of peroxide formation		0.50		
– Hydrogen collection systems		0.50		
– Vacuum distillation at less than 0.67 bar abs.		0.75		
Operation in or near flammable range	5.3			
– Storage of flammable liquids and LPGs outdoors		0.50		
– Reliance on instrumentation and/or N_2 or air purging to stay out of flammable range		0.75		
– Always in flammable range		1.00		
Operating pressure	5.4			
Low temperature	5.5			
– Between 0 and $-30\,^{\circ}C$		0.30		
– Below $-30\,^{\circ}C$				
Quantity of flammable material	5.6			
– In process				
– In storage				
Corrosion and erosion	5.7			
Leakage joints and packing	5.8			
Add: SPH	⟶			
$(1 + SPH_{tot})$ x sub-factor = fire and explosion index F				
TOXICITY INDEX T (see 6)				
$\dfrac{T_h + T_s}{100}$ x $(1 + GPH_{tot} + SPH_{tot})$ = Toxicity index T	⟶			

* The term "process" includes handling as well as storage.

** Consult 4 and 5 for the penalty to be used. For a number of process hazards the penalty to be used is fixed and can be taken from the preceding column "penalty".

a chemical. The material factors for many materials are listed in Appendix 2 (a). The material factor should be determined for every dangerous substance occurring in the plant element.

The material factor may be derived from table 2.2, using the numerical value for both flammability and reactivity as contained in NFPA literature.[3]

For example, ethylene oxide with a flammability of 4 and a reactivity of 3 leads to a material factor of 29 from table 2.2. Butyl acrylate, with a flammability of 2 and a reactivity of 2, leads to a material factor of 24 from table 2.2.

Flashpoint or H_{cv} can be used for flammability N_f. The value of H_{cv} is calculated by multiplying the heat of combustion, kJ/mol, by the vapour pressure at 300K (27° C) in bar. For materials boiling below 300K use 1.00 for vapour pressure. For N_r use the adiabatic decomposition temperature T_d.

For example, propylene oxide has the following basic properties:

– flashpoint below –20° C;

– heat of combustion 30.703 kJ/g;

– mol. weight 58;

– heat of combustion is thus 30.703 x 58 = 1780.78 kJ/mol;

– vapour pressure 0.745 bar (27° C);

– decomposition temperature 675° C.

Table 2.2. Determination of material factor

Flash point °C	H_{cv} kJ.bar/mol	flammability / N_f	N_r / reactivity 0	1	2	3	4
None	$< 4.10^{-5}$	0	0	14	24	29	40
> 100	4.10^{-5}–2.5	1	4	14	24	29	40
40 – 100	2.5 – 40	2	10	14	24	29	40
–20 – +40	40 – 600	3	16	16	24	29	40
< –20	> 600	4	21	21	24	29	40

Adiabatic decomposition temp. T_d K: < 830 | 830–935 | 935–1010 | 1010–1080 | >1080

Material Factor MF

For a flashpoint below –20° C the hazard value for flammability is 4. This may be checked by calculating H_{cv}:

$$H_{cv} = 1780.78 \times 0.745 = ca. \ 1326 \ kj. \ bar/mol.$$

An H_{cv} of 1326 gives a hazard value of 4 for flammability.

The adiabatic decomposition temperature is:

$$T_d = 675 + 273 = 948 \ K.$$

This gives a hazard value of 2 for reactivity. On the basis of table 2.2, a material factor of 24 will be applicable to propylene oxide.

4. Determination of general process hazards

4.1. Exothermic reactions

4.1.1. A 0.20 penalty is required for:

– *combustion* = the combustion of solid, liquid or gaseous fuel with air as in a furnace.

4.1.2. The following reactions require a 0.30 penalty:

(a) *hydrogenation* = the addition of hydrogen atoms to both sides of a double or triple bond; hazards are the use of hydrogen under pressure and at a relatively high temperature;

(b) *hydrolysis* = the reaction of a compound with water, such as the manufacture of sulphuric or phosphoric acids from oxides;

(c) *alkylation* = addition of an alkyl group to a compound to form various organic compounds;

(d) *isomerisation* = rearrangement of the atoms in an organic molecule, such as a change from a straight chain to a branched molecule, or displacement of a double bond; hazards are dependent on the stability and the reactivity of the chemicals involved and may in some cases require a penalty of 0.50;

(e) *sulfonation* = introduction of an SO_3H radical into an organic molecule through reaction with H_2SO_4;

(f) *neutralisation* = reaction between an acid and a base, to produce a salt and water.

4.1.3. The following require a 0.50 penalty:

(a) esterification : reaction between an acid and an alcohol or unsaturated hydrocarbon; moderate hazard, except in cases where acid is highly reactive or where the reacting substances are unstable, which may lead to a penalty of 0.75 or 1.25;

(b) oxidation = combination of oxygen with some substances, in which reaction is controlled and does not go to CO_2 and H_2O as in the case of combustion; where vigorous oxidising agents such as chlorates, nitric acid, hypochloric acids and salts are used, increase the penalty to 1.00;

(c) polymerisation = joining together of molecules to form chains or other linkages; heat must be dissipated to keep the reaction under control;

(d) condensation = joining together of two or more organic molecules with the splitting of H_2O, HCL or other compounds.

4.1.4. The following requires a 1.00 penalty:

– halogenation = introduction of halogen atoms (fluorine, chlorine, bromine or iodine) into an organic molecule; this is both a strongly exothermal and a corrosive process.

4.1.5. The following requires a 1.25 penalty:

– nitration = involves the replacement of a hydrogen atom in a compound with a nitro group; very strong exothermal reaction, possibly with explosive by-products.

Temperature controls must be good; impurities can act as catalysts for further oxidation, or nitration, and rapid decomposition can occur.

4.2. Endothermic reactions

Endothermic reactions receive a 0.20 penalty.

Examples of endothermic reactions are:

(a) calcination = heating of a material to remove moisture or other volatile material;

(b) electrolysis = separation of ions by means of electric current; there are hazards because of the presence of flammable or highly reactive products;

(c) pyrolysis or cracking = thermal decomposition of large molecules by high temperatures, pressures and a catalyst; regeneration of the catalyst by a separate combustion process can be dangerous.

If a combustion process is used as a source of energy for calcination, pyrolysis or cracking, the penalty is doubled to 0.40.

4.3. Handling and transfer of materials

(a) The loading and unloading of dangerous materials, especially with respect to the hazards involved in coupling and uncoupling of transfer lines of road-tankers, tank-cars and ships: penalty 0.50.

(b) Warehousing and yard storage (excluding tank storage) of hazardous materials in drums, cylinders, transport tanks, etc.:

– materials with process (storage) temperature below the atmospheric boiling point: penalty 0.30;

– materials with process (storage) temperature above the atmospheric boiling point: penalty 0.60.

The above penalties are applied because of possible exposure in handling and because of potential fire hazard. They are applied regardless of quantity (for which a penalty is given elsewhere).

4.4. Process units within a building

Process units which are located within a building and in which dangerous materials are processed and/or stored represent an increased hazard because of obstruction of natural ventilation:

– flammable liquids above flashpoint but below atmospheric boiling point: penalty 0.30;

– flammable liquids or LPG above atmospheric boiling point: penalty 0.60.

4.5. Miscellaneous

Packaging, filling of drums, sacks or boxes with dangerous materials, use of centrifuges, mixing of batches in open apparatus, more than one reaction in the same apparatus: penalty 0.50.

5. Determination of special process hazards

5.1. Process temperature

(a) Apply penalty of 0.25 when process or handling conditions are above flashpoint of material.

(b) Apply *penalty of 0.60* when process or handling conditions are above atmospheric boiling point.

(c) Materials such as hexane and carbon disulphide have low auto-ignition temperatures and can be ignited on hot steam lines: *penalty 0.75*.

5.2. Low pressure

No penalty is required for processes that operate at atmospheric or sub-atmospheric pressure, provided air leakage into the system will not create a hazard. *Example*: vacuum distillation of glycols.

(a) When air leakage into the system could create a hazard, apply a *0.50 penalty. Example*: handling pyrophoric materials, diolefins with hazard of peroxide formation and catalysed polymerisation.

(b) Hydrogen collection systems require a *0.50 penalty*.

(c) Any vacuum distillation at less than 0.67 bar absolute should be *penalised at 0.75* if air or contaminants leaking into the system could create a hazard.

5.3. Operation in or near flammable range

(a) Storage of flammable materials requires a *penalty of 0.50* for outdoor tanks, if the gas-air mixture in the vapour space is generally in or near the flammable range.

(b) For processes that operate close to the flammable limits or where it is necessary to use instrumentation and/or nitrogen or air purging to stay outside the explosion limits, use a *0.75 penalty. Examples*: oxidation of toluene to benzoic acid, dissolving of rubber, direct oxidation in ethylene oxide process.

(c) For processes that normally operate in the flammable range, use a *1.00 penalty. Examples*: ethylene oxide distillation and storage.

5.4. Operating pressures

Operating pressures above atmospheric pressure require a penalty which will increase as the operating pressure increases.

The penalty to be applied is given in figure 2.1.

Figure 2.1. Penalty for operating pressure

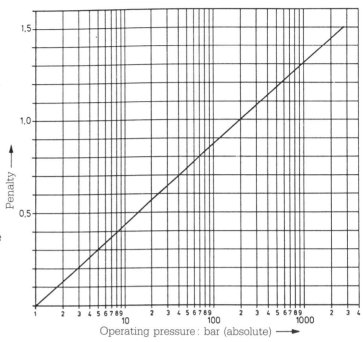

The penalty Y may also be calculated with the formula $Y = 0.435 \log P$, in which P is the absolute pressure at which the relief valve is set, expressed in bars.

The penalty curve in figure 2.1 is for flammable and combustible liquids and must be corrected for other materials as follows:

(a) for highly viscous materials such as tars, bitumen, heavy lubricating oil and asphalts, *multiply the penalty by 0.7*;

(b) for compressed gases, *multiply the penalty by 1.2*;

(c) for pressurised liquefied flammable gases, *multiply the penalty by 1.3*;

(d) *penalties are not applicable* to extrusion or moulding operations.

5.5. Low temperature

(a) For processes that operate between 0° C and −30° C, *add 0.30*.

(b) For processes that operate below −30° C, *add 0.50*.

The purpose is to make allowance for presumed brittleness. Moreover, in case of leakage, cold liquid will come into contact with the relatively hot environment, which can cause considerable evaporation.

5.6. Quantity of flammable material

(Figures 2.2 and 2.3)

5.6.1. In process

To obtain penalty, multiply kilograms of material in process by heat of combustion expressed in kJ/kg. Figure 2.2 gives the appropriate penalty. The penalty Y may also be calculated with the formula:

$\log Y = 0.305 \log eQ - 2.965$ in which e = heat of combustion of the material in kJ/kg, and Q = quantity of flammable material in kg.

Figure 2.3.   Penalty for the quantity of energy present in the flammable material in storage

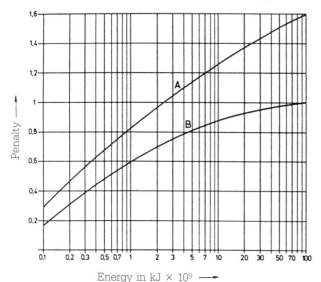

Curve A: pressurised liquefied gas.
Curve B: flammable liquids.

Use quantity of material in largest process vessel or train of process vessels connected together, in so far as that quantity can be released in its entirety because of an undesired event.

5.6.2. In storage

For flammable substances in storage, *the penalty to be used* with respect to the quantity present in a tank is determined in accordance with figure 2.3. A distinction is made here between pressurised liquefied gas (curve A) and flammable liquids (curve B).

The penalty Y may also be calculated with:

$$Y = \sqrt{185 - \left\{\log\left(\frac{eQ.10^{-9}}{700,000}\right)\right\}^2} - 11.45$$

Figure 2.2.   Penalty for quantity of energy present in the flammable material in process

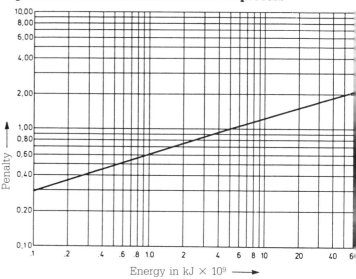

for pressurised liquefied gas (curve A); and

$$Y = \sqrt{55 - \left\{\log\left(\frac{eQ.10^{-9}}{270}\right)\right\}^2} - 6.4$$

for flammable liquids (curve B).

5.7. Loss of material through corrosion and erosion

This hazard should be assessed for both internal and external corrosion. Some areas to consider are –

– the influence of minor impurities in the process fluid on corrosion;

– external corrosion from breakdown in paint and coatings;

– resistant linings (plastics, brick, etc.) liable to damage at seams, joints or pinholes.

Apply the following penalties:

(a)   corrosion rate less than 0.5 mm/year with risk of pitting or local erosion: *0.10*;

(b)   corrosion rate over 0.5 mm/year, and less than 1 mm/year: *0.20*;

(c)   corrosion rate over 1 mm/year: *0.50.*

5.8. Leakage of joints and packing

Gaskets,[4] sealing of joints or shafts and packing can be sources of leaks, particularly where thermal or pressure cycling occurs. A penalty factor should be selected according to the design and materials chosen for these items, as follows:

(a) pump and gland seals likely to give some leakage of a minor nature: *0.10*;

(b) processes known to give regular leakage problems on pumps and flange joints: *0.20*;

(c) process fluids penetrating in nature, abrasive slurries which cause continuous sealing problems: *0.40*;

(d) sight glasses, bellows assemblies and expansion joints: *1.50*.

6. Determination of the toxicity index T

The toxicity index is primarily based on the index figures for health hazards established by the NFPA. For a number of materials, these figures, ranging from 0 to 4, are given in Appendix 2 (a).

For materials not included in this table, reference is made to the NFPA publications (see note 3 to this appendix).

The NFPA figures are translated into a toxicity factor T_h according to table 2.3.

Table 2.3. Relation between NFPA hazard figures and toxicity factor (T_h)

NFPA index figure	Toxicity factor (T_h)
0	0
1	50
2	125
3	250
4	325

In addition, the toxicity factor has to be corrected for the MAC-value of the toxic substance by adding to it a penalty T_s, which is given in table 2.4.

Table 2.4. Penalty T_s for MAC-value

Mac-ppm	Penalty T_s
≤ 5	125
5 - 50	75
> 50	50

The toxicity index (T) is now calculated as follows:

$$T = \frac{T_h + T_s}{100} (1 + GPH_{tot} + SPH_{tot}).$$

In this the material which gives the highest value of $T_h + T_s$ is determining.

GPH_{tot} = the total of General Process Hazard penalties (see section 4);

SPH_{tot} = the total of Special Process Hazard penalties (see section 5).

7. Classification in hazard categories

By comparing the indices F and/or T to the criteria stated in table 2.5, the unit in question is classified in one of the three categories established for this purpose. Category I is the category of plant elements with the lowest hazard potential and category III the one with the highest hazard potential.

Table 2.5. Categories of plant elements

	Fire and explosion index (F)	Toxicity index (T)
Category I	F < 65	T < 6
Category II	65 ≤ F < 95	6 ≤ T < 10
Category III	F ≥ 95	T ≥ 10

In cases where both for the fire and explosion index and for the toxicity index a category has been found, the highest one is adopted.

Notes

[1] Dow Chemical Company: *Fire and explosion index hazard classification guide* (Midland, Michigan, fourth edition, May 1976).

[2] In this connection a substance is considered flammable if the process temperature is higher than or equal to the flashpoint.

[3] National Fire Protection Association: *Identification of the fire hazards of materials*, NFPA Nos. 704M, 325M and 49.

[4] In principle, this concerns only gaskets for the sealing of moving parts or connections that must be opened regularly.

Appendix 2 (a)

Hazard figures and material factors as derived from National Fire Protection Association data

Name	NFPA classification			Material factor
	Health	Fire	Reac-tivity	
Acetaldehyde	2	4	2	24
Acetic acid	2	2	1	14
Acetic anhydride	2	2	1	14
Acetone	1	3	0	16
Acetonitrile	2	3	1	16
Acetyl chloride	3	3	2	24
Acetyl peroxide	1	2	4	40
Acetyl salcyl acid	1	1	0	4
Acetylene	1	4	3	29
Acrolein	3	3	2	24
Acrylic acid	3	2	2	24
Acrylamide	2	1	1	14
Acrylonitrile	4	3	2	24
Allyl alcohol	3	3	1	16
Allylamine	3	3	1	16
Allyl chloride	3	3	1	16
Allyl ether	3	3	2	24
Ammonia	3	1	0	4
tert-Amylacetate	1	3	0	16
Aniline	3	2	0	10
Barium stearate	0	1	0	4
Benzaldehyde	2	2	0	10
Benzene	2	3	0	16
Benzoic acid	2	1	0	4
Benzoyl chloride	3	2	1	14
Benzoyl peroxide	1	4	4	40
Bisphenol A	2	1	0	4
Bromobenzene	2	2	0	10
Butane	1	4	0	21
1,3-Butadiene	2	4	2	24
Butanol	2	3	0	16
1-Butene	1	4	0	21
n-Butyl acetate	1	3	0	16
Butyl alcohol	1	3	0	16
n-Butylamine	2	3	0	16
Butyl bromide	2	3	0	16
n-Butyl ether	2	3	0	16
tert-Butyl hydroperoxide	1	4	4	40
Butyl nitrate	1	3	3	29
tert-Butyl peroxide	1	3	3	29
Butylene	1	4	0	21
Butylene oxide	3	3	2	24
Calcium carbide	1	4	2	24
Calcium stearate	0	1	0	4
Carbon disulphide	2	3	0	16
Carbon monoxide	2	4	0	21
Chlorine dioxide	3	4	3	29

Name	NFPA classification			Material factor
	Health	Fire	Reac-tivity	
1-Chlorobutane	2	3	0	16
Chloroform	2	0	0	0
Chloromethylethyl ether	2	1	0	4
o-Chloro phenol	3	2	0	10
Chloropicrin	4	0	3	29
1-Chloropropane	2	3	0	16
Chlorostyrene	2	2	2	24
Coumarin	2	1	0	4
o-Cresol	2	2	0	10
Cumene	2	3	0	16
Cumene hydroperoxide	1	2	4	40
Cyanuric acid	2	0	1	14
Cyclobutane	1	4	0	21
Cyclohexane	1	3	0	16
Cyclohexanol	1	2	0	10
Cyclopropane	1	4	0	21
Diesel fuel	0	2	0	10
Dibutyl ether	2	3	0	16
o-Dichlorobenzene	2	2	0	10
p-Dichlorobenzene	2	2	0	10
1,2-Dichloroethylene	2	3	2	24
1,2-Dichloropropene	2	3	0	16
2,3-Dichloropropene-crude	2	3	0	16
3,5-Dichlorosalicylic acid	0	1	0	4
Dicumyl peroxide	0	2	3	29
Dicyclopentadiene	1	3	1	16
Diethyl amine	2	3	0	16
Diethyl benzene	2	2	0	10
Diethyl carbonate	2	3	1	16
Diethyl peroxide	0	4	4	40
Diethanolamine	1	1	0	4
Diethylene glycol	1	1	0	4
Diethylamine triamine	3	1	0	4
Diethyl ether	2	4	1	21
Diisobutylene	1	3	0	16
Diisopropylbenzene	0	2	0	10
Dimethyl amine (anhy.)	3	4	0	21
2,2-Dimethyl propanol	2	3	0	16
n-Dinitrobenzene	3	1	4	40
2,4-Dinitro phenol	3	1	4	40
m-Dioxane	2	3	0	16
Dioxolane	2	3	2	24
Diphenyl oxide	1	1	0	4
Dipropylene glycol	0	1	0	4
Di-tert-Butyl peroxide	1	3	4	40
Divinyl benzene	1	2	2	24
Divinyl ether	2	3	2	24

67

Name	NFPA classification			Material factor
	Health	Fire	Reactivity	
Dowtherm A heat tr. agt.	2	1	0	4
Epichlorohydrin	3	3	2	24
Ethane	1	4	0	21
2-Ethanolamine	2	2	0	10
Ethyl acetate	1	3	0	16
Ethyl acrylate	2	3	2	24
Ethyl alcohol	0	3	0	16
Ethyl benzene	2	3	0	16
Ethyl bromide	2	3	0	16
Ethyl chloride	2	4	0	21
Ethylene	1	4	2	24
Ethylene carbonate	2	1	1	14
Ethylene diamine	3	2	0	10
Ethylene dichloride	2	3	0	16
Ethylene glycol	1	1	0	4
Ethylene oxide	2	4	3	29
Ethylenimine	3	3	2	24
Ethyl nitrate	2	4	4	40
Ethylamine	3	4	0	21
Formaldehyde	2	4	0	21
Glycerine	1	1	0	4
Heptane	1	3	0	16
Hexane	1	3	0	16
n-Hexanol	2	2	0	10
Hydrazine	3	3	2	24
Hydrogen	0	4	0	21
Hydrogen sulphide	3	4	0	21
Isobutane	1	4	0	21
Isobutyl alcohol	1	3	0	16
Isopentane	1	4	0	21
Isopropanol	1	3	0	16
Isopropyl acetate	1	3	0	16
Isopropyl chloride	2	4	0	21
Isopropyl ether	2	3	1	16
Jet fuel	1	3	0	16
Lauroyl peroxide	0	2	3	29
Maleic anhydride	3	1	1	14
Magnesium	0	1	2	24
Methane	1	4	0	21
Methanol	1	3	0	16
Methyl acetate	1	3	0	16
Methyl acetylene	2	4	2	24
Methyl amine	3	4	0	21
Methyl chloride	2	4	0	21
Methyl chloracetate	2	2	1	14
Methyl cyclohexane	2	3	0	16
Methylene chloride	2	0	0	0
Methyl ether	2	4	0	21

Name	NFPA classification			Material factor
	Health	Fire	Reactivity	
Methyl ethyl ketone	1	3	0	16
Methyl hydrazine	3	3	1	16
Methyl isobutyl ketone	2	3	0	16
Methyl mercaptan	2	4	0	21
Methyl styrene	2	2	0	10
Mineral oil	0	1	0	4
Monochlorobenzene	2	3	0	16
Monoethanolamine	2	2	0	10
Naphtha	1	3	0	16
Naphthalene	2	2	0	10
Nitroethane	1	3	3	29
Nitroglycerine	2	2	4	40
Nitromethane	1	3	4	40
Nitropropane	1	2	3	29
2-Nitrotoluene	2	1	4	40
Octane	0	3	0	16
Pentane	1	4	0	21
Peracetic acid	3	2	4	40
Phenol	3	2	0	10
p-Phenylphenol	3	1	0	4
Potassium perchlorate	1	0	2	24
Propane	1	4	0	21
Propargyl alcohol	3	3	3	29
Propargyl bromide	4	3	4	40
Proprionitrile	4	3	1	16
Propylene	1	4	1	21
Propylene dichloride	2	3	0	16
Propylene glycol	0	1	0	4
Propylene oxide	2	4	2	24
Sodium dichromate	1	0	1	14
Stearic acid	1	1	0	4
Styrene	2	3	2	24
Sulphur	2	1	0	4
Sulphur dioxide	2	0	0	0
Toluene	2	3	0	16
1,2,3-Trichlorobenzene	2	1	0	4
1,1,1-Trichloroethane	3	1	0	4
Trichoethylene	2	1	0	4
Triethanolamine	2	1	1	14
Triethylene glycol	1	1	0	4
Triethyl aluminium	3	3	3	29
Triisobutyl aluminium	3	3	3	29
Triisopropanol amine	2	1	0	4
Triisopropyl benzene	2	3	0	16
Trimethyl aluminium	3	3	3	29
Trimethyl amine	2	4	0	21
Tripopylamine	2	2	0	10
Vinyl acetate	2	3	3	24
Vinyl acetylene		4	3	29

Name	NFPA classification			Material factor
	Health	Fire	Reac-tivity	
Vinyl allyl ether	2	3	3	24
Vinyl benzyl chloride	2	1	0	4
Vinyl chloride	2	4	1	21
Vinyl cyclohexane	2	3	2	24
Vinyl ethyl ether	2	4	2	24
Vinyl toluene	2	2	1	14
Vinylidene chloride	2	4	2	24
Xylene	2	3	0	16
Zinc stearate	0	1	0	4

Appendix 3

A guide to hazard and operability studies

(Originally published as Chemical Industry Safety and Health Council of the Chemical Industries Association: *A guide to hazard and operability studies* (London, 1977): reproduced by permission of the United Kingdom Chemical Industries Association Ltd., by whom copyright of the material is held.)

(Prepared initially in ICI and edited for general industry use by representatives of BP Chemicals Ltd, Chemical Industries Association Ltd, ICI Central Safety Dept., Shell Chemicals (UK) Ltd, under the aegis of the CISHEC Safety Committee.)

Foreword

The Chemical Industry is an industry concerned with innovation. It produces a continual stream of new processes and products which sometimes involve working at extremes of temperature, pressure, scale of operation or of toxicity. Major changes lead in turn to a series of minor changes as knowledge increases and processes are optimised.

There is within the Industry great and growing awareness of the necessity to apply more systematic approaches to safety—particularly in plant design. In addition, there is increasing pressure from society at large for improved standards of safety.

Whenever something new is carried out there is the danger that some part of the process will not behave in the expected manner and that such a deviation could have serious effects on other parts of the process.

One technique designed to study such deviations is known as a *Hazard and Operability Study*. This is defined in the British Chemical Industry Safety Council publication *Safety Audits* in the following manner:

> *The application of a formal systematic critical examination to the process and engineering intentions of the new facilities to assess the hazard potential of mal-operation or malfunction of individual items of equipment and the consequential effects on the facility as a whole.*

The technique aims to stimulate the imagination of designers in a systematic way so that they can identify the potential hazards in a design. It is extremely flexible. It can be applied to all types of plant within the Industry ranging from large continuous ones such as petrochemical or ammonia plants, through small batch units to individual proprietary items of equipment such as autoclaves or machines for making sheets of plastic. The technique can be used by small organisations as well as by large ones.

This guide introduces the technique and has been written to give an appreciation of the method itself, its scope and its value.

Note on presentation

The sequence of chapters has been arranged firstly to convey the basic principles of the technique and then to place it in context.

The distinguishing feature of Hazard and Operability Studies is the 'Examination Session' during which a multi-disciplinary team systematically examines all relevant parts of a design using a structured but creative approach. As this is the key to the whole enterprise it is described first in a chapter devoted to the principles of examination.

Some preparative work is necessary before the examination and naturally there is follow-up work to deal with and document the hazards exposed. Chapter 3 deals with the practical procedures for carrying out a Hazard and Operability Study. Hazard and Operability Studies are not an end in themselves but are part of an overall procedure for the initiation, design, construction, commissioning and operation of facilities. Studies can be undertaken at various stages, the timing of which is discussed in chapter 4.

Further aspects are discussed in Appendices. The first three deal with practical applications including worked examples for various types of plant. Practical advice is given subsequently on how to make a start with Hazard and Operability Studies, how to train people to carry them out and how to provide a continuing support for those engaged in them.

Contents

Contents

1   INTRODUCTION

Primarily, safety in the design of chemical plants relies on the application of various codes of practice or design codes which are based on the wide experience and knowledge of professional experts and specialists in the industry. Such application is backed up by the experience of local plant managers and engineers who have been involved in similar plants and who have had direct experience in their operation.

All new projects embody some element of change but in the chemical industry the degree of change from one plant to the next is often considerable. It is important to recognise that the body of established experience expressed in codes, etc is limited by the extent of existing knowledge and can only be relevant to the extent to which it is possible to apply it to new products, new plant and new methods of operation involved in the new design. It has become increasingly clear in recent years that although codes of practice are extremely valuable, it is particularly important to *supplement* them with an imaginative anticipation of hazards when new projects involve new technology.

The need to check designs for errors and omissions has been recognised for a long time, but this has traditionally been done on an individual basis. Experts have usually applied their special skills or experience to check particular aspects of design. For example the instrument engineer would check the control systems and having satisfied himself that the systems were satisfactory would put his mark of approval on the design and pass it to the next 'expert'. This kind of individual checking, provided it is carried out conscientiously, will obviously improve the design but clearly it has little chance of detecting hazards concerned with the interaction of a number of functions or specialisms. These hazards are likely to result from the unexpected interaction of seemingly safe components or methods of operation under exceptional conditions. If it is wished to study such interactions in new designs, the combined skills of a group of experts is required. Their total knowledge and informed imaginations can be used to anticipate whether the plant will operate as intended under all possible circumstances.

This report provides a method of working for such a group so that they can carry out their task systematically and thoroughly.

2   THE PRINCIPLES OF EXAMINATION

Because the examination procedure is the fundamental part of a Hazard and Operability Study, it is highlighted and described separately in this chapter.

2.1 The Basic Concept

Essentially the examination procedure takes a full description of the process, systematically questions every part of it to discover how deviations from the intention of the design can occur and decides whether these deviations can give rise to hazards.

The questioning is focussed in turn on every part of the design. Each part is subjected to a number of questions formulated around a number of *guide words* which are derived from method study techniques. In effect, the *guide words* are used to ensure that the questions, which are posed to test the integrity of each part of the design, will explore every conceivable way in which that design could deviate from the design intention. This usually produces a number of theoretical deviations and each deviation is then considered to decide how it could be caused and what would be the consequences.

Some of the causes may be unrealistic and so the derived consequences will be rejected as not meaningful. Some of the consequences may be trivial and would be considered no further. However, there may be some deviations with both causes that are conceivable and consequences that are potentially hazardous. These potential hazards are then noted for remedial action.

Having examined one part of the design and recorded any potential hazards associated with it, the study progresses to focus on the next part of the design. The examination is repeated until the whole plant has been studied.

The purpose of the examination is to identify all possible deviations from the way the design is expected to work and all the hazards associated with these deviations. In addition, some of the hazards can be resolved. If the solution is obvious and is not likely to cause adverse effects on other parts of the design, a decision can be taken and the design modified on the spot. This is not always possible—for example, it may be necessary to obtain further information. Thus the output from examinations normally consists of a mixture of decisions and questions for answering at subsequent meetings.

Although the approach as described may appear to generate many hypothetical deviations in a mechanistic way, the success or failure depends on four aspects

i   The accuracy of drawings and other data used as the basis for the study
ii The technical skills and insights of the team
iii The ability of the team to use the approach *as an aid* to their imagination in visualising deviations, causes and consequences
iv The ability of the team to maintain a sense of proportion, particularly when assessing the seriousness of the hazards which are identified

Because the examination is so systematic and highly structured, it is necessary that those participating use certain terms in a precise and disciplined way. The most important of these terms are

Intention   The *intention* defines how the part is expected to operate. This can take a number of forms and can be either descriptive or diagrammatic. In many cases it will be a flowsheet or line diagram. Other forms are described in section 3.3.

Deviations   These are departures from the intention which are discovered by systematically applying the *guide words*.

Causes   These are the reasons why *deviations* might occur. Once a *deviation* has been shown to have a conceivable or realistic cause, it can be treated as meaningful.

Consequences   These are the results of the *deviations* should they occur.

Hazards   These are *consequences* which can cause damage, injury or loss.

Guide Words   These are simple words which are used to qualify the *intention* in order to guide and stimulate the creative thinking process and so discover *deviations*. A list of *guide words* is given in Table 1.

2.2 A Simple Example

To illustrate the principles of the examination procedure, consider a plant in which chemicals A and B react together to form a product C. Let us suppose that the chemistry of the process is such that the concentration of raw material B must never exceed that of A otherwise an explosion may occur.

Referring to Figure 1 start, say, with the pipeline extending from the suction side of the pump which delivers raw material A to where it enters the reaction vessel.

Figure 1 AN EXAMPLE OF A SIMPLE FLOWSHEET

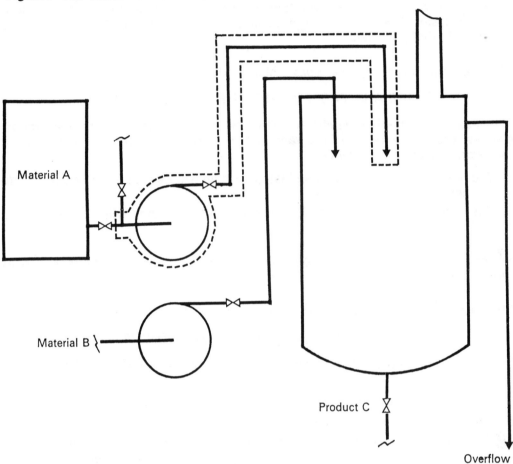

Reaction: A + B = C
Component B must not exceed Component A to avoid an explosion
The part of the plant examined is outlined thus – – – – – – – – – – –

The *intention* is partly described by the flowsheet and partly by the process control requirements to transfer A at some specified rate. The first *deviation* is that obtained by applying the *guide word* NOT, DON'T or NO to the *intention*. This is combined with the *intention* to give

DON'T TRANSFER A

The flowsheet is then examined to establish the *causes* which might produce a complete cessation of flow of A. These *causes* could be

i   Supply tank is empty

ii Pump fails to turn—mechanical failure
                        —electrical failure
                        —pump is switched off, etc

iii Pipeline is fractured

iv Isolation valve is closed

Clearly some at least of these are conceivable *causes* and so we can say that this is a meaningful *deviation*.

Next we consider the *consequences*. Complete cessation of flow of A would very soon lead to an excess of B over A in the reaction vessel and consequently to a risk of explosion. We have therefore discovered a *hazard* in the design and this is noted for further consideration.

We now apply the next *guide word* which is MORE. The *deviation* is

MORE A IS PASSED INTO THE REACTION VESSEL

The *cause* would be that the characteristics of the pump may, under some circumstances, produce excessive flow rate. If this *cause* is accepted as realistic, we then consider the *consequences*

i   The reaction produces C contaminated with an excess of A which goes on into the next stage of the process
ii The excess flow into the reaction vessel means that some will leave the vessel by the overflow

Further information will have to be obtained to decide whether these *consequences* would constitute a *hazard*.

The next *guide word* is LESS. The *deviation* is

LESS A IS PASSED INTO THE REACTION VESSEL

The *causes* are a little different from those when the *deviation* was the complete cessation of flow of A

i   The isolation valve is slightly closed
ii   The pipeline is partly blocked
iii The pump fails to produce full flow—because the impellers are eroded, or
                                        —because valves are worn, etc

The *consequence* is similar to complete cessation of flow and so the potential *hazard* is of a possible explosion.

Four further *guide words* are in turn applied to the design *intention* of this part, to ensure that all conceivable *deviations* are explored.

When the pipeline which introduces raw material A has been examined, it is marked on the flowsheet as having been checked. The next part of the design is then chosen for study and this could be the pipeline which introduces raw material B into the reaction vessel. This sequence is repeated for every part of the design, each line, the vessel auxiliaries such as stirrers, any services to the vessel such as the provision of heating and cooling and the vessel itself. A chart of the sequence is given in Figure 2. This particular approach is sometimes called the 'line by line' method.

Only under exceptional circumstances is a written record made of every step of the examination. It is more usual to carry out the steps mentally and verbally in discussion and to write down only the potential *hazards* and their *causes*.

The proposed action is also noted if it can be agreed straight away. If there is some doubt about the action or if further information is required, the matter must be brought forward to a subsequent meeting.

Figure 2 DETAILED SEQUENCE OF EXAMINATION

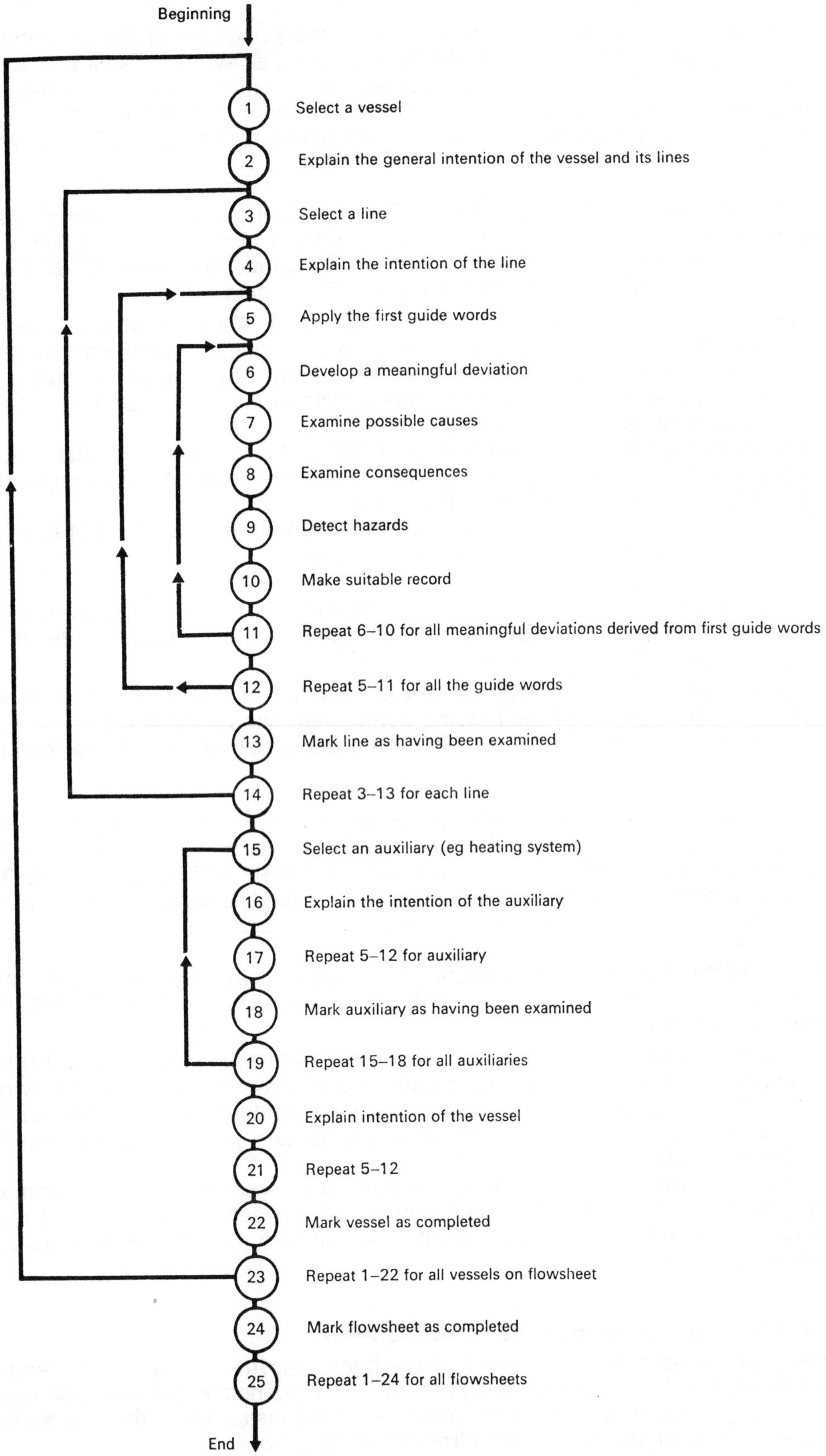

Beginning

1 Select a vessel

2 Explain the general intention of the vessel and its lines

3 Select a line

4 Explain the intention of the line

5 Apply the first guide words

6 Develop a meaningful deviation

7 Examine possible causes

8 Examine consequences

9 Detect hazards

10 Make suitable record

11 Repeat 6–10 for all meaningful deviations derived from first guide words

12 Repeat 5–11 for all the guide words

13 Mark line as having been examined

14 Repeat 3–13 for each line

15 Select an auxiliary (eg heating system)

16 Explain the intention of the auxiliary

17 Repeat 5–12 for auxiliary

18 Mark auxiliary as having been examined

19 Repeat 15–18 for all auxiliaries

20 Explain intention of the vessel

21 Repeat 5–12

22 Mark vessel as completed

23 Repeat 1–22 for all vessels on flowsheet

24 Mark flowsheet as completed

25 Repeat 1–24 for all flowsheets

End

2.3 Meanings of *guide words*

In the simple example we have demonstrated the principles of the examination method by showing how to apply the first three guide words. These are usually straightforward and produce easily-understood deviations. The remaining four guide words are not so easily applied and require some further explanation. Their meanings are now illustrated—again by reference to the example shown in Figure 1.

The next two deviations are both qualitative and all or part of the original design intention is retained. The first of these is a deviation in which some other effect occurs concurrently with the design intention. The guide words are AS WELL AS and the deviation AS WELL AS TRANSFER A. This could mean

i   The transfer of some component in addition to A. A search of the flowsheet in Figure 1 shows an additional line with an isolation valve on the pump suction. If this valve were not shut, another component might be transferred together with A. This raises the possible effects of such a component either in its own right or as an inert diluent of A

ii The transfer of A somewhere else in addition to its transfer to the reactor. Inspection of the flowsheet shows this is possible. It could for example flow up the line on the suction side of the pump

iii The carrying out of another activity concurrently with the transfer. For example, can A boil or decompose in the pipelines or pump?

The other related deviation is that which occurs when the design intention is incompletely achieved. The guide words are PART OF and the deviation PART OF TRANSFER A. This could mean

i   A component of A is missing. Here a knowledge of the composition of A is required so the effects of the missing component can be assessed

ii The omission of one or more reactors if the pump delivers A to more than one reactor.

The final two deviations are again qualitative but none of the original design intention is retained. The first of these is the opposite of the design intention. The guide word is REVERSE and the deviation REVERSE TRANSFER OF A. This means flow from the reactor back through the pump. The flowsheet is examined to see if this is possible and the consequences are assessed.

Lastly, there is the complete substitution of the design intention by something else. The guide words are OTHER THAN and the deviation is OTHER THAN TRANSFER A. This could mean

i   The transfer of a different material. The flowsheet is examined to see if this is possible. Substitution could arise in a number of ways. For example, the wrong material could be delivered or another material admitted via the T piece on the suction side of the pump. Information would be gathered on possible materials and their effects

ii A change in the implied destination, ie transfer of A somewhere other than the reactor. Inspection of the flowsheet shows that this can happen via the T piece

iii A change in the nature of the activity. For example, can A solidify instead of being transferred?

2.4 Further advice on the use of *guide words*

In the previous section, guide words have been presented as a set of standard terms which can be applied to design intentions to generate notional deviations. Their value and applicability depend upon the intentions to which they are applied and the possible modes of deviation from those intentions.

When they are used on broadly-expressed intentions they are all applicable. They may also be applied at the detailed level of descriptive words or phrases. However, when they are applied to intentions expressed in fine detail, some restrictions and even some modifications may be found necessary.

When they are applied to an activity such as REACT or TRANSFER it is usual to find that all the guide words will generate intelligible notional deviations. Sometimes more than one deviation will be generated by one guide word. Similarly when they are applied to substances, all guide words, with the possible exception of REVERSE, will be intelligible. Again, more than one deviation may be developed. For example, MORE STEAM can mean a greater quantity or rate of steam (a capacity increase) or steam at higher pressure (an intensity increase).

When dealing at a more detailed level of design intention, some restriction will be found because the possible modes of deviation are reduced. For example, suppose the design intention for a temperature of 100°C was being considered. The only possible modes of deviation (if we forget about the absolute zero) are MORE, ie above 100°C and LESS, ie below 100°C.

When the guide words are applied to time aspects, MORE and LESS may mean longer and shorter duration or higher and lower frequencies. However, when dealing with sequence or absolute time, the extra guide words SOONER or LATER give more insight than OTHER THAN. Similarly when dealing with position, sources or destination, WHERE ELSE is more useful than OTHER THAN. Again HIGHER and LOWER will give more meaning than MORE and LESS for deviations in elevation.

When dealing with a design intention involving a complex specification of temperatures, rates, composition, pressures, etc, it may be better to apply the whole sequence of guide words to each element individually rather than apply each guide word across the whole range of the specification. Also, when applying

Table 1 A LIST OF GUIDE WORDS
Guide words are applied to the design intention. The design intention tells us what the equipment is expected to *do.*

GUIDE WORDS	MEANINGS	COMMENTS
NO or NOT	The complete negation of these intentions	No part of the intentions is achieved but nothing else happens
MORE LESS	Quantitative increases or decreases	These refer to quantities + properties such as flow rates and temperatures as well as activities like 'HEAT' and 'REACT'
AS WELL AS	A qualitative increase	All the design and operating intentions are achieved together with some additional activity
PART OF	A qualitative decrease	Only some of the intentions are achieved; some are not
REVERSE	The logical opposite of the intention	This is mostly applicable to activities, for example reverse flow or chemical reaction. It can also be applied to substances, eg, 'POISON' instead of 'ANTIDOTE' or 'D' instead of 'L' optical isomers
OTHER THAN	Complete substitution	No part of the original intention is achieved. Something quite different happens

guide words to a sentence it may be more useful to apply the sequence of guide words to each word or phrase separately, starting with the key part which described the activity.

3 THE PROCEDURE FOR A STUDY

The principles described in the previous chapter are put into practice in a procedure which consists of the following steps

i   Define objectives and scope
ii Select the team
iii Prepare for the study
iv Carry out the examination
v   Follow-up
vi Record the results

Each of these is discussed in more detail.

3.1 Definition of objectives

The objectives and scope of a study should be made explicit as soon as possible. Some examples of reasons for a study are

i   To check a design
ii To decide whether and where to build—but see section 4.1
iii To decide whether to buy a piece of equipment
iv To obtain a list of questions to put to a supplier
v   To check running instructions
vi To improve the safety of existing facilities

It is also necessary to decide the types of hazard to be considered, for example
i   To people working in a plant
ii To plant and equipment
iii To or from product quality
iv To the general public
v   To the environment

The physical limits of the plant to be studied must be decided and whether interactions with neighbouring units or buildings should be included. Any time or financial constraints must be specified. It will also be necessary to state whether any aspects such as the civil engineering or the chemistry can be taken for granted and deliberately excluded.

The general objectives for a study are normally set by the person responsible for the project or for the plant; for example, the project manager, project engineer or the plant manager. He is usually assisted in this definition by a study leader (see 3.2). The study will be carried out by a team and the degree of authority given to that team must be decided. The definition is made easier if the manager has an appreciation of the approach; training courses for managers are discussed in Appendix 5.

3.2 Team composition

Hazard and Operability Studies are normally carried out by multi-disciplinary teams. There are two types of team member, namely those who will make a technical contribution and those who play a supporting and structuring role.

Technical team members

The examination requires the team to have a detailed knowledge of the way the plant is intended to work. This means a blend of those concerned with the design of the plant and those concerned with its operation. The technique of using guide words generates a very large number of questions. For most purposes it is essential that the team contains enough people with sufficient knowledge and experience to answer the majority of those questions without recourse to further expertise.

As an example, a typical small chemical plant would be examined by a team consisting of each of the following

> Mechanical engineer
> Chemical engineer
> R & D chemist
> Production manager
> Project manager responsible for the project as a whole

This group should contain sufficient expertise to provide the necessary technical input. Additionally if some members of the team are drawn from those who also have some responsibility for the design of a plant, they will be particularly motivated to produce a successful design and a safe operating procedure. Normally these members of the team will have the necessary authority to make changes. The blend of disciplines will vary with the type of project. Some projects will require the inclusion of different disciplines for example

> Instrument and electrical engineers
> Civil engineers
> Pharmacists, etc

The team should not be too large, ideally between three and five technical members. If a study seems to require a large number of people it is worthwhile trying to break it down into several disparate parts with some variation of team composition for each part.

The training of team members is discussed in Appendix 5.

Supporting team members
Because examination sessions are highly structured and very systematic, it is necessary to have someone to control the discussion. We will call this person the 'study leader'.

The study leader has a role to play throughout a study. He should help whoever has commissioned the study to define its scope. He may help with the selection and training of the team. He will advise on the assembly of the necessary data and may help convert this into a suitable form. However, his most obvious role emerges during the examination sessions where he guides the systematic questioning and he must be thoroughly trained for this job. It is not desirable that he should be responsible for making a major technical contribution. If possible, he should not have been closely associated with the subject of the study as there is a danger of developing blind spots and failing to use the technique objectively. But he should have sufficient technical knowledge to be able to understand and control the team discussions. The characteristics and training required are discussed in Appendix 5.

In addition to the study leader it is sometimes desirable to have a further supporting member of the team to make a note of the hazards as they are detected. This person is known as the study 'secretary' or 'scribe'. It may appear extravagant to employ two people in a supporting role. However, experience indicates that this arrangement greatly increases the rate of working of the team as a whole. It is better to employ seven people for two days rather than six people for four days on a given study. The training of secretaries is also discussed in Appendix 5.

The attitude of team members
It is imperative that the team as a whole should have a positive and constructive

attitude to a study as its success ultimately depends upon the imaginative thinking of the members.

This positive attitude must be built up from the definition stage onwards. Suitable training is a great help and should create a climate in which the team members are anxious to start the study. At times during the examination sessions, some team members feel the approach is tedious but a well-led team ultimately derives considerable satisfaction from its design work receiving such a thorough analysis.

3.3 Preparative work

The amount of preparative work required depends upon the size and complexity of the plant. In the simplest case, a group of people can work together for a couple of hours on a simple flowsheet and complete a study. In general, rather more preparation is required. The preparative work consists of four stages

i   Obtain the data
ii Convert the data into a suitable form
iii Plan the sequence for the study
iv Arrange the necessary meetings

Typically, the data consists of various drawings in the form of line diagrams, flowsheets, plant layouts, isometrics and fabrication drawings. Additionally there can be operating instructions, instrument sequence control charts, logic diagrams and computer programmes. Occasionally there are plant manuals and equipment manufacturers' manuals.

The data must be inspected to make sure it is sufficiently comprehensive to cover the defined area of study and any discrepancies or ambiguities in the data must be resolved. The amount of work required to convert the data into a suitable form and plan the sequence for the study varies with the type of plant.

With continuous plants the preparative work is minimal. The existing flowsheets or pipe and instrument diagrams contain sufficient information for the study and it is merely necessary to see that there are enough copies of each drawing available. Likewise the sequence for the study is straightforward. The study team starts at the beginning of the process and progressively works downstream. A list of typical plants of this type together with a worked example of part of a study are shown in Appendix 1.

In view of the relative simplicity of the study of continuous processes, most of this section and the greater weight of material in the worked examples (see Appendices 2 and 3) are devoted to the more complex situations found in batch operations.

With batch plants the preparative work is usually more extensive. In addition to drawings which describe the plant itself, it is necessary to know the sequence of plant operations. This can be in a variety of forms—for example running instructions, logic diagrams or instrument sequence diagrams. In some circumstances (eg when more than one batch of material is being processed at the same time) it may be necessary to prepare a display indicating the status of each vessel on a time basis. Again, operators may be physically involved in the process (eg in charging vessels) as opposed to simply controlling the process and their activities will need to be represented by means of flow process charts.

Sometimes it will not be possible to start at the beginning of a flowsheet and work downstream. Instead the team will start with the first operating instruction and apply the guide words to it (or to part of it) and refer to the line diagram, flow process charts, etc. The study leader will usually prepare a plan for the sequence of study before the study starts. A list of typical plants of this type together with a simplified example is given in Appendix 2.

With some kinds of complicated, proprietary items of equipment, the preparative work can be extensive and occupy more man-days than the examination itself. Equipment manufacturers rarely supply sufficient information in a form suitable for a study, and as a rule flowsheets do not exist which show the full integration of a proprietary item of equipment with existing plant. Occasionally several proprietary items from different manufacturers are assembled in series.

The study leader will often have to prepare a suitable model tailored to suit the application of the technique to the equipment. This may include a display of its relationships with operators and with other plant. This preparative work will often involve a lengthy dialogue between the project engineer and the study leader and sometimes involves the manufacturers as well. The study leader will prepare a plan for the study and discuss both the model and the plan with the team prior to starting the study. A list of typical equipment which might be treated in this way and an example are given in Appendix 3.

Once the data has been assembled and the model made (if necessary) the study leader is in a position to start to arrange meetings. The first requirement is to estimate the team-hours needed for the study. This can be built up in a number of ways. As a general rule each individual part to be studied, eg each main pipeline into a vessel, will take an average of fifteen minutes team time. The simple example shown in Figure 1 should take one and a half hours made up of fifteen minutes each for the two inlets, two exits, the vent and the vessel itself.

Thus an estimate can be made by considering the number of pipelines and vessels. Another way to make a rough estimate is to allow two and a half hours for each vessel. Fifteen minutes should also be allowed for each simple verbal statement such as 'switch on conveyor', 'motor starts', 'conveyor starts'.

Having arrived at an estimate of the team hours required, the study leader (or secretary) can consider arranging meetings. Ideally the duration of examination sessions should be restricted to three hours (preferably in the morning). Longer periods of examination are undesirable because it is usually found that effectiveness begins to fall off. Under extreme time-pressures, examination sessions have been held for two consecutive days but such a programme should be attempted only in very exceptional circumstances.

Ideally there should be not more than two sessions per week to allow for the follow-up work described in Section 3.5. This might give rise to difficulties when individual members of the team have to travel to the meeting place.

Examination sessions should be arranged to be carried out in rooms which are free from distractions and with plenty of table space for flowsheets, charts, etc.

With large capital projects, it is often found that one team cannot carry out all the studies within the time constraints imposed. It may therefore be necessary to use a multiplicity of teams and team leaders. One of the team leaders should then act as a co-ordinator and allocate sections of the design to different teams and prepare time schedules for the study as a whole.

3.4 The examination in practice

The principles have already been described in Section 2 and the purpose of this chapter is to add practical advice on how these principles are put into effect.

Examination sessions are highly structured with the study leader controlling the discussion by following his predetermined plan. If the approach is based on the flowsheet he selects the first vessel and asks the team to explain its broad function. He selects the pipeline or other element of the design and asks the team to make its purpose explicit. This is not always straightforward but until every member of the team knows exactly what something is supposed to do, deviations cannot be generated. A similar approach is used if the study sequence is based on operating instructions.

The study leader then applies the first guide word and the team discussion starts. It is sometimes necessary, particularly with an inexperienced team, for the study leader to stimulate the team discussion by asking further questions such as 'Can the flow stop?' or 'Does it matter if it stops?' As far as possible only probing questions should be asked by the study leader. The team should not only provide the technical answers but be encouraged to be creative and think of all the deviations and hazards themselves.

As hazards are detected the study leader should make sure everyone understands them. As mentioned earlier, the degree of problem-solving during the examination sessions can vary. There are two extreme positions

i   A solution is found for each hazard as it is detected before looking for the next hazard
ii No search for solutions is started until all hazards have been detected

In practice there is a compromise. It may not be appropriate or even possible for a team to find a solution during a meeting. On the other hand, if the solution is straightforward and local, a decision can be taken and the design and operating instruction modified immediately. To some extent, the ability to take instant decisions depends upon the type of plant being studied. With a continuous plant, a decision taken at one point in a design may not invalidate previous decisions concerning parts of the plant upstream which have already been studied. But this possibility always has to be considered. For batch plants with sequence control, any alteration to the design or mode of operation could have extensive implications.

If a question is noted for future evaluation, a note is also made of the person nominated to follow it up.

The study leader should sum up at the end of the team discussion before starting with the next guide word. However, he must maintain sufficient pace to avoid the team becoming bored and also he must keep as far as possible to an agreed timetable. To this end it may be necessary to terminate an erudite discussion between two experts by suggesting the point of disagreement be noted and resolved outside the meeting.

Although the study leader will have prepared for the study, the technique is very penetrating and may expose gaps in the model or in the knowledge of the team members. It may sometimes be necessary to elaborate on some aspects during the meeting or even postpone certain parts of the study in order to obtain more information.

Once a section of pipeline or a vessel or an operating instruction has been fully examined, the study leader should mark his copy to this effect. This ensures comprehensive coverage. Another way of doing this is that once every part of a drawing has been examined, the study leader certifies that the examination has been completed in an appropriate box in the flowsheet.

It has already been mentioned that sometimes a study secretary is used as well as a study leader. Secretaries are frequently employed in either of the following circumstances

i   When the examination must be carried out very quickly because of time pressures on members of the team

ii The study is complex and the leader must guide the team using a number of sources of information simultaneously, eg a combination of flowsheets, operating instructions, sequence control charts and bar-charts. The use of a secretary enables the leader to concentrate on directing the study

3.5 Follow-up work

The follow-up to the examination sessions is generally straightforward. If decisions have been taken concerning changes in design or operating methods, these must be communicated to those responsible. Any outstanding problems must be resolved by obtaining more information followed by action and there must be some form of progress-chasing.

Sometimes the output from examination sessions consists largely or exclusively of questions to be answered later. A list of these may be compiled by the study leader (or secretary) and circulated to the team members. After an interval the team reconvenes in what are called 'Evaluation and action sessions'. At these, each question is reviewed, progress is noted and where possible, decisions taken. One evaluation and action session can usually deal with the output of two or three examination sessions.

Once a hazard has been discovered, the kind of action needed to provide a safe system will usually be agreed quite quickly because in many cases there is an obvious remedy to hand. However in some cases it will become apparent that there are a number of possible actions and the team may have some difficulty in agreeing which is the most effective course to take. Actions to contain hazards are generally of four kinds

i   A change in the process (recipe, materials, etc)

ii A change in process conditions (pressure, temperature, etc)

iii An alteration to the physical design

iv A change of operating method

It is important to consider a wide range of possible actions and not to except that every hazard can and should be contained merely by an alteration to the physical design.

When choosing between a number of possible actions it may be useful to put them into two categories

i   Those actions which remove the cause of the hazard

ii Those actions which reduce the consequences

In general it is better and more effective to remove the hazard and provided the study is carried out at the design stage this can usually be done without undue expenditure (see also Section 4.1). If there is no reasonable prospect of removing the hazard the team will have to consider what can be done to protect people and plant if the accident takes place.

To illustrate the kind of reasoning which may be applied, consider a reaction vessel where in an examination session it was discovered that if an impurity was to be introduced with one of the raw materials, there might be a sudden evolution of gas and pressure would develop in the vessel.

Let us assume that the hazard might be contained by taking one of three actions

i   Eliminating the possibility of gas evolution by changing the raw material responsible for the problem ii Eliminating the possibility of gas evolution by altering one of the process conditions

iii Fitting an appropriate pressure relief and vent system to protect the plant

Solution i will be 100% effective and should be the first choice.

Solution ii has to be considered with care, because its adequacy will depend on the reliability of the control system which governs the process condition.

Solution iii is only adequate if the vent system can be designed to cope with the gas evolution and the reliability of such a system is acceptable.

Hazard Analysis is one technique for deciding on the course of action when a number of possibilities have to be considered. A discussion of this technique is outside the scope of this book and References 2 to 7 give further information. However, it should be emphasised that evaluated risks are only as convincing as the information which is used in their calculation. The results are a statistical risk to life or property and should be accepted only as a guide to indicate whether action should be taken and which course of action is likely to be most effective for the expenditure involved.

When it has been decided to alter a design, operating method etc, it is often necessary to subject the new design intention to a second round of examination to make sure that the change has not introduced a new and unsuspected hazard.

Finally it must be emphasised that follow-up work is not complete until all the acknowledged hazards have been dealt with by implementation of all the agreed actions.

3.6 Recording

An important activity of the study team is to record the results of the study. One useful form of record is a 'Hazard file'. This contains

i A copy of the data (flowsheets, running instructions, bar charts, models, etc) used by the team during the examination sessions and marked by the study leader to the effect that they have been examined

ii A copy of all the working papers, questions, recommendations, redesigns, etc produced by the team and others as a result of the study

The file should be retained on the plant so that it is a source of information if changes are subsequently contemplated by the operating personnel.

In addition, the results of a study may also be the subject of a specially prepared report. This is usual if the study includes a quantification of particular risks. Reports can also be written for the guidance of managers or other practitioners if a study has some interesting or unique features.

The formal recording of the study may in future have further implications. For example, insurance premiums may be affected or planning permission may be assisted by evidence of a well-conducted study.

Finally, the information generated by studies can be used to improve future designs.

4 THE PROGRAMMING OF STUDIES

Until now, the Hazard and Operability Study procedure has been discussed on its own and not in relationship to capital projects as a whole. By far the best time to carry out a study is at the 'design freeze' stage, ie when the design is fairly firm. At this stage sufficient detail has been formally given to the design intention to allow the essentially questioning mechanism of Hazard and Operability Studies to obtain meaningful answers. At the same time it is possible to change the plant design without incurring unnecessary expense.

Attempts to carry out a proper Hazard and Operability Study at an early stage—before the design is fully defined—will result in failure because insufficient detail will be available. However a supplementary 'check list' approach can be used at a very early stage in a project, at the 'project definition' stage, when the main design parameters and layouts are being decided but before the detailed design commences. This approach is described in Section 4.1.

Hazard and Operability Studies can be carried out when construction has been largely completed but before start up. Studies at this stage are particularly useful as a check on operating instructions. However, the correction of design faults at this stage can be expensive and will lead to delays.

Studies can also be carried out on existing plant. The main benefit is again to improve operating methods.

4.1 Early checking for major hazards

It is highly desirable to look for *major hazards*—including the potential for disastrous interactions between plants—at a very early stage in the development of a project. A technique for doing such a check, although not strictly speaking a Hazard and Operability Study, is included in this guide because if it has been used it will considerably facilitate a full Hazard and Operability Study when this is subsequently carried out at the 'design-freeze' stage.

A basic requirement is to identify the major hazards. Once these are known, it is possible to make certain *fundamental decisions* such as

i   Where the plant will be sited
ii What should be the location of the plant within the site with respect to the site boundaries, other plants, etc
iii What particular aspects of design will require special development in order to contain the hazards
iv What further research is required to obtain the information (toxicity, flammability, etc) needed to produce an effective design

The identification of major hazards can be done quite easily once certain *general parameters* are established. These are

i   Materials   —Raw materials
                     —Intermediates
                     —Products
                     —Effluents
ii Unit operations—Mixing
                     —Distillation
                     —Drying etc
iii Layout   —Arrangement between unit operations within the plant
                     —Space relationships with other facilities

These general parameters should then be considered in turn when a check-list of *potential hazards* are applied to them. A useful check-list for most chemical plants is the following

Fire	Noise
Explosion	Vibration
Detonation	Noxious material
Toxicity	Electrocution
Corrosion	Asphyxia
Radiation	Mechanical failure

Other hazards can of course be added for particular kinds of processes.
When the potential hazards are in turn applied to the general parameters any meaningful combination may indicate a major hazard and these should then be considered against the list of fundamental decisions.

A few examples will illustrate the procedure

A meaningful combination of INTERMEDIATE X and FIRE may expose that flammability limits are unknown and must be obtained before a dryer can be properly designed.

A meaningful combination of EFFLUENT GAS and TOXICITY will lead to a reconsideration of the siting and of effluent gas treatment.

A meaningful combination of RAW MATERIAL, FIRE and LIQUID NITROGEN STORAGE will lead to reconsideration of layout in the storage area.

The procedure which has been outlined can be carried out by a small group of experienced people very quickly.

This check-list approach helps to ensure compatibility at an early stage and it can be used to assess plant to plant and plant to environment interactions.

The check for major hazards should be used when there is sufficient time to make major and fundamental alterations to the design concept. When a more detailed Hazard and Operability Study is carried out at a later stage it should then detect only minor hazards which will require only minor redesign or alteration to operating methods in order to contain them.

4.2 Studies at 'design freeze'

This is the most convenient time for a Hazard and Operability Study. The drawings are, by definition, accurate. The design staff will then know why the plant has been designed in a particular way. If a substantially modified flowsheet is produced for each session, the team will find it difficult to know whether any particular section has been studied in its final form.

However, it is possible to carry out a study of proprietary items of equipment at any time, even before a decision is taken to purchase, because the design will already have been established by the manufacturer.

Similarly it is possible to carry out a study of sections of plant, the designs of which are established and detailed in advance of others. Care should be taken however to review these later to ensure that interactions with other sections of plant have not introduced new hazards.

4.3 Studies pre start-up

It is possible to carry out a study when construction is substantially complete and the preliminary operating instructions have been written. If a full study has been carried out at 'design freeze' and if the person who will prepare the operating instructions was a member of the study team, it should not be necessary to carry out a further study at this stage. However, under the following conditions it can be useful

i There has been a substantial change of intent at a very late stage
ii The operating instructions are very critical
iii The new plant is a copy of an existing plant with mainly process changes rather than equipment changes

It will be necessary to make sure that the line diagrams accurately describe the plant as built.

4.4 Studies on existing plants

While emphasis will continue to be placed on new plants there should also be an understanding of the hazard potential of existing plants. The latter can continue in operation for many years and can be modified or debottlenecked several times during this life. Unless such modifications have been very carefully handled they could have compromised the safety margins or safety concepts built into the original plant design.

Resources are bound to be limited and therefore some method is required whereby existing plants can be selected for study. Selection may result from an emotional reaction to some recent incident on that or similar plant. While such a reaction is understandable, it does not necessarily mean that limited resources are being directed to the study of plants with the greatest overall hazard. Therefore it is suggested that a number of factors might be taken into account such as

i   A safety audit has shown that a more detailed study is desirable
ii Abnormal occurrences or accidents have taken place
iii A ranking procedure such as the *Dow Index* has shown that this plant has a high potential for hazards
iv The plant will remain in service for a long time
v   The plant has been extensively modified
vi It is convenient to study a particular plant in sequence with respect to other interacting plants

When making arrangements for a study on existing plant, extra time must be allowed for preparative work since line diagrams and operating instructions are often found to be out of date.

Even more care than usual is required at the definition stage. The team will produce recommendations and some of these might require significant changes being made to the plant. It is important to be quite clear who will be responsible for acting on these recommendations. Also, it will be necessary to install a vigorous follow-up and progress-chasing procedure. This normally exists with a new capital project but may not exist to the same extent when modifications are being carried out on an existing plant.

5 GLOSSARY OF TERMS

HAZARD AND OPERABILITY STUDIES

The application of a formal systematic critical examination to the process and engineering intentions of new or existing facilities to assess the hazard potential of mal-operation or mal-function of individual items of equipment and their consequential effects on the facility as a whole.

STUDY DEFINITION

A statement of the object and scope of a study.

DESIGN AND OPERATING INTENTIONS

The way the process and equipment is intended to work under both normal and anticipated abnormal conditions.

MODEL

A representation of these intentions in a form suitable for study by the technique. In the majority of cases conventional drawings, etc, are adequate and no special representation is necessary.

FLOW-PROCESS CHART

A chart setting out the sequence of a flow of activities using symbols such as ASME standards.

DEVIATION

A departure from the design and operating intention.

HAZARD

A deviation which could cause damage, injury or other form of loss.

STUDY TEAM

A small group of people (normally three to six) who carry out the study.

EXAMINATION SESSIONS

Periods of time (usually about three hours) in which the study team systematically analyses the design to detect hazards.

GUIDE WORDS

During examination sessions the study team tries to visualise all possible deviations from every design and operating intention. Broadly speaking, there are seven kinds of deviation, each of which can be associated with a distinctive word or phrase. Collectively, these are called 'guide words' because when used in association with a design and operating intention they guide and stimulate creative thinking towards appropriate deviations.

TEAM DISCUSSION

That part of an examination session which follows the application of a guide word to a design intention and during which the team members derive meaningful deviations, decide whether these are hazardous and what action should be taken as a consequence.

EVALUATION AND ACTION SESSIONS

Under certain circumstances, it is inappropriate to take firm decisions during examination sessions and instead, a series of questions are posed for subsequent evaluation. Under these circumstances further meetings are held in which each question is reviewed, the results of any investigation are reported and decisions taken.

TECHNICAL TEAM MEMBERS

Those members of a study team whose main contribution consists of explaining the design, using their knowledge, experience and imagination during team discussion and taking decisions on changes.

TEAM LEADER

A person trained in the methodology of Hazard and Operability Studies who will advise and assist the study in general and in particular, use the guide words, stimulate the team discussion and ensure comprehensive coverage during examination sessions. In the absence of a study secretary (see below) he will also note actions or questions which arise during these sessions.

STUDY SECRETARY

This is an optional role. He helps organise the various meetings, takes notes during the examination sessions and circulates the resultant lists of actions or questions.

6 ACKNOWLEDGEMENTS

This guide is based on a report by Mr R. E. Knowlton and Dr D. K. Shipley of ICI Pharmaceuticals Division. Helpful comment from practitioners of Hazard and Operability Studies in other parts of ICI were also taken into account and permission to use Dr H. G. Lawley's example from Chem. Eng. Prog., April 1974, in Appendix 1 is gratefully acknowledged.

The guide was edited for general industry use by representatives of
BP Chemicals Ltd
The Chemical Industries Association Ltd
ICI Central Safety Department
Shell Chemicals (UK) Ltd

7 REFERENCES

1 Lawley, H. G., *Operability Studies and Hazard Analysis*, Chem. Eng. Prog., April 1974.

2 Farmer, F. R., I. Chem. E. Symposium Series No. 34, *Major Loss Prevention in the Process Industries*, 1971, p. 82.

3 Stewart, R. M., I. Chem. E. Symposium Series No. 34, *Major Loss Prevention in the Process Industries*, 1971, p. 99.

4 Houston, D. E. L., I. Chem. E. Symposium Series No. 34, *Major Loss Prevention in the Process Industries*, 1971, p. 210.

5 Bullock, B. C., *The development and application of quantitative risk criteria for chemical processes*, Fifth Chemical Process Hazard Symposium, I. Chem. E., Manchester, April 1974.

6 Kletz, T. A., *Hazard Analysis—A Quantitative Approach to Safety*, I. Chem. E. Symposium Series No. 34, 1971.

7 Melinek, S. J., *Methods of determining the optimum level of safety expenditure*, Building Research Establishment Current Paper, CP88/74.

8 Raybould, E. B., and Minter, A. L., *Problem Solving for Management*. London, Management Publications, 1971, pp. 86–90.

9 Nadler, G., *Work Design*. Homewood (Illinois), Irwin, 1963.

10 Whitmore, D. A., *Work Study and Related Management Services*. London, Heinemann, 1968, p. 183.

APPENDIX 1

Application to a continuous plant

The original development of the method based on plant flowsheets occurred when the technique was applied to large, continuous, single-stream plants and the technique has been widely used in this application.

The following are typical of continuous plants which have been studied
Methanol plants
Ammonia plants
Petrochemical plants
Chlorine plants
Soda-Ash plants

As an example of the use of the technique for identifying inadequacies in design and for drawing attention to important operating requirements in the case of a continuous process, a synopsis of part of a paper by H. G. Lawley (Reference 1) is given below.

The system considered is the feed section of a proposed olefin dimerisation unit, the preliminary design being as shown in Figure 3 and the process description is as follows

'An alkene/alkane fraction containing small amounts of suspended water is continuously pumped from bulk intermediate storage via a half-mile pipeline section into a buffer/settling tank. Residual water is settled out prior to passing via a feed/product heat exchanger and preheater to the reactor section. The water, which has an adverse effect on the dimerisation reaction, is run off manually from the settling tank at intervals. Residence time in the reaction section must be held within closely defined limits to ensure adequate conversion of the alkene and to avoid excessive formation of polymer.'

Table 2 summarises the results for the first line section from intermediate storage up to the buffer tank and also indicates the manner in which the need for action was recognised.

It is imperative to ensure that before starting an examination, the design intention is clearly defined. In the particular case given in this example the intention is

To transfer alkene/alkane fraction of a specified composition from intermediate storage to the feed buffer/settling tank at a specified rate and temperature and as shown in Figure 3.

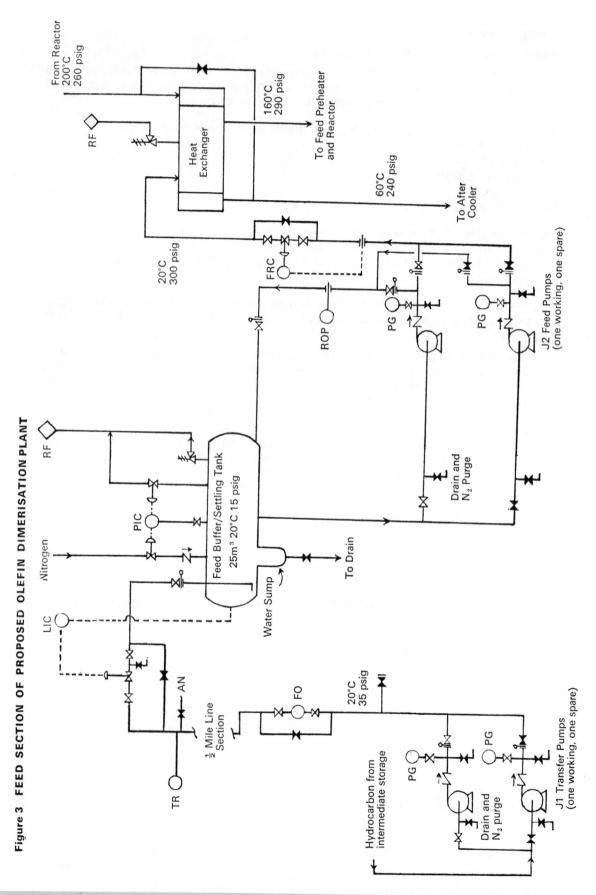

Figure 3 FEED SECTION OF PROPOSED OLEFIN DIMERISATION PLANT

**Table 2   OPERABILITY STUDY OF PROPOSED OLEFIN DIMERISATION UNITS: RESULTS OF LINE SECTION FROM INTER-
MEDIATE STORAGE TO BUFFER/SETTLING TANK**

The guide words are applied to the design intention which states what the equipment is expected to DO

Guide Word	Deviation	Possible Causes	Consequences	Action Required
Not, No	NO FLOW	(1) No hydrocarbon available at intermediate storage	Loss of feed to reaction section and reduced output. Polymer formed in heat exchanger under no flow conditions	(a) Ensure good communications with intermediate storage operator (b) Install low level alarm on settling tank LIC
		(2) J1 pump fails (motor fault, loss of drive, impeller corroded away, etc)	As for (1)	Covered by (b)
		(3) Line blockage, isolation valve closed in error, or LCV fails shut	As for (1) J1 pump overheats	Covered by (b) (c) Install kickback on J1 pumps. (d) Check design of J1 pump strainers
		(4) Line fracture	As for (1) Hydrocarbon discharged into area adjacent to public highway	Covered by (b) (e) Institute regular patrolling and inspection of transfer line
More	MORE FLOW	(5) LCV fails open or LCV bypass open in error	Settling tank overfills Incomplete separation of water phase in tank leading to problems on reaction section	(f) Install high level alarm on LIC and check sizing of relief opposite liquid over-filling (g) Institute locking off procedure for LCV bypass when not in use (h) Extend J2 pump suction line to 12 in above tank base
	MORE PRESSURE	(6) Isolation valve closed in error or LCV closes, with J1 pump running	Transfer line subjected to full pump delivery or surge pressure	(j) Covered by (c) except when kickback blocked or isolated. Check line, FQ and flange ratings, and reduce stroking speed of LCV if necessary. Install a PG upstream of LCV and an independent PG on settling tank

Guide Word	Deviation	Possible Causes	Consequences	Action Required
More (contd.)	MORE TEMPERATURE	(7) Thermal expansion in an isolated valved section due to fire or strong sunlight	Line fracture or flange leak	(k) Install thermal expansion relief on valved section (relief discharge route to be decided later in study)
		(8) High intermediate storage temperature	Higher pressure in transfer line and settling tank	(l) Check whether there is adequate warning of high temperature at intermediate storage. If not, install
Less	LESS FLOW	(9) Leaking flange or valve stub not blanked and leaking	Material loss adjacent to public highway	(m) Covered by (e) and the checks in (j)
	LESS TEMPERATURE	(10) Winter conditions	Water sump and drain line freeze up	(m) Lag water sump down to drain valve, and steam trace drain valve and drain line downstream
As well as	ORGANIC ACIDS PRESENT	(11) Disturbance on distillation columns upstream of intermediate storage	Increased rate of corrosion of tank base, sump and drain line	(n) Check suitability of materials of construction
Part of	HIGH WATER CONCENTRATION IN STREAM	(12) High water level in intermediate storage tanks	Water sump fills up more quickly. Increased chance water phase passing to reaction section	(p) Arrange for frequent draining off of water from intermediate storage tank. Install high interface level alarm on sump
	HIGH CONCENTRATION OF LOWER ALKANES OR ALKENES IN STREAM	(13) Disturbance on distillation columns upstream of intermediate storage	Higher system pressure	(q) Check that the design of settling tank and associated pipework, including relief valve sizing, will cope with sudden ingress of more volatile hydrocarbons
Other than	MAINTENANCE	(14) Equipment failure flange leak etc	Line cannot be completely drained or purged	(r) Install low-point drain and N_2 purge point downstream of LCV. Also N_2 vent on settling tank

NB No hazards were evident from consideration of REVERSE or LESS PRESSURE.

APPENDIX 2

Application to a batch plant

Many of the more specialised materials produced by the chemical industry are made in plants which are partially or completely batch operations.

The following list gives typical products made by batch processes
General organic intermediates
Dyestuffs
Speciality chemicals such as antioxidants
Bulk drugs
Fermentation products
Some polymers
A number of 'formulated products' are made by batch processes including
Pharmaceuticals
Paints
Catalysts
Photographic emulsions
Cosmetics
Specialised formulations

The general characteristics of batch plants as compared with continuous plants are as follows
i   By definition, the status of the various parts of the plant are changing cyclically with respect to time and therefore a line diagram alone gives a very incomplete picture
ii The processes are usually multistage, the individual units multipurpose and the plant as a whole multiproduct. Therefore there is a large number of possible interconnections between units
iii The operators may take part physically in some of the process activities such as removing product from filters

As an example of the application of the technique to a batch process, consider the hypothetical plant shown in Figure 4. This shows a plant consisting of two measure vessels, four reaction vessels, a condenser, an absorption tower with its circulation system and a nutsche filter with its filtrate receiver. This plant is typical, although it has been simplified with the omission of most of the connections to vessels, vents, inert gas inlets, bursting discs, stirrers, heating and cooling supplies to jackets, etc.

In addition to the flowsheet, operating instructions will have been prepared. Typically these consist of tables containing the operation number, a description of the operation, the precautions to be taken and finally a column for the operator to initial once the operation has been completed. A typical layout of operating instructions concerning this hypothetical example is shown in Table 3.

It may be desirable to prepare a bar-chart which shows the status of each piece of equipment throughout a complete batch cycle. For instance, in this example, while batch 1 is being filtered, batch 2 could be reacting in vessel 3, with batch 3 being transferred from vessel 1 to vessel 2 and the measure vessels being filled in preparation for batch 4. These bar-charts are usually produced by the plant management.

Finally, it may be necessary to flow-chart the operators' movements. This aspect will be dealt with in detail in Appendix 3.

As part of the preparative work the study leader should prepare (at least mentally) and plan a programme for the study. His first decision must be whether to study the plant in a sequence derived from the flowsheet or the sequence of the operating instructions.

Let us suppose he has decided to use the sequence of operating instructions. The early instructions will be concerned with a number of preparative activities, starting stirrers and turning cooling water on, checking vessels and starting the absorption tower circulation etc, so let us start this example with Instruction 23 (Table 3) which states 'Charge 100 l of material C from the drum to the general purpose measure vessel using the air ejector'.

While this instruction is perfectly adequate for operational purposes with a trained operator it is too complex to be used to generate deviations. The study leader should decide how to tackle each instruction either as part of his preparation or during the actual examination sessions. In this instance, the instruction can be split into a part dealing with the air ejector and the rest dealing with the liquid transfer.

The study leader will ask a member of the team to describe the purpose of the air ejector. The purpose could be stated as 'Remove some air from the measure vessel'. The guide words are applied to this statement and the attention of the team is directed to the measure vessel and its attachments with the results shown in Table 4.

The second part of Instruction 23 will then be 'Charge 100 l of material C to measure vessel' and this instruction can be used as it stands. The guide words are applied to it with the results shown in Table 5.

The team may carry out some quick problem-solving. For example, a number of the identified hazards can be removed by substituting in Instruction 23 the final phrase 'using residual vacuum' and this alteration could be agreed by the team at this point. The instruction is marked as having been examined.

The team would then proceed to Instruction 24 which reads 'Transfer 100 l of material C from the general purpose measure vessel to vessel 1 via the orifice plate'. While this instruction is sufficiently simple for it to be examined without breaking it up into parts, it is not entirely explicit. The study leader would ask a member of the team to make the exact intention clear. The aim could be to supply C at a restricted rate to avoid an excessive reaction. The examination then starts with the results shown in Table 6.

Again the team may carry out some problem-solving. For example, it could decide to install another dedicated measure vessel complete with orifice plate for material C and thus avoid some of the hazards. Provided this could be carried out simply, the drawing and the instructions would be modified and checked on the spot. If however there were any complications—for example, coupling two measure

Table 3 TYPICAL FORMAT FOR OPERATING INSTRUCTIONS

No	Operation	Precautions	Initials
23	Charge 100 l of material C from the drum to the general purpose measure vessel using the air ejector	Wear air fed hood, PVC gloves and apron	
24	Transfer 100 l of material C from the general purpose measure vessel to vessel 1 via the orifice plate	Ensure flow is solely via the orifice plate	

Figure 4 A SIMPLIFIED BATCH PLANT

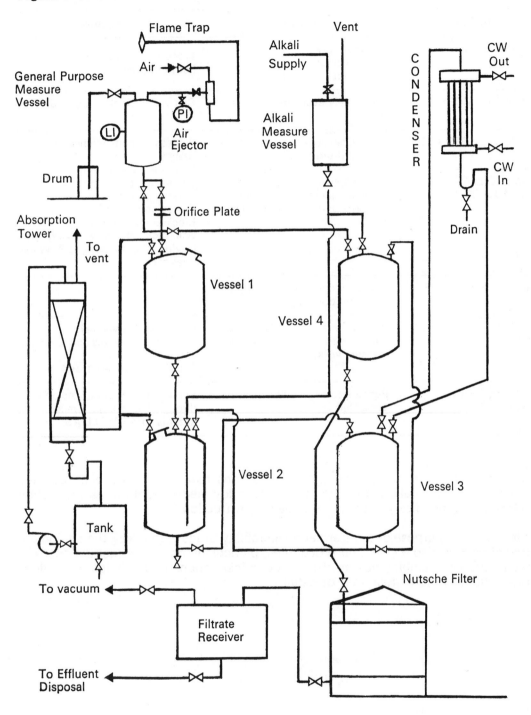

Table 4   DEVIATIONS FROM 'REMOVE SOME AIR FROM THE MEASURE VESSEL'

Deviations	Causes	Consequences
DON'T REMOVE AIR	No air supply Faulty ejector Valve shut	Process inconvenience but no hazard
REMOVE MORE AIR	Completely evacuate measure vessel	Can vessel stand full vacuum?
REMOVE LESS AIR	Insufficient suck to transfer contents of drum	Process inconvenience but no hazard
AS WELL AS REMOVE AIR	Pull droplets of material C or other materials from drums or vessels 1 or 4 along exhaust line	Fire hazard? Static hazard? Corrosion hazard? Blocked flame trap? Will material be a hazard after leaving the flame trap? Where does it go?
REMOVE PART OF AIR	Remove oxygen or nitrogen only: not possible	
REVERSE REMOVAL OF AIR	If line from air ejector is blocked compressed air will flow into measure vessel	Over-pressure vessel? Blow air into drums and spray out contents? Put air into vessels 1 or 4?
OTHER THAN REMOVE AIR	Put air ejector on when measure vessel full	Spray contents along line and out through flame trap. Similar hazards to AS WELL AS

vessels to a single air ejector—the modifications may well have to be decided outside the examination sessions. Again the study leader would mark Instruction 24 as having been examined and proceed to Instruction 25.

Although one purpose of a Hazard and Operability Study is to check the equipment for safety, it is also a check on procedures, particularly operating instructions. The technique finds ambiguities or obscurities in instructions and it helps to produce instructions at the correct level of detail.

Table 5 DEVIATIONS FROM 'CHARGE 100 LITRES OF MATERIAL C TO MEASURE VESSEL'

Deviations	Causes	Consequences
DON'T CHARGE C	No material C available. Valve shut	No hazards
CHARGE MORE C	Charge a quantity greater than 100 l	If vessel is over-filled with ejector running, C is pulled into air ejector with hazards already raised in Table 4. If excess were put into the measure vessel, how could it be removed safely?
CHARGE LESS C	Charge a quantity less than 100 l	No hazard at this stage
CHARGE AS WELL AS C	Obtain a mixture of C and something else in the vessel. List mixtures which are possible	Possibly hazardous mixtures present
CHARGE PART OF C	No meaning. C is not a mixture of materials	
REVERSE CHARGE OF C	Flow from measure vessel to drum	Spillage of material. Possible spray hazard
CHARGE OTHER THAN C	Mix-up with drums. List the other materials	Possible reactions in measure vessel or corrosion of measure vessel

Table 6 DEVIATIONS FROM 'TRANSFER 100 LITRES OF MATERIAL C FROM THE GENERAL PURPOSE MEASURE VESSEL TO VESSEL 1 AT A CONTROLLED RATE'

Deviations	Causes	Consequences
DON'T TRANSFER C	Blocked line. Shut valves. Pressure too high in vessel 1	Process inconvenience but no hazards
TRANSFER MORE C	Transfer more than 100 l Transfer at a higher rate by by-passing the orifice plate or fitting too large an orifice plate	Excess C in vessel 1 List chemical consequences State whether vessel will overflow State where it will overflow to Consider consequences of excessive reaction rate. Static hazard?
TRANSFER LESS C	Transfer less than 100 l Leave some C in the transfer lines Leave some C in the general purpose measure vessel	Inadequate amount of C in reaction vessel. Chemical consequences Note whether there is a danger of locked pressure State the next material to be put into C and consequences of mixing with C
TRANSFER AS WELL AS C	Contaminated C. List possible contaminants. A mixture of air and C	Determine the effects of these contaminants. Consider the effect of air in vessel 1
TRANSFER PART OF C	No meaning	
REVERSE TRANSFER OF C	A flow of material from vessel 1 to the measure vessel is possible if vessel 1 is full and under pressure	State the consequences
OTHER THAN TRANSFER C (WHERE ELSE?)	Transfer wrong material. List what else could be present. Transfer C to vessel 4	Determine consequences Find out from 'Bar Chart' what is in vessel 4 at this stage and determine consequences of adding C

APPENDIX 3
Application to a proprietary item of equipment

Studies have been carried out on unit operations such as mixing, separation, reacting, drying, distillation, milling, tabletting, sterilisation packing, polymerisation, cracking and blending. Often such operations are conducted in proprietary items of equipment such as centrifuges and spray driers which may need to be studied in depth both in terms of the principles of their operation and in their interaction with materials, facilities and other equipment. The technique can also be applied to service facilities such as boilers, incinerators and storage vessels.

As an example, let us consider the proprietary sterilisation autoclave shown in Figure 5.

Sterilisation of stillage-loaded materials is achieved by treatment with steam humidified sterilising gas in a jacketted autoclave chamber under specified conditions. Two entries are provided to the chamber—from the sterile and from the non-sterile working areas of the facility.

Steam is admitted to the chamber via a let-down system and sterilising gas via a vaporiser. The chamber may be evacuated via a cooler either directly to drain or via a luted sealed catchpot to a vent stack. Filtered atmospheric air may be admitted via a non-return valve. A relief valve is fitted to the chamber which exhausts to the vent stack and may be by-passed by opening a vent valve if it is required to dump the contents to stack. Water is circulated through the jacket and heated indirectly by means of steam.

Once the autoclave is charged and the doors closed, automatic sequence control takes over and programmes the process as shown in Figure 6. The machine itself checks the progress of the process cycle, monitoring the status of the chamber and auxiliaries. Certain checks (see Figure 6: Autochecks) control progress in association with timers.

In modelling this type of equipment, it must be borne in mind that both the operator and the machine control the overall process between them and that the operator is physically involved in moving process materials. The latter activity is expressed in the form of a flow process chart (Figure 7) using method study charting symbols. A complete list of such symbols is shown in Figure 8.

For this type of study a stage by stage plan for the examination would be appropriate as shown in Table 7. The equivalent of Stages 1, 3 and 5 have already been considered earlier in the guide. The purpose of this Appendix is to demonstrate the method of handling Stages 2 and 4.

Stage 2: Autocycle of operations

Following the general principle that when a plant's condition can vary with time, the model must describe this by linking the equipment and the design intention. In this case a dot chart fulfils the requirement. Detailed knowledge of the equipment should be possessed by the examination team and the interrelation of components is described by the arrangement drawing Figure 5.

Guide words are applied to the machine's in-built instructions for achieving each process step and each deviation must be followed until further progress is prevented by the controller. This may involve following a deviation through several (or indeed all) of the subsequent process steps looking via the arrangement drawing for all consequences which could be hazardous.

This is demonstrated in Table 8 which shows the deviations arising from the programmed instruction HUMIDIFY AUTOCLAVE CHAMBER.

Figure 5 AUTOCLAVE ARRANGEMENT

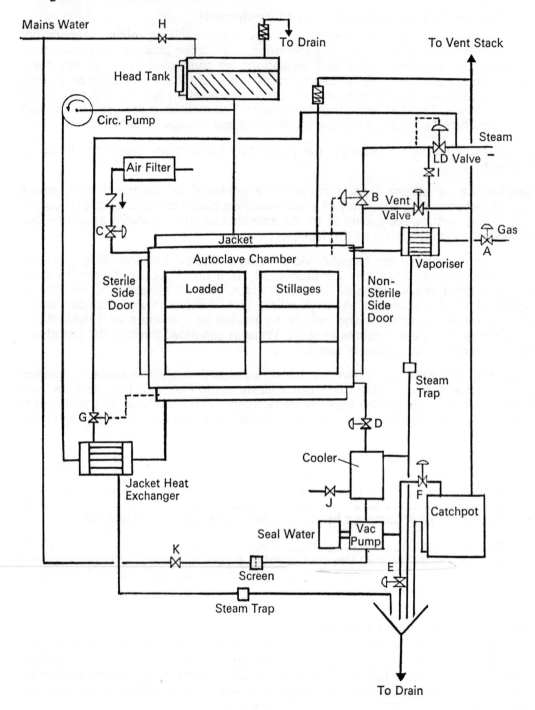

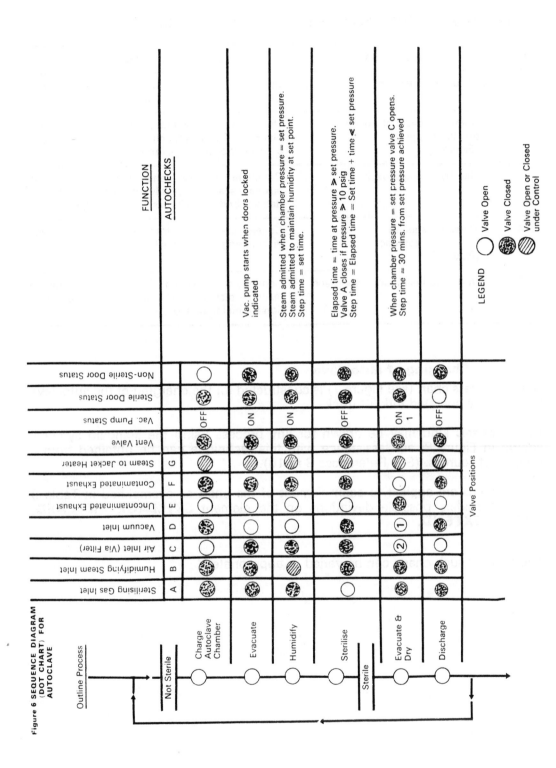

Figure 6 SEQUENCE DIAGRAM (DOT CHART) FOR AUTOCLAVE

Table 7 PLAN FOR AUTOCLAVE EXAMINATION SESSIONS

Stage	Description	Scope and Features
1	Check-list approach	Interactive. Looks at machine in its *context.* Seeks 'worst disaster' situation
2	Autoclave cycle of operations dot chart approach (Figure 6)	Uses sequence diagram in conjunction with line diagram. Covers machine control aspects and auto-controlled part of process
3	Line-by-line approach	Complete process and service lines and auxiliaries and manually operated systems, to defined battery limits, as shown in Figure 5
4	Material handling Flow chart approach (Figure 7)	Covers operating instructions for charging and discharging of stillages by fork lift truck
5	Operating instructions approach	Completes operating instructions including machine start-up and shut-down and preparation for maintenance

Stage 4: Charging of autoclave

A flow process chart (see Figure 7) is constructed for the charging of the autoclave by manually operated fork lift truck.

Charts of this kind may be drawn for any process using the standard symbols shown in Figure 8, and assistance with this technique can be obtained from a number of sources. (See References 8 to 10).

Guide words are applied to each element of the chart as exemplified in Table 9 which considers possible deviations on the element **STILLAGE ENTERED, FORKS EXTEND.**

The scale of such charts can be varied as appropriate.

Figure 7 FLOW PROCESS CHART: CHARGING AUTOCLAVE

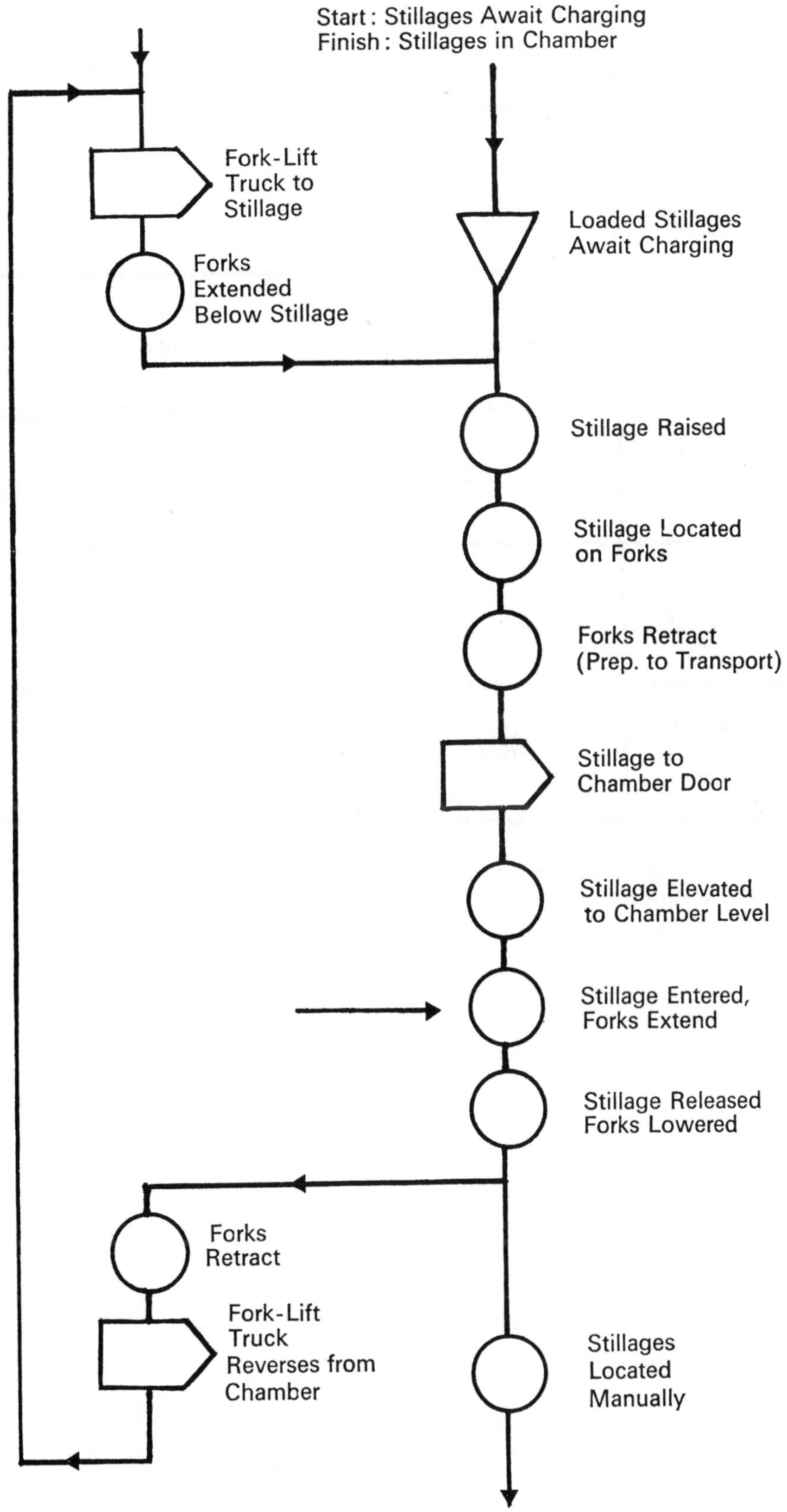

Start : Stillages Await Charging
Finish : Stillages in Chamber

Fork-Lift Truck to Stillage

Forks Extended Below Stillage

Loaded Stillages Await Charging

Stillage Raised

Stillage Located on Forks

Forks Retract (Prep. to Transport)

Stillage to Chamber Door

Stillage Elevated to Chamber Level

Stillage Entered, Forks Extend

Stillage Released Forks Lowered

Forks Retract

Fork-Lift Truck Reverses from Chamber

Stillages Located Manually

Figure 8 EXPLANATION OF PROCESS CHART SYMBOLS (TAKEN FROM METHOD STUDY)

SYMBOL	ACTIVITY	PREDOMINANT RESULT
(a)  ⬤	OPERATION	Produces, accomplishes, changes furthers the process
(b) ▢	INSPECTION	Verifies quantity or quality
(c) 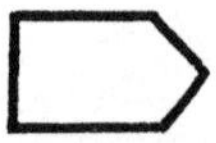 ⬠	TRANSPORT	Moves or carries
(d)  D	DELAY	Interferes or delays
(e)  ▽	STORAGE	Holds, retains or stores

The above examples are those approved by the ASME (American Society of Mechanical Engineers)

Table 8 DEVIATIONS FROM 'HUMIDIFY AUTOCLAVE CHAMBER'

Deviations	Causes	Consequences
DON'T HUMIDIFY	Valve B not open. LD valve closed. Steam line choked. Vent valve open. All steam to vaporiser. Line fractured	Hazard to product—sterilising gas not effective dry
MORE HUMIDIFY	Too much steam— LD valve failed open	Could chamber be overpressured? Is RV sized for full bore ingress of steam to chamber?
	Too high steam pressure/temp	Is product temp/pressure sensitive? Effect of high temp and pressure on sealing components of autoclaves eg door seals?
LESS HUMIDIFY	Too little steam, too low steam pressure/temp	Is condensation on product deleterious?
AS WELL AS HUMIDIFY	Contaminants in steam eg CO_2, condensation, air, rust, etc.	Effect on product?
	Sterilising gas (valve A passing)	Waste gas by evacuation. Gas into plant atmosphere—is second IV required?
	Air (valve C passing)	Reduces effectiveness of humidification
	Contaminants from vent stack (vent valve passing)	Might induce gases from other autoclaves
	Plant atmosphere (door seals leaking)	No hazard at this stage, but could be leak at sterilising stage
	Vacuum pump fails	Contaminants from drain enter autoclave
PART OF HUMIDIFY	Steam in but loss of vac. pump (or valve D closes)	Chamber will be partly pressurised. Load very wet, temperature too high. Chamber partly filled with water. Cycle will continue and sterilising gas may not enter due back pressure
	Vacuum, but no steam in	Cycle will continue; if lack of humidity is not detected and action taken, load will *not* be sterile
REVERSE HUMIDIFY	Vacuum drying	No steam in, as above
OTHER THAN HUMIDIFY	Sterilise by omission of humidifying step	Cycle will continue—load will not be sterile (as above)

Table 9 DEVIATIONS FROM 'EXTEND FORKS TO CHARGE STILLAGE INTO CHAMBER'

Deviations	Causes	Consequences
DON'T	Fork lift truck mechanism failed	Production stopped How is load recovered?
MORE	Extend too far	Load collides with opposite door. Opposite door forced open or damaged Sterile area integrity lost Door may no longer seal, leading to leak of sterilising gas later
LESS	Extend insufficiently	Load insecure and falls back
AS WELL AS	Raise forks	Load trapped between forks and chamber roof—load damaged Chamber raised from foundations? Humidity detector probe broken—leads to leak of sterilising gas later
	Lower forks	Forks foul door landing face and damage seal—leads to leaks
	Move truck	Load insecure with forks extended
PART OF	Too rapid operation	Part of load shaken from stillage How are spillages dealt with? Material damaged—how is this dealt with on sterile side later?
REVERSE	Stillage does not disengage from forks	Load discharged—spillage? Load damaged
OTHER THAN	Procedural faults	Wrong load to right autoclave Right load to wrong autoclave Wrong load to wrong autoclave

APPENDIX 4

How to start Hazard and Operability Studies

Hazard and Operability Studies may be started in an organisation because there is a desire to improve safety, even though the current performance may be good, or because some members of the organisation have read or heard about the technique and its benefits and want to try it.

The way in which a study is started will of course depend on the organisation but it usually follows one of four approaches

A *Do-it-Yourself* approach
The *Evolutionary* approach
The *Educational* approach
A *Crash* programme.

A *Do-it-yourself* approach

Although expert help is desirable and will reduce costs by speeding up the process of gaining competence, it is not essential. The early pioneers had no expert advice and at least five organisations have started to carry out Hazard and Operability studies from a foundation much less firm than that now possessed by the reader. The first step is to agree a trial should be carried out and appoint a person to act as a study leader for this trial. The person selected should preferably have a technical background with production experience together with some knowledge of method study in general and critical examination in particular.

This person should make himself very familiar with this booklet. It is suggested that he then carries out a small exercise on his own in applying the technique to something very simple such as a solvent storage vessel which is supplied by a tanker.

Armed with this experience he should, in discussion with management, select the first real subject for a trial. The subject could be a project around 'design freeze' or an existing unit. He will then select the team in the usual way.

At this stage he will be in a position to arrange an appreciation training course for the team members together with others who may be involved in later studies. The training could be built up from the following

i   A general introduction including course objectives
ii The principles of examination with the tutor basing his talk on 2.1 then working through 2.2, followed by 2.3
iii He can then explain the detailed sequence as in Figure 2
iv He could use his personal experience with the storage tank example (or other simple example) to provide an exercise which the course members would work on in (say) groups of 4 aided by Table 1

The study leader will then have a team sufficiently trained to start a study on the selected topic. Progress is likely to be slow for the first few examination sessions until both the leader and the team start to feel at home with the technique.

The *Evolutionary* approach

The first step is to gain the preliminary agreement of colleagues including the safety adviser. The next step is to arrange a preliminary meeting between colleagues and a study leader, who has been engaged for an introductory study. The purposes of this meeting are

i   To determine whether the technique can be applied and to convince those involved that it is worth trying

ii To select the project which should be studied as a try-out
iii To determine the objectives of the study
iv To obtain a time-estimate for the study
v To select a team for the study
vi To ensure there are sufficient resources available to provide the technical back-up for the team and to see that their decisions can be implemented

There are a number of criteria for project selection but basically it should be something which will not be too time-consuming, be effective and have a fairly immediate impact. In selecting a team for the first study, thought should be given to the long-term implications of Hazard and Operability Studies. For example, is there a need to develop an in-house study leader?

The next stage is to discuss the proposal with the team members and, together with the study leader, plan the steps in the procedure. The data available are reviewed and steps are taken to fill any gaps.

The rest of the study follows the basic procedure mentioned earlier. If the chosen project is a small one lasting say two or three team days, the study leader may remain in charge throughout, and this is the ideal. If the study is lengthy, then it may be worthwhile training an in-house study leader to take over.

After the first (hopefully successful) demonstration, the technique is gradually extended to cover the relevant parts of the organisation and become one of its standard procedures.

The *Educational* approach

This is usually initiated by senior management and since the approach requires a significant commitment, particularly of management and training resources, it will have resulted from a policy decision to use the technique. Adopting this approach, it is advisable to carry out the following steps

i Obtain the necessary training and experience to produce one or if necessary more study leaders
ii Develop and present appreciation courses for senior and middle management so that they can give their managerial support to the teams
iii Develop and present suitable appreciation and team-membership training courses for those who will actually carry out the studies

More details of the training courses are given in Appendix 5.

The *Crash* programme

The approach is usually precipitated by the realisation, at board level, of a need for rapid action.

The approach is straightforward. Teams are set up and study leaders are obtained to train and lead the teams and to train other study leaders from within the organisation.

The requirements for such a programme are

i Recognition by all levels of management of the need
ii Availability of the technique in a form appropriate to the problem
iii Availability of experienced study leaders at short notice
iv Availability of resources to ensure that follow-up actions are implemented

APPENDIX 5

Training

There are four main kinds of training concerned with Hazard and Operability Studies

Senior management appreciation course
Course for team members
Study Leader training
Secretary training

Hazard and Operability Studies can also be included in a general management training course.

Senior manager training

Courses should be presented so that senior managers can have an understanding of the technique, an appreciation of when it can be used with advantage and the benefits to be obtained from it in terms of reduced hazard, improvement in methods and an improvement in the general competence of the operation.

This training should also deal with the human relationships aspect of studies. It is important to have a 'no recrimination' policy if and when faults are detected. On the positive side, an opportunity is provided by studies for the professional development of staff.

Such training should take about half a day.

Team member training

This training places greater emphasis on actually carrying out studies and particularly on the *examination* stage. It should be possible to complete this course in a period of from half a day to two days, depending upon the method of instruction and the amount of practice the members are given.

There can also be informal training for a team about to carry out a study if some of the members are unfamiliar with the technique. This is given by the study leader immediately prior to starting a study and takes one to three hours.

Study leader training

Study leaders develop their ability to plan and control Hazard and Operability Studies by combination of a wide range of technical and management skills, prior experience as team members and as team secretaries, succeeded by conducting studies themselves under the supervision of an experienced leader.

Ideally, the study leader should have the following background and training
i   Several years' experience in production as a line manager or engineer
ii Experience in design
iii Training and experience in problem solving including training in method study and consultancy skills
iv Extensive reading of the literature on the technique
v   Experience as a team member
vi Experience as a team secretary
vii Experience as a trainee study leader under supervision

Secretary training

The secretary must have an appreciation of the technique. In addition, he must be given some guidance on how to record succinctly, but in a way which immediately identifies the section of plant referred to, the nature of the hazard and the circumstances in which it can occur.

APPENDIX 6

The formalisation of Hazard and Operability Studies

Appendices 4 and 5 have indicated how to start Hazard and Operability Studies in an organisation and the kinds of training which should be provided, but these steps are only preliminaries. To obtain full benefit the ultimate aim should be to make the approach part of the 'way of life' within the organisation.

It is difficult to lay down rules for the formalisation of the technique because organisations differ greatly in structure; the manner in which studies are introduced could also influence the situation. Nevertheless, the following guidelines have emerged as a result of experience.

In parts of the chemical industry where Hazard and Operability Studies are most fully established, there are specialist groups providing overall leadership in the technique. They contain skilled study leaders and provide training, advice and assistance in the application of the technique. They do some, but not necessarily all, of the study leading. In addition, they develop the technique for new, wider or more specialised applications. This group can be part of a management services department, a safety department or that part of an engineering department which handles the capital programme.

In addition to the specialist group, there will be trained study leaders who can assist on a part-time basis. All appropriate people concerned with plant design and operation should in time have some training and experience as team members. Although the technique may initially be introduced on an experimental or optional basis, it will tend to be deployed in an increasing number of projects. Ideally its growth should increase to the extent that it becomes a natural part of the design process. Formalisation at this stage will then be seen as evidence of commitment at, say, board level, and should ensure that the appropriate resources will be made available to carry out the studies and to implement the actions which are produced. The formalisation usually takes the form of company instructions which cover the following points

i   The time in the development of a project at which a study should be carried out
ii The criteria by which it is decided to study existing facilities
iii The responsibility for initiating the studies
iv The methods of reporting and recording of the information generated during a study.

Appendix 4

Consequence calculation methods

1. INTRODUCTION

This appendix gives examples of the calculations necessary to assess the consequences of major accidents. Considerable international research has been undertaken to improve the methods involving both theoretical analysis and large-scale trials, and this is continuing, including a large European Commission programme.

Hence the examples given represent the state of the art in 1987, although some areas, e.g. assessment of vapour cloud explosions, are currently under review.

LIQUEFIED PETROLEUM GAS (LPG)

1.1. BLEVE fireball

(a) Fireball radius: $R = 29M^{1/3}$

where R = fireball radius (m)
      M = mass of fuel (te)

(b) Fireball duration: $t = 4.5M^{1/3}$

where t   = duration (sec.)
      M = mass of fuel (te)

M is usually taken as half the tank capacity, i.e. for a 50te LPG tank, M = 25te. If, however, storage is in a close grouping of three or more vertical tanks, it is recommended that M is taken as 90 per cent of the tank capacity.

(c) The radiative flux incident on a target some distance away from the LPG tank is given by:

$q_t = EFT$,

where q_t = radiative flux incident on target (kWm^{-2});
       E = surface emissive power (kWm^{-2});
       F = view factor;
       T = atmospheric transmissivity.

E is taken as 270 kWm^{-2} for cylinders, horizontal and vertical tanks and 200 kWm^{-2} for spheres.

F is taken as $\dfrac{R^2r}{(R^2+r^2)^{3/2}}$,

where r is the ground-level distance between target and LPG tank. For application of this formula r should be greater than 2R.

T is determined by the relationship

$T = 1 - 0.058 \ln r$.

Once q_t has been determined, then a thermal dose or pulse can be calculated as $q_t \times t$

where t = duration of fireball.

For example, determine the incident thermal radiation flux of a BLEVE fireball at a distance of 300 m from a 100te LPG tank:

$R = 29M^{1/3} = 29 \times 50^{1/3} = 107$ m;

$t = 4.5M^{1/3} = 4.5 \times 50^{1/3} = 16.6$ sec.;

$E = 270$ kWm^{-2};

$T = 1 - 0.058 \ln r = 1 - 0.058 \ln 300 = 0.67$;

$F = \dfrac{R^2r}{(R^2+r^2)^{3/2}} = \dfrac{107^2 \times 300}{(107^2+300^2)^{3/2}} = 0.016$;

$q_t = EFT = 270 \times 0.106 \times 0.67 = 19.2$ kWm^{-2};

∴ thermal dose or pulse = $q_t \times t = 19.2 \times 16.6 = 317$ kJm^{-2}.

1.2. Vapour cloud explosion

Assumptions:

(a) LPG tank full when catastrophic failure causes quasi-instantaneous release;

(b) vapour/aerosol cloud is twice adiabatic flash fraction at 15°C, i.e. 62 per cent and 34 per cent of the tank contents for propane and butane respectively;

(c) 1te LPG ≏ 0.42te TNT.

For example, determine the overpressure at a distance of 300 m from a 100te propane tank:

$$\text{Scaled distance} = \frac{\text{distance}}{(0.42M \times 62)^{1/3}}$$

where M = mass of fuel in cloud (te)

$$= \frac{300}{(0.42 \times 62)^{1/3}} = 101 \text{ m te}^{1/3}.$$

From graph of scaled distance versus overpressure (figure 4.1),

Overpressure = 2.23 psig.

1.3. Maximum liquid release rates for commercial LPGs

This can be determined from figure 4.2.

1.4. Maximum gas release rates for commercial LPGs

This can be determined from figure 4.3.

1.5. Maximum two-phase release rates for commercial LPGs

This can be determined from figure 4.4.

CHLORINE

The consequences of releases of toxic gases like chlorine are time-dependent and will vary with distance and prevailing weather conditions. Concentrations and durations can be estimated using computer models which combine a physical description of the gas cloud behaviour with experimental data. Box-type computer models are frequently used to predict the dispersion behaviour of gases like chlorine which are denser than air. A model known as DENZ can be used for instantaneous releases (e.g. failure of a storage vessel) and gives information shown in figure 4.5.

For continuous releases (e.g. from a leaking pipe), a model known as CRUNCH will give information shown in figure 4.6.

This information can be used in conjunction with table 10 in section 6.1.4 of the manual to estimate the effects of a release on people.

Figure 4.1. TNT curve overpressure versus scaled distance

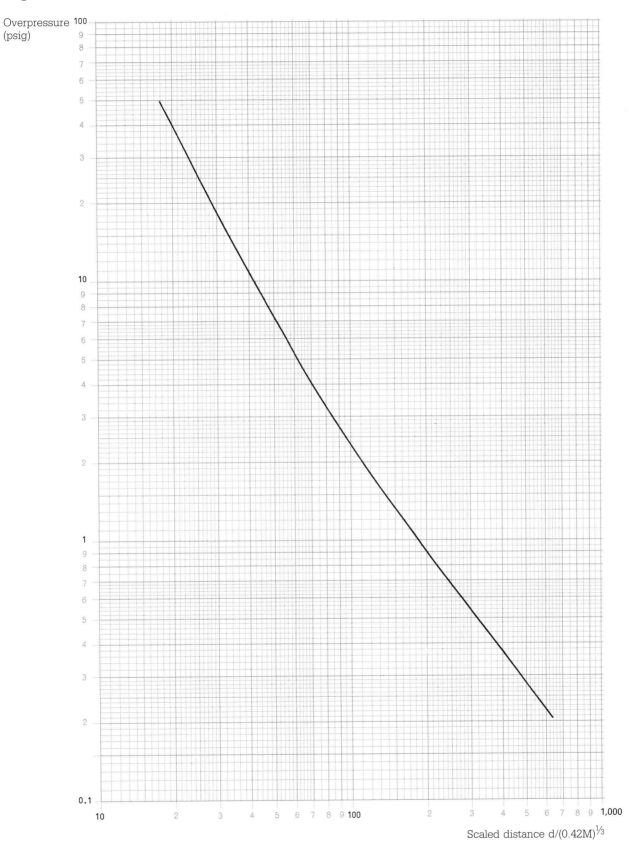

Scaled distance $d/(0.42M)^{1/3}$

Figure 4.2. Maximum liquid release rates for commercial LPGs

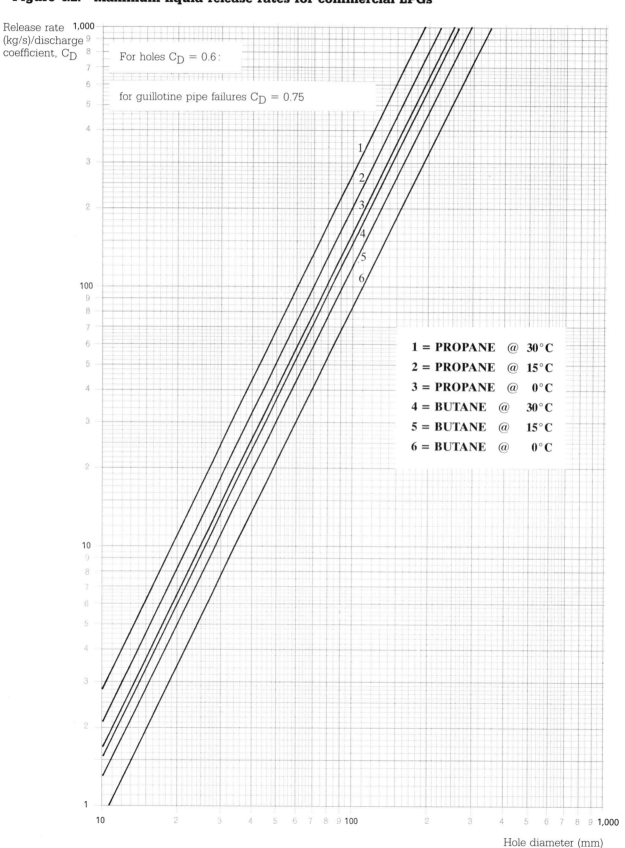

Release rate (kg/s)/discharge coefficient, C_D

For holes $C_D = 0.6$:

for guillotine pipe failures $C_D = 0.75$

1 = PROPANE @ 30°C
2 = PROPANE @ 15°C
3 = PROPANE @ 0°C
4 = BUTANE @ 30°C
5 = BUTANE @ 15°C
6 = BUTANE @ 0°C

Hole diameter (mm)

Figure 4.3. Maximum gas release rates for commercial LPGs

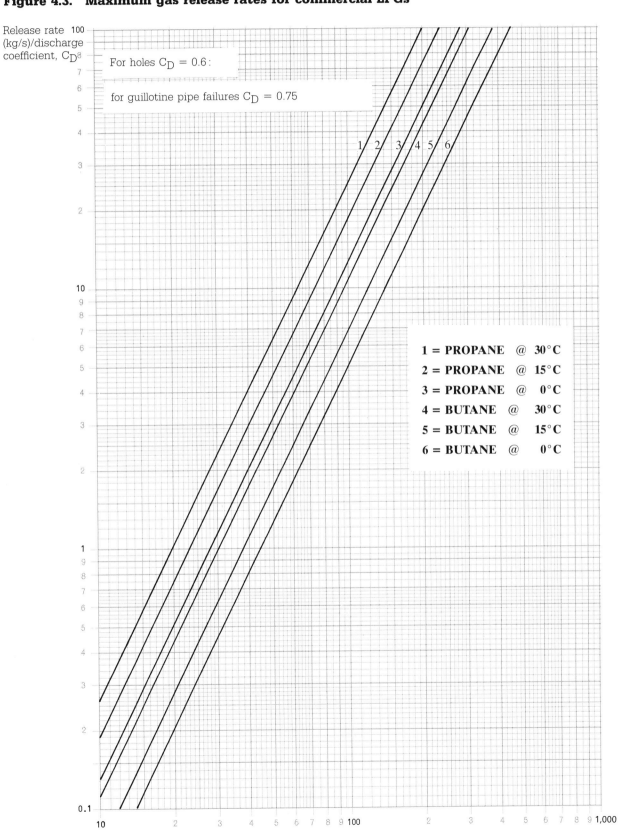

Release rate (kg/s)/discharge coefficient, C_D

For holes $C_D = 0.6$:

for guillotine pipe failures $C_D = 0.75$

1 = PROPANE @ 30°C
2 = PROPANE @ 15°C
3 = PROPANE @ 0°C
4 = BUTANE @ 30°C
5 = BUTANE @ 15°C
6 = BUTANE @ 0°C

Hole diameter (mm)

Figure 4.4. Maximum two-phase release rates for commercial LPGs

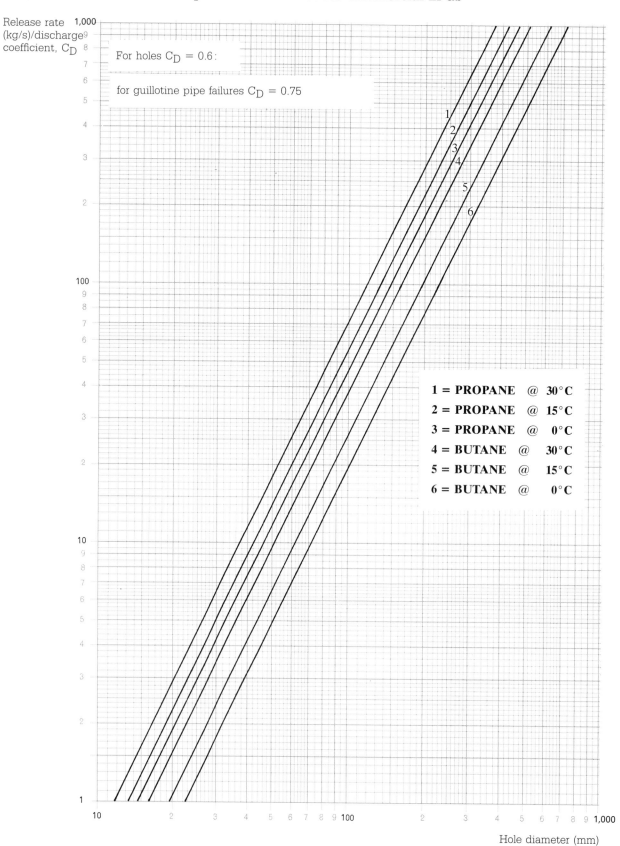

Figure 4.5. **Relationship between mass chlorine, maximum ground-level concentrations and downwind distances from leak source for instantaneous releases (D5 weather)**

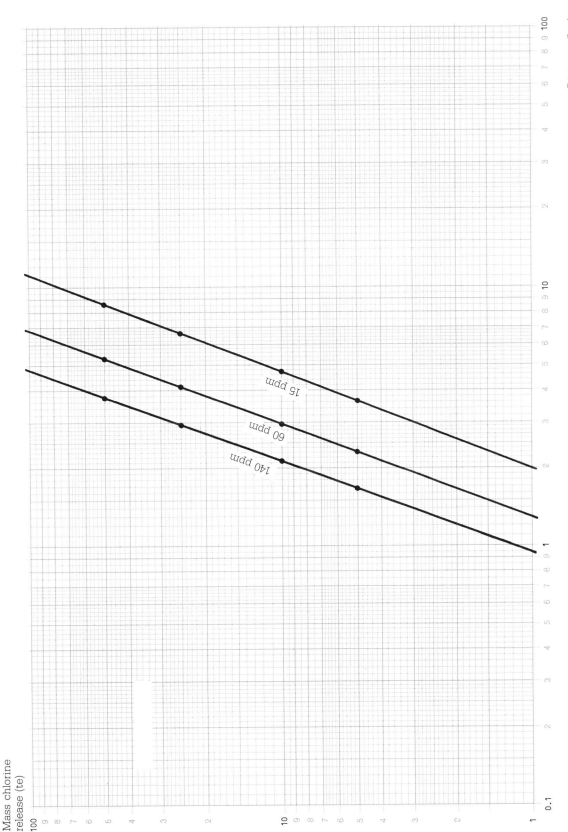

Mass chlorine release (te)

Distance (km)

Figure 4.6.   Relationship between chlorine release rates, equilibrium ground-level concentrations and downwind distances from leak source for continuous release (D5 weather)

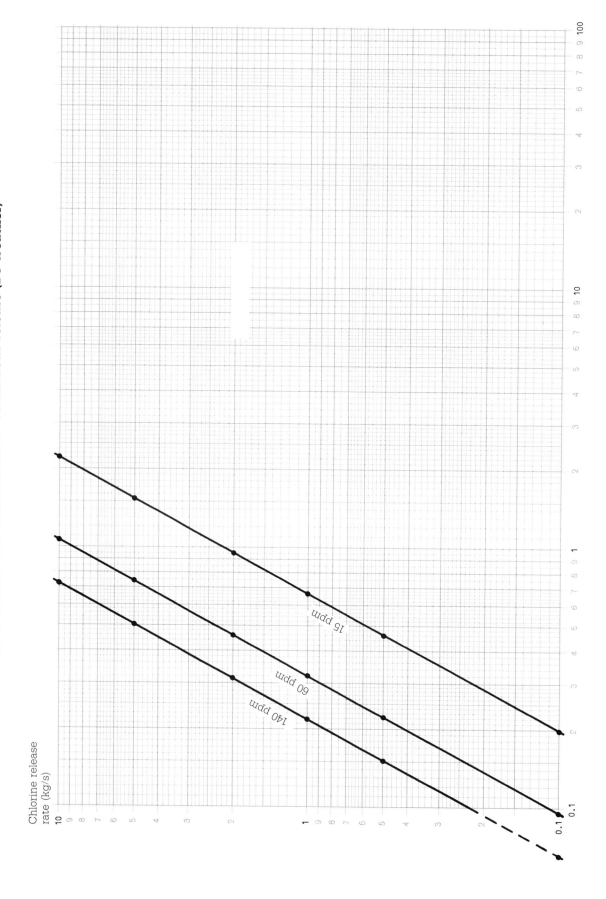

Appendix 5 (a)

The storage of LPG at fixed installations

(Reproduced from Health and Safety Executive : *The storage of LPG at fixed installations,* Health and Safety series booklet HS (G) 34 (London, HMSO, 1987).)

Contents

Glossary

Catchment pit A pit or trench, sited in a safe place, in which LPG can collect to enable it to evaporate in a controlled manner.

Element of construction Any wall, floor, ceiling, roof, door or window (including the frame) etc which forms part of a building, room or other enclosure.

Enforcing authority The authority with a responsibility for enforcing the Health and Safety at Work etc Act 1974 (HSW Act) and other relevant statutory provisions. This is normally HSE or the local authority for the area as determined by the Health and Safety (Enforcing Authority) Regulations 1977.

Evaporation area An area of ground in a safe place adjacent to the storage vessel or vessels where LPG can collect, evaporate and disperse safely.

Fire wall A wall, screen or separating partition erected in the open air to reduce the effects from radiated heat on an LPG vessel and to ensure an adequate dispersion distance for LPG leaking from the vessel.

Fire resisting A fire resisting element of construction is one that would have at least the stated period of fire resistance (ie stability, integrity and insulation) if tested, from either side, in accordance with British Standard BS 476:Part 1: 1953 or Part 8: 1972.

(a) where two or more elements of construction together provide separation, the junction between them should be bonded or fire stopped to prevent or retard the passage of flames or hot gases, thus giving effective fire separation between the rooms or spaces on either side;

(b) elements of construction should be of sufficiently robust construction so that their fire resisting properties are not impaired by damage caused by everyday wear and tear. Additional protection, eg crash barriers, reinforcing plates, wearing strips etc, may be required when mechanical damage is foreseeable.

Liquefied Petroleum Gas (LPG) A generic term used to describe liquefiable gases consisting predominantly of C_3 and C_4 hydrocarbons.

Mounded vessel A storage vessel which may be sited above ground or partly buried and which is completely covered by a mound of earth or similar inert material.

Noncombustible material A material that can be classified as noncombustible when tested for noncombustibilty in accordance with BS 476 Part 4: 1970.

Remotely operated emergency valve A shut-off valve capable of remote operation which will close automatically on loss of the actuating power or fire engulfment and which, preferably, is fire safe in accordance with BS 5146: 1984, API 607 or API 6FA. Electrically driven valves need not close automatically on fire engulfment if the power supply is adequately fire protected.

Separation distance The horizontal distance between the nearest part of a storage vessel and the specified feature.

Skid mounted vessel A storage vessel mounted on a structural frame enabling it to be readily moved and transported.

Underground vessel A storage vessel situated below ground level in a pit or trench which has been back filled with sand or other suitable material.

Vessel A container or tank of greater than 150 litres water capacity designed and constructed to a recognised pressure vessel code eg BS 5500.

Vessel capacity The capacity of a vessel is quoted as the volume in litres of water required to completely fill the vessel. The nearest metric tonne (te) equivalent is also quoted in brackets as this is commonly used. However, this second figure is only an approximation because of the different densities of propane and butane.

Introduction

1 This publication provides a general guide to safe practice in storing and handling liquefied petroleum gas (LPG) at fixed storage installations. It provides a guide to safe practice both for

people storing LPG and those enforcing safety requirements. This guide may be used where people have duties under the HSW Act and may also be used as good practice in other circumstances such as storage vessels at domestic premises. The recommendations are intended to minimise the risks of fire and explosion from escaping LPG and from a fire at or near a store.

2   The information in this guidance gives one way of achieving an acceptable standard of safety. Each case must be considered on its merits, and special circumstances may necessitate variations from the recommendations. It is not intended to preclude the use of alternative designs, materials and methods where these provide equivalent safety standards. Neither is it the intention that the recommendations should be applied rigidly to existing premises, where for a variety of reasons it may not be practicable to comply with them, although such alterations as are considered to be reasonable or essential for safety should be made. New installations should comply with the advice in this guidance from the date of publication.

Scope

3   This guidance deals solely with installations where LPG is stored under pressure at ambient temperatures in fixed vessels larger than 150 litres. It applies to all such installations whether or not the material is stored for use on site or transhipment and subsequent use off site and includes guidance on the design, construction and examination of LPG storage vessels. Information is also presented on the precautions to be taken during loading and offloading of road tankers and rail tankers.

4   Guidance is not given on the storage of cylinders or cartridges containing LPG. Advice on these matters can be found in Guidance Note CS4 and Guidance Note CS8. Advice on the storage of refrigerated LPG, previously contained in Guidance Note CS5 should be obtained from your local HSE office.

Legal requirements

5   The storage of LPG will usually be subject to

the general duties of the HSW Act. It may also be subject to additional legal requirements:

(a)   at the premises subject to the Factories Act 1961, the Highly Flammable Liquids and Liquefied Petroleum Gases Regulations 1972 (HFL Regulations) will apply;

(b)   the Notification of Installations Handling Hazardous Substances Regulations 1982 (NIHHS) require that all premises at which 25 tonnes or more of LPG are kept should be notified to the Health and Safety Executive (HSE). Guidance on these regulations can be found in HSE booklet HS(R)16;

(c)   the general requirements of the Control of Industrial Major Accident Hazards Regulations 1984 (CIMAH) apply to all premises where LPG in any quantity is produced or processed or where 50 tonnes or more are stored. Guidance on the CIMAH Regulations can be found in HSE booklet HS(R)21 and on the emergency plans required by the regulations in HSE booklet HS(G)25;

(d)   at premises subject to the Fire Certificates (Special Premises) Regulations 1976, enforced by HSE, and the Fire Precautions Act 1971, enforced by the Fire Authority, the presence of LPG may be taken into account when considering the general fire precautions;

(e)   the operation of loading and unloading road tankers and tank containers with a capacity greater than $3m^3$ when they are loaded or unloaded while still on a vehicle, is subject to the requirements of the Dangerous Substances (Conveyance by Road in Road Tankers and Tank Containers) Regulations 1981;

(f)   if LPG is supplied through a pipeline, the Pipeline Act 1962 may apply. However the Act does not apply to certain specified pipelines including those wholly within factory premises, mines, quarries and petroleum depots. This Act is enforced by the Pipelines Inspectorate of the Department of Energy to whom enquiries should be made;

(g)   where LPG is supplied as a gas through pipes to premises, the supply must be

Table 1 Typical physical properties of liquefied petroleum gas

Physical property		Commercial butane	Commercial propane
Relative density (to water) of liquid at 15.6°C		0.57—0.58	0.50—0.51
Litres/tonne of liquid at 15.6°C		1723—1760	1957—2019
Relative density (to air) of vapour at 15.6°C and 1015.9 mbar		1.90—2.10	1.40—1.55
Ratio of gas to liquid volume at 15.6°C and 1015.9 mbar		233	274
Volumes of gas/air mixture at lower limit of flammability from 1 volume of liquid at 15.6°C and 1015.9 mbar		12 900	12 450
Boiling point °C		−2	−45
Vapour pressure at 20°C	bar	2.5	9
	psig	40	130
at 50°C	bar	7	19.6
	psig	100	283
Lower limit of flammability,	% v/v	1.8	2.2
Upper limit of flammability,	% v/v	9.0	10.0

Source: LPGITA An Introduction to Liquefied Petroleum Gases.

authorised by or under the Gas Act 1986, subject to certain exceptions. It is an offence for any person to supply gas through pipes without authorisation in circumstances where authorisation is required. Further particulars may be obtained from the Office of Gas Supply, Southside, 105 Victoria Street, London SW1E 6QT.

Note: although LPG itself is not subject to the Petroleum (Consolidation) Act 1928 the Petroleum Licensing Authority may take its presence into account in determining the condition of any licence that may be issued under the Act.

Properties and hazards of LPG

6 The two liquefied petroleum gases in general use are commercial butane and commercial propane. Their main physical properties are given in Table 1. These hydrocarbons exist as gases at normal temperatures and pressures but can be liquefied under moderate pressure. If the pressure is subsequently released, the hydrocarbons again become gaseous.

7 LPG is colourless and its density as a liquid is approximately half that of water. If LPG is spilt on water, it will float on the surface before vapourising. The liquid has approximately 1/250th of the gas volume.

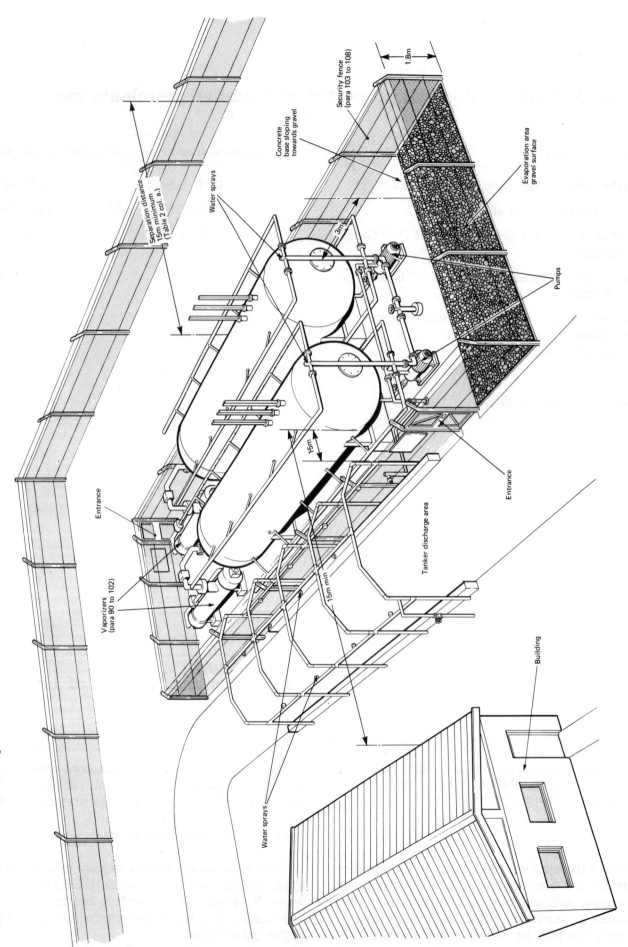

Fig 1 Two 60 tonne vessels with vapourisers

Security fence
(para 103 to 108)

1.8m

Concrete
base sloping
towards gravel

Evaporation area
gravel surface

Water sprays

Separation distance
15m minimum
(Table 2 col. a.)

3m

Pumps

15m

Entrance

Entrance

Vaporizers
(para 90 to 102)

Tanker discharge area

15m min

Water sprays

Building

8   The gas or vapour is at least 1½ times as dense as air and does not disperse easily. It will tend to sink to the lowest possible level and may accumulate in cellars, pits, drains or other depressions.

9   LPG forms flammable mixtures with air in concentrations of between approximately 2% and 10%. It can, therefore, be a fire and explosion hazard if stored or used incorrectly. There have been incidents in which escapes of LPG have been ignited, resulting in serious fires. If LPG escapes into a confined space and is ignited, an explosion could result. If an LPG vessel is involved in a fire, it may overheat and rupture violently giving an intensely hot fireball and may project pieces of the vessel over considerable distances.

10   Vapour/air mixtures arising from leakage or other causes may be ignited some distance from the point of escape, and the flame travel back to the source.

11   At very high concentrations, when mixed with air, LPG vapour is anaesthetic and subsequently an asphyxiant by diluting or decreasing the available oxygen.

12   LPG can cause severe cold burns to the skin owing to its rapid vaporisation and the consequent lowering of temperature. Vaporisation of LPG can also cool equipment to the extent that it may be cold enough to cause cold burns. Protective clothing such as gloves and goggles should be worn if this cooling is likely to occur.

13   LPG is normally odorised before distribution so that is has a characteristic smell which can easily be recognised. This enables detection by smell of the gas at concentrations down to one fifth of the lower limit of flammability (approximately 0.4% of the gas in air). Significant leaks may also be detected by a hissing sound or by icing in the area of the leak. Small leaks may be detected by brushing the suspect areas with a detergent/water mixture where bubbles will form at the leak. **On no account should a naked flame or other source of ignition be used to detect a leak.**

14   A vessel which has held LPG and is nominally empty may still contain LPG in vapour form and be potentially dangerous. In this state the internal pressure is approximately atmospheric and, if a valve is leaking or left open, air can diffuse into the vessel forming a flammable mixture and creating a risk of explosion. LPG will also be displaced to the atmosphere.

Location, separation and grouping

15   LPG vessels sited above ground should be located in the open air in a well ventilated position in accordance with the separation distances given in Table 2, column (a). Underground or mounded vessels should be located so that the manhole and pressure relief valves are in a well ventilated position in accordance with the separation distances given in Table 2, column (d). Advice should be obtained from the enforcing authority before using separation distances less than those in Table 2. The siting of installations involving vessels greater than 337 500 litres (150 te) should be discussed with HSE.

16   LPG vessels should not be located one above the other. The ground beneath or adjacent to connections into vessels or ancillary equipment containing LPG should be concreted or compacted and free from pits, depressions, drains and culverts. When all the vessel connections are grouped at one end, the concrete or compacting may only be necessary beneath the connections. The ground within the separation distance given in Table 2, column (a) should, as far as possible, be flat and level, other than beneath the vessel and where it is sloped to an evaporation area or catchment pit.

17   Weeds, long grass, deciduous shrubs and trees and any combustible material should be removed from an area within the separation distance in Table 2 column (a) of any LPG vessel of up to 2500 litres capacity (1.1 te) and within 6m of larger vessels. Sodium chlorate should not be used to clear weeds near LPG vessels.

18   Shrubs or trees provided to screen LPG vessels from view should not interfere with ventilation and therefore should only be located on one side of the installation. Evergreen shrubs or trees may be located 1m from vessels up to

Fig 2 Small bulk vessel adjacent to a building

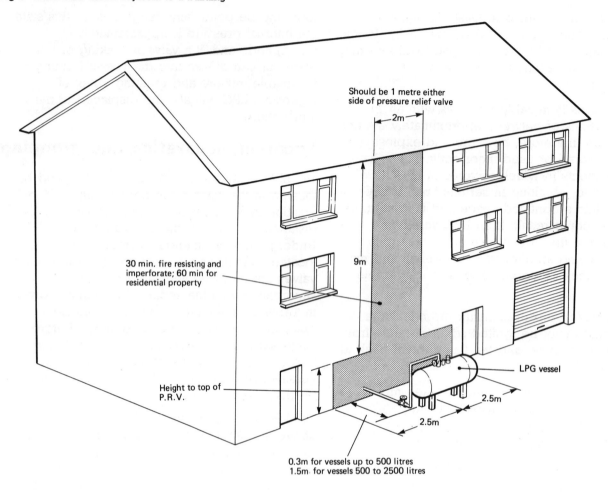

Should be 1 metre either
side of pressure relief valve

2m

30 min. fire resisting and
imperforate; 60 min for
residential property

9m

Height to top of
P.R.V.

LPG vessel

2.5m

2.5m

0.3m for vessels up to 500 litres
1.5m for vessels 500 to 2500 litres

Fig 3 Small bulk vessel at domestic premises

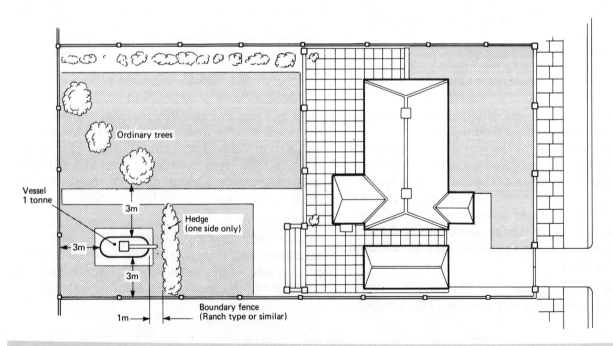

Ordinary trees

Vessel
1 tonne

3m

3m

Hedge
(one side only)

3m

Boundary fence
(Ranch type or similar)

1m

Table 2 Location and spacing for vessels

Maximum water capacity   Minimum separation distances

Of any single vessel in a group			Of all vessels in a group		Above ground vessels			Buried or mounded vessels		
Litres	Gallons	Nominal LPG Capacity (tonnes)	Litres	Gallons	From buildings, boundary, property line or fixed source of ignition (a)	With fire wall (b)	Between vessels (c)	From buildings etc to		Between vessels (f)
								Valve Assembly (d)	Vessel (e)	
					m (ft)	m	m	m	m	m
150 to 500	28 to 100	0.05 to 0.25	1 500	330	2.5 (8)	0.3*	1	2.5	0.3	0.3
>500 to 2500	100 to 500	0.25 to 1.1	7 500	1 650	3 (10)	1.5	1	3	1	1.5
>2500 to 9000	500 to 2000	1.1 to 4	27 000	6 000	7.5 (25)	4	1	7.5	3	1.5
>9000 to 135000	2000 to 30 000	4 to 60	450 000	100 000	15 (50)	7.5	1.5	7.5	3	1.5
>135 000 to 337 500	30 000 to 75 000	60 to 150	1 012 500	225 000	22.5 (75)	11	¼ of sum of the dia of 2 adjacent vessels	11	3	‡
>337 500	>75 000	>150	2 250 000	500 000	30 (100)	15	"	15	3	‡

*For vessels up to 500 litres capacity, the fire wall need be no higher than the top of the vessel and may form part of the site boundary. The fire wall for a vessel up to 2500 litres water capacity may form part of a building wall in accordance with Figure 2. Where part of the building is used for residential accommodation the wall, including any overhanging but excluding the eaves, against which the LPG is stored should be of 60 minutes fire-resisting construction and imperforate.

‡The spacing between adjacent vessels should be determined by the site conditions and the needs for safe installation, testing, maintenance and removal of vessels.

5000 litres capacity for this purpose. For larger vessels the separation distances in paragraph 17 apply.

19 For all vessels with connections below the liquid level the ground beneath the vessel or connections should be sloped to prevent the accumulation of liquid beneath them and ensure a flow away from the vessel, adjacent vessels or ancillary equipment towards a safe area. It is not necessary to compact or concrete the ground beneath connections that are plugged or blanked off.

20 Propane vessels with a capacity of 56 250 litres (25 te) or more and butane vessels with a capacity of 11 250 litres (5 te) or more, and in each case with connections below the liquid level should have provision made for directing

any large spillage of LPG to an evaporation area or catchment pit. These should be sited in a safe place away from occupied buildings, boundaries or sources of ignition. Escaping LPG should be diverted to the evaporation area or catchment pit by sloping the ground in the required direction and where necessary by installing low walls, usually no more than 500mm high, to direct the flow in the right direction. Catchment pits will normally only be appropriate at large installations.

21 Catchment pits should have sufficient capacity to contain the largest credible leak and should be sufficiently well ventilated to permit the safe dispersion of small leaks. Gas detectors should be installed in the pit to provide warning of the presence of LPG vapour.

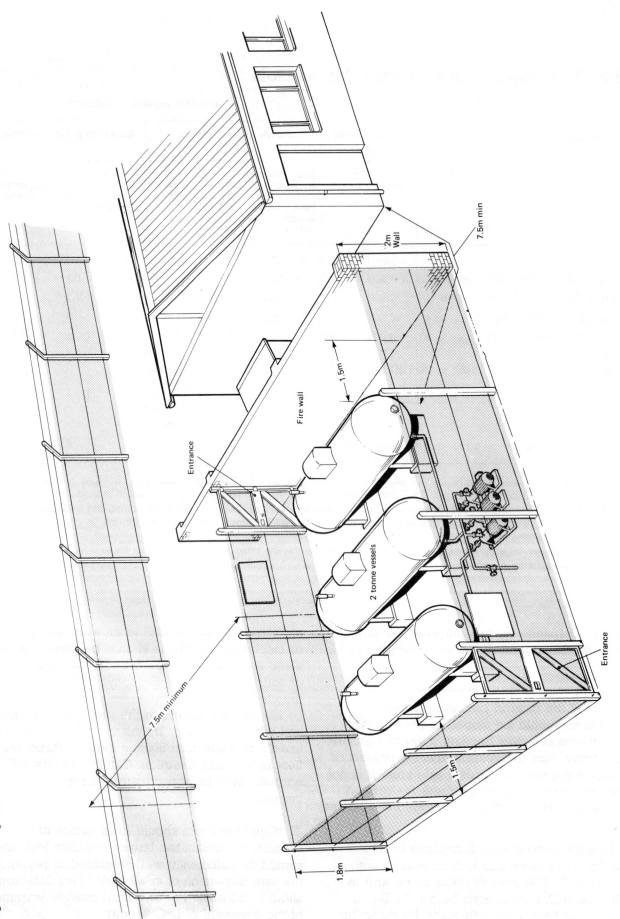

Fig 4 Vessel compound with a fire wall

22 Any catchment pit should be far enough away from LPG vessels, buildings, boundaries etc so that if filled with LPG which ignites, the thermal radiation would not exceed the following levels:

(a) 7.8 Kw/m² at work areas, process facilities and unprotected LPG vessels;

(b) 12.6 Kw/m² at boundaries;

(c) 31.5 Kw/m² at LPG vessels protected by water sprays or thermal insulation.

23 Evaporation areas should be at least 3m from LPG vessels. The area should be surfaced with stone chippings or similar materials to increase the surface area and promote evaporation and dispersion of the gas.

24 Vessels should not be sited in places that are known to be susceptible to flooding.

25 LPG storage vessels should be installed at least 6m from the bund wall of any tank containing a flammable liquid with a flash point below 32°C and from any tank containing a flammable liquid with a flash point in the range 32 to 65°C. The minimum separation distance between an LPG storage vessel and the top of the bund of any tank containing a flammable liquid should be 3m. See Table 3.

26 Vessels containing liquid oxygen should be sited not less than the separation distance given in Table 4 from vessels containing LPG. Vessels containing toxic or other hazardous materials stored under pressure eg chlorine should be at least 15m from LPG storage vessels or at the separation distances given in Table 2, column (a), whichever is the greater.

27 LPG storage vessels should not be located within the bunded enclosure of a vessel containing a flammable liquid, any heated storage vessel eg heavy fuel oil vessel, liquid oxygen or any other hazardous substance.

28 The number of above ground LPG storage vessels in one group should not exceed six subject to the maximum total capacity of a group given in Table 2. Any vessel in one group should be 7.5m or the separation distance given in Table 2, column (c) whichever is the greater, from the nearest vessel in another group unless a fire wall is erected between the two groups.

29 LPG cylinders in excess of 50kg total quantity with pressure relief valves which vent horizontally should not be stored within 7.5m of vessels of more than 5000 litres capacity or 3m of vessels below this size. Up to 300kg of LPG in cylinders fitted with vertically venting pressure relief valves eg most fork lift truck cylinders, may be stored within the vessel security compound at least 1m from the vessel. See Table 3.

30 Up to 300kg of propane in cylinders may be kept within 7.5m or 3m of a vessel (see paragraph 29) for the purposes of pressure augmentation of a butane vessel in cold weather or to provide an emergency supply of propane in the event of a failure of the bulk supplies. The cylinders should be positioned at least 1m from the vessel. The pressure relief valves should be directed away from the vessel or a fire wall should be built between the cylinders and vessel.

31 Buildings or structures in which cylinders are filled with LPG or other flammable gases should be sited 10m from bulk LPG vessels up to 135 000 litres capacity (60 te) and 15m from larger vessels. This separation distance is not necessary where only a small number of cylinders are filled eg for fork lift trucks. See Table 3. For underground vessels this distance may be reduced to 5m or the separation distance in Table 2 column (d), whichever is the greater.

32 So far as is reasonably practicable, horizontal storage vessels should be sited so that their long axes do not point towards nearby occupied buildings, important items of equipment or storage tanks containing hazardous materials.

Fire walls

33 The purpose of a fire wall is to protect the vessel or vessels from thermal radiation from a fire nearby and to ensure an adequate dispersion distance to boundaries, buildings and sources of ignition for LPG leaking from the vessel or its fittings.

34 A fire wall should be imperforate and of solid masonry, concrete or similar construction. Except for vessels up to 500 litres (0.25 te) a fire wall should be at least 2m high or as high as the top of the vessel whichever is the greater and should be sited between 1m and 3m from the

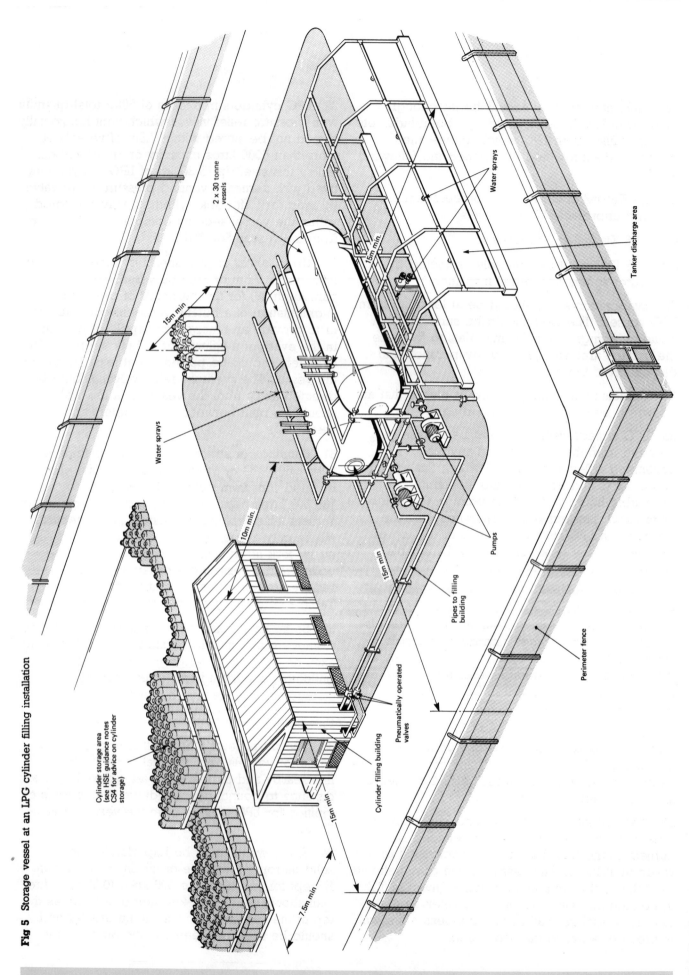

Fig 5 Storage vessel at an LPG cylinder filling installation

2 x 30 tonne vessels

15m min.

Water sprays

Tanker discharge area

15m min

Water sprays

Pumps

10m min.

15m min

Pipes to filling building

Cylinder storage area (see HSE guidance notes CS4 for advice on cylinder storage)

Pneumatically operated valves

Cylinder filling building

Perimeter fence

15m min

7.5m min

Table 3 Separation of hazardous substances and operations from LPG vessels

Substance	Minimum separation distance	See paragraph
Flammable liquids f.pt. <32°C f.pt. 32—65°C	6m to bund wall 6m to tank and 3m to a bund wall	25
Tank containing toxic or hazardous substance	15m or the separation distance in Table 2 column (a) whichever is the greater	26
LPG cylinders total quantity of LPG >50kg	3m for LPG vessels <5000 litres capacity	29
	7.5m to LPG vessels >5000 litres capacity	29
Except LPG cylinders with vertically venting PRVs ≤300kg	1m	29
Propane cylinders for pressure augmentation or emergency supply, PRVs to point away from vessel ≤300kg	1m	30
Cylinder filling building	10m for vessels up to 135 000 litres and 15m for larger vessels	31

Table 4 Separation distance between LPG vessels and liquid oxygen tanks

Water capacity of LPG vessels (litres)	Nominal capacity of LPG vessels (tonnes)	Liquid oxygen capacity (litres)	Separation distance (metres)
>up to 2500	0 — 1.1	up to 125 000	6
>2500 to 9000	>1.1 — 4	"	7.5
>9000 to 135 000	>4 — 60	"	15
>135 000 to 337 000	>60 — 150	"	22.5
>337 000	>150	"	30
up to 5000	0 — 2	Over 125 000	30
>5000 to 500 000	>2 — 220	"	45
>500 000	>220	"	Expert advice should be sought

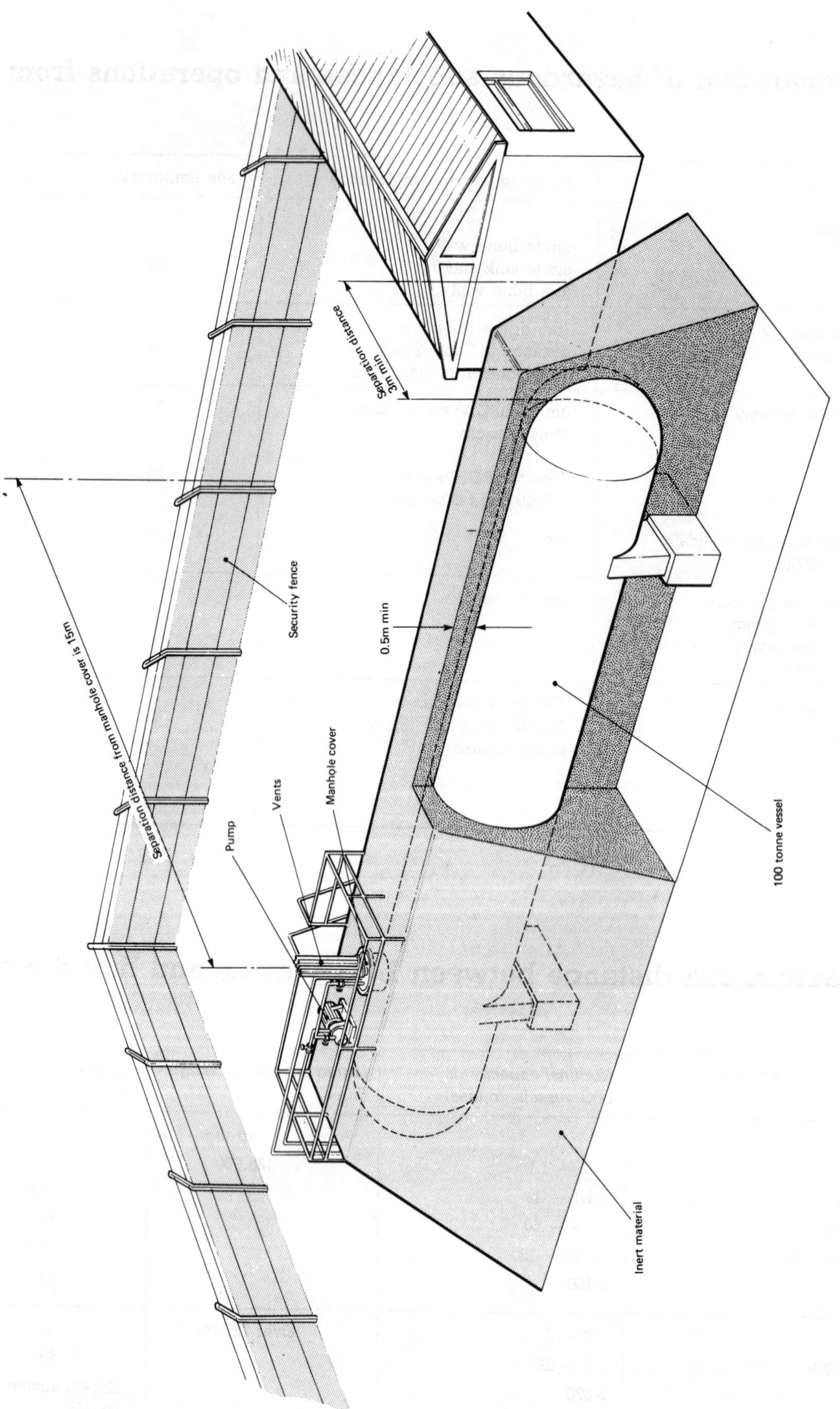

Fig 6 Mounded vessel

Security fence

Separation distance from manhole cover is 15m

Pump

Vents

Manhole cover

Separation distance 3m min

0.5m min

100 tonne vessel

Inert material

nearest point of the vessel. With the provision of a fire wall, the separation distances may be reduced to the values given in Table 2 column (b). For vessels up to 500 litres see footnote to Table 2.

35 The distance between the vessel and any specified feature measured around the ends of the fire wall should be equal to or greater than the separation distance given in Table 2 column (a).

36 Normally a fire wall should only be provided on one side of a vessel or group of vessels.

Mechanical integrity

37 The mechanical integrity of LPG vessels will not initially be assured unless the correct design criteria are adopted. These should reflect process needs and environmental conditions and particular attention should be paid to vacuum and low temperature use. The design of underground and mounded vessels will require an appreciation of the more arduous conditions introduced.

38 LPG vessels should be designed, constructed, tested and certified to an appropriate standard eg BS 5500 for new vessels. They should be constructed from steel which is suitable for use at the minimum safe operating temperature. Their design requirements should meet or exceed the following criteria.

	Propane	Butane
Maximum safe operating pressure	14.5 bar gauge (210 psig)	4.83 bar gauge (70 psig)
Minimum safe operating pressure	0 bar gauge	480 millibar absolute (7 psi absolute)
Minimum safe operating temperature	-40°C	-18°C

The design requirements for vessels to be used interchangeably for propane and butane storage should be:

Maximum safe operating pressure	14.5 bar gauge (210 psig)
Minimum safe operating pressure	480 mbar absolute (7 psi absolute)
Minimum safe operating temperature	-40°C

39 Existing butane installations should be checked by a competent person to determine whether they meet the design criteria in paragraph 38. If not the vessel or installation should be modified to meet the criteria or a vacuum prevention system installed. See Appendix.

40 All vessels should be marked with the minimum safe operating pressure. Where this is not known and cannot be determined it should be assumed to be 1 bar absolute (zero bar gauge) and the vessel marked accordingly.

Underground and mounded vessels

41 Underground vessels should be located in ground which is well drained. The vessel should preferably be located within a concrete or brick lined pit which will allow sound installation and backfill and provide easy access for inspection. Vessels may be installed in open ground excavations where these criteria can be met.

42 Underground and mounded vessels should be placed on a firm foundation and installed so as to prevent movement or flotation. The surface of vessels should be suitably prepared and treated to protect them from corrosion. Methods of protection may include surface coatings and cathodic protection.

43 The excavation should be large enough to allow for easy installation and should permit a clear gap of at least 1m between the shell of the vessel and the walls before backfilling. When lowering the vessel into place, care should be taken to avoid damage to the coating. When the vessel is in place, the coating should be checked by suitable fault detection apparatus and any damage repaired.

44 The backfill material should be inert, non-corrosive, free from abrasive materials or particles likely to damage the vessel coating and carefully consolidated to give a minimum cover of 500mm.

45 Mounded vessels should be covered by a suitable material which is inert, non-corrosive, free from particles or abrasive materials likely to damage the vessel coating and carefully consolidated to give a minimum cover of 500mm. The mound should protect the vessel from the effects of thermal radiation and should be sufficiently robust to remain in place in the event of jet flame impingement.

46 Underground and mounded vessels should normally be fitted with a manhole of not less than 560mm internal diameter to allow access for inspection. Where a manhole is not provided, inspection ports may be needed and it may be

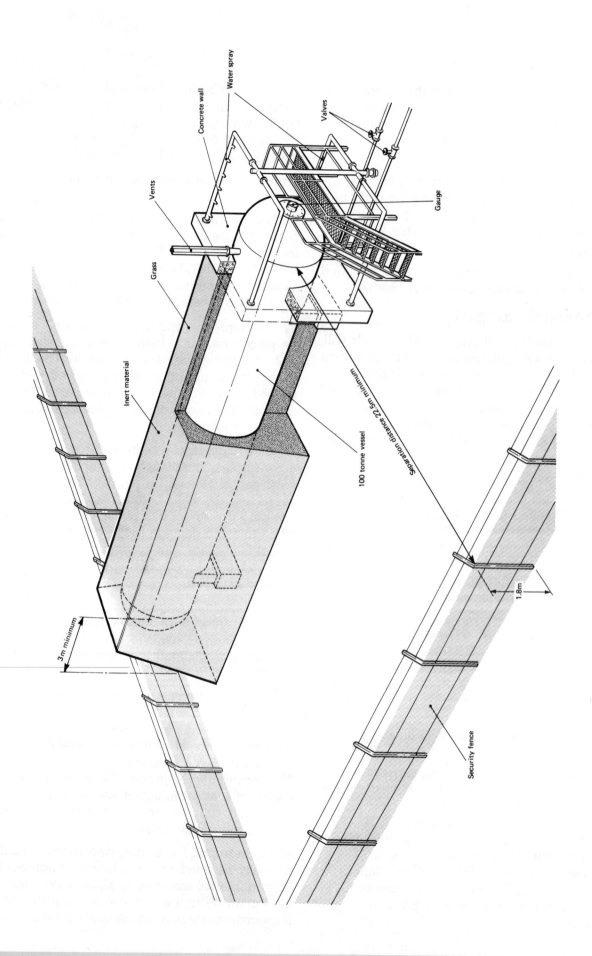

Fig 7 Semi-mounded vessel

Water spray

Concrete wall

Valves

Vents

Gauge

Grass

Inert material

100 tonne vessel

Separation distance 22.5 m minimum

3m minimum

1.8m

Security fence

necessary to excavate the vessel to thoroughly inspect it. Vessel fittings and connections may be mounted on the manhole cover or attached directly to the vessel. If this latter method is used, excavation may be necessary for inspection.

Skid mounted vessels

47 Skid mounted vessels whether used from a vehicle or placed on the ground, should conform to the guidance for fixed vessels given in this booklet.

48 The vessel should be constructed to an accepted pressure vessel standard and meet the requirements of paragraphs 37 to 40 and 55 to 57 for mechanical integrity and paragraphs 58 to 71 for fittings.

49 When it is necessary to move the vessel, all liquid should be removed from it before it is lifted or moved from its position unless the vessel has been designed to transport LPG. Any vessel greater than 3m^3 in volume will be subject to the Dangerous Substances (Conveyance by Road in Road Tankers and Tank Containers) Regulations 1981, in which case it should also meet the requirements of those regulations.

50 The vessel should be properly mounted on a vehicle to prevent undue stresses on it. Any sides or tailboards on the vehicle should not inhibit ventilation around the vessel. No part of the vessel should overhang the sides or ends of the vehicle, unless the vessel is purged of LPG.

51 If the vessel is to be used while on the ground:

(a) the ground on which the vessel is sited should be compacted and substantially level;

(b) the vessel should stand on legs which are an integral part of it, or alternatively on suitable supports.

52 Vessels should only be used from a vehicle if the vehicle has been designed for the transport of hazardous substances in accordance with the Dangerous Substances (Conveyance by Road in Road Tankers and Tank Containers) Regulations 1981.

53 The ground on which the vehicle is parked should be firm and substantially level and in

addition to an effective parking brake, wheel chocks should be provided.

54 Because of the temporary nature of skid mounted vessels it is particularly important that the piping is to a high standard and thoroughly checked for leakage before use, each time the vessel is moved.

Certification of all vessels

55 After installation and before being filled with liquid the vessel should be examined by a competent person. Particular attention should be paid to site fittings, protective devices, site loadings, vessel supports and foundations. The vessel should be certified as fit-for-purpose with the particular LPG. Any additional site inspection or testing necessary should be determined by a competent person and the safe operating limits of pressure, temperature and loading should be certified. For underground or mounded vessels the examination should take place before backfilling or mounding.

56 Existing vessels should carry similar current fit-for-purpose certification issued by a competent person. Before the first periodic examination this will relate to the as-new condition. After the first and subsequent examinations the safe working limits should be endorsed or reassessed by the competent person dependant on the inspection findings. For guidance on in-service examination and inspection see paragraphs 182 to 191.

Marking

57 If not already included in the requirements of the manufacturing standard the following additional information should be plated on the vessel or included in documentation which is available for inspection:

(a) plated;
     manufacturers name
     date of manufacture
     standard to which it was built
     reference number
     maximum safe operating pressure
     minimum safe operating pressure - *where this is other than atmospheric. If no minimum is marked - assume atmospheric.*
     test pressure
     minimum safe operating temperature

water capacity
inspection authority

(b) included in documentation;
maximum permissible fill (contents)
Maximum permissible load on supports.

Fittings

58 All fittings should be suitable for use with
LPG at the temperatures and pressures likely to
be encountered in service. To reduce the
probability of a liquid leak the number of direct
connections below the liquid level should be
minimised and wherever possible only one
branch, excluding drain lines, should be
provided. All other branches should terminate in
the vapour space.

59 Each vessel should be fitted with at least one
of each of the following items:

(a) a pressure relief valve connected directly to
the vapour space;

(b) a drain or other means of emptying the
vessel of liquid;

(c) a maximum level indicator and preferably a
contents gauge. The maximum level indicator
should be independent of the contents
gauge;

(d) a filling connection;

(e) a means for preventing excessive vacuum if
dictated by vessel design. (See Appendix);

(f) a pressure gauge connected to the vapour
space if the vessel is over 5000 litres capacity
(2.2 te). For vessels below this size provision
should be made for determining the pressure
in the vessel eg a valved tapping in the
vapour space of the vessel or adjacent
pipework.

Pressure relief valves

60 All above ground vessels should be fitted
with a pressure relief valve or valves designed to
protect the vessel under fire exposure in
accordance with a recognised code eg LPGITA
Code of Practice No 1, API 520, API RP2000,
BS 6759: Part 3: 1984.

61 The full flow capacity of pressure relief
valves on underground or mounded vessels may

be reduced to not less than 30% of the capacity
required for an equivalent size of above ground
vessel or such other value as will adequately
protect the vessel.

62 Every relief valve should be permanently
marked with:

(a) manufacturer's name and identification,
including catalogue or type number;

(b) start to discharge pressure;

(c) certified capacity in terms of air at 15.6°C
and 1 bar pressure;

(d) date of last inspection or setting.

63 An isolation valve should not be fitted
between a single pressure relief valve and the
vapour space of the vessel. For multiple relief
valves, if provision is made to isolate a relief
valve for maintenance or testing interlocks should
be provided to ensure the remaining valves
continue in use. They should be capable of
providing the relief capacity required by
paragraph 60. For vessels fitted with single relief
valves, provision may be made for their removal
for testing or servicing by using an automatic
shut-off valve. This valve should remain in the
fully open position with the relief valve in place
and close before the relief valve is completely
removed. It is essential that the storage vessel is
not left unprotected and a replacement relief
valve should be fitted immediately.

64 For above ground vessels over 5000 litres
capacity (2.2 te) and for all underground and
mounded vessels, the relief valve should be
fitted with vent pipes. These should be
adequately supported and have outlets at least
1.8m above the top of the vessel to which they
are fitted and at least 3m above ground level.
Vent pipes should be designed to ensure that, if
the discharge products ignite flames do not
impinge on the vessel, or on any adjacent vessel,
piping or equipment. Vent pipes may be
provided with loose-fitting rain caps and should
allow for the drainage of water. For large vessels
the pressure relief system may discharge to the
vent collecting system of a flare.

65 A vent or vents sufficient to permit the free
discharge of LPG from the relief valve or from
any protective cover fitted should be provided
on smaller vessels. The vents should be

positioned so as not to spread the LPG or resultant flame over the vessel shell.

Drain connections

66 Drain connections should be less than 50mm in diameter and fitted with two shut-off valves in series. The length of piping between the valves should be at least 0.5m to minimise the risk of sumultaneous obstruction of both valves by the freezing of any water present in the LPG. The piping down stream of the second valve should not discharge beneath the vessel. The second valve and piping should be adequately supported and secured to prevent mechanical damage or breakage by vibration or jet forces. Both valves on the drain systems should have a means of actuation which cannot be readily removed or moved from the closed position except by intentional operation. (See paragraph 195).

67 Alternatively, a satisfactory arrangement for drain lines could be a single valve and a plug or blanking plate fitted on the discharge side of the valve. Additional pipework and a second valve should be fitted, when required, in accordance with paragraph 66.

68 No drain line should discharge within 6m of any drainage system where this would be liable to create a hazard.

Contents gauges

69 Any gauging device that relies on bleeding LPG to atmosphere should be fitted with an opening no greater than 1.4mm diameter. Gauging devices should clearly indicate when the vessel is full to its maximum normal capacity. Sight glasses should not be used for measuring the liquid level in LPG storage vessels except in special applications eg LPG meter provers.

Valves

70 All liquid and vapour connections on vessels should be fitted with a shut-off valve which preferably is fire safe, except for relief valves and where the connection through the tank shell is not greater than 1.4mm diameter. The valve should be located as close to the vessel as practicable. However, where there are no mechanical joints between the shut-off valve

flange and the vessel and the intervening piping is designed, constructed, and tested in accordance with the vessel's design code, the shut-off valve may be located at the downstream end of that length of piping. All connections in a vessel greater than 3mm diamater for liquids, and 8mm diameter for vapour should have an emergency shut-off valve eg an excess flow valve, a non-return valve or a remotely operated emergency valve.

71 Remotely operated emergency valves capable of local manual operation should be fitted to all piping greater than 19mm internal diameter which carries liquid if:

(a) the supply of LPG is to an activity requiring frequent making and breaking of connections eg tanker filling, cylinder filling; or

(b) the activity occurs where the general public has access or where a significant number of people not familiar with the specific emergency procedures are likely to be nearby and whose number and location would make it difficult for them to evacuate quickly eg automative fuel dispensing; or

(c) the vessel is of 225 000 litres (100 te) water capacity or greater.

Pumps

72 Pumps should not be sited beneath an LPG vessel. Pumps should be securely installed and located in accordance with Table 5. Positive displacement pumps should have a bypass or other suitable protection against over-pressure.

Compressors

73 Vapour compressors should preferably be installed in the open air in a well ventilated position at least 4.5m from an LPG vessel, buildings and boundaries. If installed in a building, then the building should be made of non-combustible material with a lightweight roof and should have good natural ventilation, particularly at low level. The building should not be used for any purpose other than compression and distribution of LPG and other gases. Compressors should have at least one:

(a) high pressure cut-off switch, or similar

Table 5 Area classification

Factor			Area classification
Storage vessels	(a)	Within 1.5m in all directions from the discharge orifice of fixed liquid level gauges, rotary or dip gauges, filler openings	Zone 1
	(b)	Up to 1.5m above ground level and within the distances set out for a fixed source of ignition in Table 2 column (a)	Zone 2
Relief valve discharge	(a)	Within direct path of discharge	Fixed electrical equipment should not be installed.
	(b)	Within 1.5m in all other directions from point of discharge	Zone 1
	(c)	Beyond 1.5m but within 4.5m, or the separation distance in Table 2 column (a) in the case of vessels with a capacity not exceeding 2500 litres, in all directions from point of discharge	Zone 2
Tanker loading and unloading	(a)	Within 1.5m in all directions from a point where connections are regularly made or disconnected for a product transfer	Zone 1
	(b)	Beyond 1.5m but within 4.5m or the separation distance in Table 2 column (a) in the case of vessels with a capacity not exceeding 2500 litres, from point of connection or disconnection	Zone 2

Pumps, compressors and vaporisers other than direct fired

(a) Outdoors in open air, at or above ground level	(a)	Within 1.5m in all directions	Zone 1
	(b)	Beyond 1.5m but within 4.5m in all directions or the separation distance in Table 2 column (a) in the case of vessels not exceeding 2500 litres capacity.	Zone 2

Note: Where there is a high standard of maintenance of pumps and pump seals the area within 1.5m in all directions from the pump may be classified as Zone 2

(b) Indoor location with adequate ventilation		The entire room and any adjacent room not separated by a vapour-tight partition	Zone 1

Notes

1 Where any area is classified under more than one factor the higher classification should prevail

2 Any pit, trench or depression falling within a Zone 1 or Zone 2 area should be treated as a Zone 1 area throughout

3 The term 'outdoors in open air' includes pumps, compressors and vaporisers which are covered by a canopy.

device, on the discharge side of the compressor;

(b) means to prevent liquid LPG entering the compressor; eg a catchpot with a liquid level sensor.

Piping

74 Piping should be properly designed and constructed with due regard to low temperature service. The materials used should be suitable for use with LPG. In general steel piping should be used but for vapour lines solid drawn copper tubing may be used. When using copper pipe the potential hazards from work hardening of the material should be recognised. Cast iron pipe should not be used. Pipes conveying propane vapour should be constructed from materials suitable for use at temperature down to -20°C. Where these pipes may be subject to two-phase flow eg on flare and blowdown systems, lower design temperatures may be appropriate.

75 Detailed advice on piping for use with LPG can be found in LPGITA CoP No 22. All metal piping with a nominal bore greater than 50mm, all piping at full vessel pressure and all pipes carrying liquid should be designed and constructed to an acceptable standard such as BS 3351 or ANSI B31.3.

76 Joints in piping should be kept to a minimum. Piping more than 50mm outside diameter should have welded or welded flanged joints except when connecting to equipment fitted with screwed connections. Piping 50mm diameter and less may have screwed joints. Where piping has screwed joints which may be subject to vibration, consideration should be given to tack welding them to prevent them from coming loose. Jointing compounds for screwed connections and joint rings should be suitable for use with LPG.

77 To prevent the accumulation of static electricity metal piping should be electrically continuous so that the resistances to earth of the installation does not exceed 10^6 ohms. In practice a value of less than 100 ohms is readily attainable and is unlikely to deteriorate with time to a level above 10^6 ohms unless the plant is subject to serious corrosion. Reference should be made to BS 5958: Part 1:1980 for further information.

78 Piping should be sized and routed so as to restrict the contents of the pipe to the minimum and thus reduce the potential hazard. The route selected should minimise the possibility of physical damage particularly from vehicles but where such damage may be foreseen, protective barriers, bollards etc should be provided. Piping should preferably be run above ground and routed away or protected from excessive heat or cold. The routing of piping containing liquid LPG or vapour at pressure above 37 mbar gauge in buildings should be avoided. Where this is not reasonably practicable any such piping within a building should be in a well ventilated position protected from physical damage. The length of pipe within the building should be kept to a minimum.

Underground pipes

79 Where piping carrying liquid is installed underground:

(a) the piping design should make due allowance for any additional loading or constraint imposed by backfill or underground location;

(b) corrosion protection should be provided where necessary eg proprietary wax-impregnated tape, tar/bitumen overwraps, or cathodic protection. Specialist advice should be sought;

(c) piping should be run, adequately supported and laid, in a shallow open concrete or masonry-lined trench with open grid covers, where necessary, to allow safe movement of pedestrians;

(d) the trench may be backfilled with an inert, non-corrosive material free from abrasive particles likely to damage the corrosion protection. See paragraph 188 for advice on maintenance requirements;

(e) protection should be provided in the form of load bearing slabs or covers for those sections over which traffic passes or where superimposed loads will occur;

(f) all pipe joints underground should be welded;

(g) as an alternative to running a liquid filled pipe in a concrete or masonry trench, the pipe may be run inside an outer pipe. The outer pipe should be sealed to the inner pipe at both ends and the space between the two should be monitored to detect leakage, normally by registering a pressure change. The outer sleeve should terminate above ground or in a suitable inspection pit;

(h) isolation valves should be provided at both ends of the underground section;

(i) the route of the pipe-run should be recorded and, where practical permanently marked;

(j) piping conveying inert or flammable liquids, may be laid in the same trench but that containing corrosive or toxic materials and steam should not be;

(k) it is recommended that electric cables are not laid in the same trench as LPG piping. Electric cables may be laid in the same trench if protected by an outer pipe or sleeve.

80 Suitable polyethylene (PE) pipe may be used to convey LPG vapour and LPG/air mixtures. PE pipe should be buried but where at the terminals it is brought above ground it should be as short as possible and not longer than 2m. It should also be protected against ultra-violet light and mechanical damage eg by sleeving. Alternatively, the transition to metal pipework may be made with a suitable fitting below ground.

80 Piping conveying LPG vapour may be buried in an open excavation backfilled with a material which is non-corrosive. Metal piping should be protected from corrosion eg using proprietary wax impregnated tape, tar/bitumen overwraps, cathodic protection. The backfill for metal piping should be free from abrasive particles likely to damage the protective coating.

Hydrostatic relief valves

82 Piping in which liquid LPG may be trapped, for example, between shut-off valves, should be protected against excessive pressure by fitting hydrostatic relief valves. If these devices discharge to atmosphere, the discharge should be to the open air and should not endanger people or equipment. Where possible the

devices should not be sited beneath the vessel. Hydrostatic relief valves located under vessels should be positioned so that escaping LPG is not directed towards the vessel surface or adjacent access ways. At oil refineries and similar large installations alternative arrangements may be provided to prevent overpressurisation of piping.

Flexible connections

83 Hoses for conveying LPG should comply with BS 4089. They should only be used where necessary, and should be as short as reasonably practicable. Where flexible connections are used for conveying liquid LPG, a hydrostatic relief valve should be installed to limit the internal pressure to not more than the design pressure of the hose or the operating pressure of the fixed piping whichever is the lower. See paragraph 152 for guidance on hoses used for loading and unloading.

84 Emergency isolation devices eg non-return valves, excess flow valves or remotely operated emergency valves should be installed in piping conveying liquid LPG to which hoses are connected, to prevent the prolonged discharge of LPG in the event of failure of the hose.

Supports for vessels and piping

Vessel supports

85 The design of supports should follow the recommendations in the code to which the vessel is constructed. Supports should permit movement of the vessel due to changes in temperature and should be designed to prevent or drain any accumulation of water. Supports for horizontal vessels should be located to give minimum moments and deflections to the vessel shell. Additional supports may be required to meet special circumstances.

86 Vessels should be properly installed on firm foundations and supported on concrete, masonry or structural steel supports. These supports (excluding supporting feet 460mm or less in height, vessel saddles, or skirts of vertical vessels) should be so constructed or protected as to be at least 2hr fire resisting.

87 Where piers are used as part of the vessel support for horizontal vessels with a capacity

exceeding 5000 litres (2.2 te), provision should be made for securing the vessel at one end, the other being free to move. The end secured should be that to which the principal liquid and the vapour pipes are attached. Saddles should normally be welded to the vessel shell. Where saddles are not welded to the vessel, their support should be shaped to conform with the vessel shell and wear pads provided to prevent damage or weakening of the vessel shell.

88 Vertical vessels should be supported by an open structure which will allow good natural ventilation under the vessel and provide adequate explosion relief. If a cylindrical skirt is used to support the vessel, pipes from the vessel, within the skirt, should have welded or welded flanged joints.

Pipe supports

89 Supports should be adequately designed, spaced and secured to suit the pipe configuration and to withstand anchorage and guide friction forces.

Vaporisers

General

90 Vaporisers can be low pressure steam-heated, hot water heated, electrically heated, or direct gas fired. They should be of sufficient capacity to vaporise LPG at the maximum vapour offtake required from the installation. For butane, precautions against the accumulation of condensate in the vapour discharge line should be taken. This may require insulation and heat

tracing of the vapour discharge line with the provision of condensate pockets capable of containing the quantity likely to be condensed during a plant shut-down. With hot water heated vaporisers, anti-freeze may be added to the water to prevent freezing.

91 Vaporisers should be designed, fabricated and tested in accordance with an appropriate pressure vessel code eg BS 5500.

92 Heating coils should not be installed inside a storage vessel to act as a vaporiser.

93 If not already included in the requirements of the manufacturing standard the following additional information should be plated on the vaporiser or included in documentation which is readily available:

(a) the manufacturer's name and vaporiser serial number;

(b) the code to which it was made;

(c) the maximum safe operating pressure;

(d) the maximum and minimum safe operating temperature;

(e) the year of manufacture.

94 Vaporisers should be installed in a well ventilated position, preferably in the open air and not in or near a pit or depression. They should be separated from important buildings, boundaries or adjoining property lines as in Table 6. The ground beneath vaporisers should be concreted and sloped so that any leak of LPG flows towards a safe place away from the vaporiser and any LPG vessel.

Table 6 Separation distances from vaporisers

Capacity of vaporiser		Minimum distance of vaporisers from nearest important building or line of adjoining property
kg/hr	lb/hr	metres
Up to 36	Up to 80	3
>36-227	>80-500	7.5
Over 227	Over 500	15

Fig 8 Installation supplying gas to houses on a metered supply

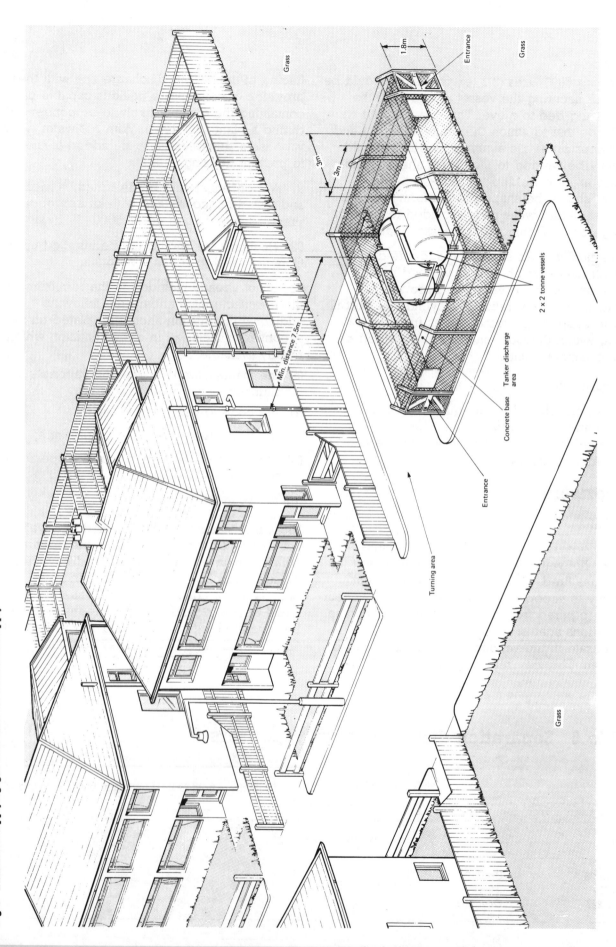

Grass

Entrance

1.8m

Grass

3m

3m

Min. distance 7.5m

2 x 2 tonne vessels

Concrete base

Tanker discharge area

Entrance

Turning area

Grass

95   Direct fired and non-explosion protected electrical vaporisers should be installed no closer to LPG vessels than the separation distances quoted in Table 2 column (a) for sources of ignition.

96   Vaporisers, other than direct fired or non-explosion protected electrical types, should be installed at least 1.5m from the nearest LPG vessel.

97   If a vaporiser is installed in a building then the building should be made of non-combustible material with a lightweight roof to provide explosion relief and should have good natural ventilation, particularly at low level. The building should only be used for vaporisation and distribution of LPG.

98   Shut-off valves should be installed in the liquid and vapour connections between the LPG storage vessel and the vaporiser.

Drain connections

99   Vaporiser systems should be equipped with a drain to allow the safe removal of any heavy products which may collect in the LPG part of the system. Drain connections fitted to vaporisers should be to the same standard as that required for bulk vessels (paragraph 66).

Pressure relief

100   Vaporisers should have pressure relief valves directly connected to the vapour space and set to discharge and reach full flow conditions, in accordance with the design code of the vaporiser. The relief valves should either discharge directly into the open air away from the vaporiser or any adjacent LPG vessel or to the collecting system of a flare stack. The relief capacity should be sufficient to protect the vaporiser from overpressurisation from fire engulfment and the maximum heat input from the heating system.

Liquid level control

101   Vaporisers should be provided with adequate automatic means to prevent liquid LPG passing through the vaporiser to the gas discharge piping under all operating conditions.

Maximum temperature control

102   Vaporisers should be fitted with an automatic device to prevent overheating.

Security

103   The installation, its fittings and attachments should be protected to minimise inadvertent or deliberate interference.

103   Vessels, vaporisers and pumps should be enclosed by a security fence. It should be at least 1.8m high and set at a distance of at least 1.5m from any vessel or vaporiser. Two gates should be provided from the enclosure which provide a ready means of escape but are not adjacent to each other. They should open outwards, should not be self-locking and should be unlocked when the compound is occupied. Certain exceptions to these general guidelines are dealt with in paragraphs 106 and 108.

105   The security fence should be of a construction which does not substantially interfere with the natural ventilation of the installation. A fence of robust industrial type wire mesh eg 12 gauge x 52mm x 52mm mesh welded panels or 12 gauge chain link fencing secured to concrete uprights would be satisfactory. Wooden fencing, particularly interwoven or lap fencing, should not be used since it is combustible, and may interfere with natural ventilation.

106   Vessels to which the public may have uncontrolled access, such as those supplying housing estates or modern open plan industrial estates, should be provided with a security fence. For vessels with capacities up to 9000 litres (4 te) at this type of installation this fence should be at least 3m from the vessel. For vessels with capacities between 2500 (1.1 te) and 9000 litres (4 te) arrangements should be made to control the accumulation of combustible materials and the positioning of sources of ignition within the remainder of the area which is within the separation distance and outside of the security fence. Advice should be sought from the enforcing authority regarding the siting of the security fence for vessels of greater than 9000 litres capacity (4 te).

107   At industrial sites where there is

surveillance of the installation, the site perimeter fence may suffice for security. However, where the installation is remotely located on the site, subject to infrequent surveillance, and particularly where trespass on to the site is known, the installation should be enclosed by its own security fence to supplement that at the perimeter.

108   The requirement for a security fence may be relaxed for vessels of less than 9000 litre (4 te) capacity provided that access to the valves and fittings is denied, eg, by a substantial lockable cover, an open mesh wire fence between the support piers. Where a lockable cover is provided it should be kept locked at all times other than during vessel filling. The key to the cover should be readily available in an emergency. This relaxation should not be applied where the public have uncontrolled access.

Protection against vehicular damage

109   The location of vessels and their attachments, eg piping, in areas used by motor traffic should be avoided. Where protection is required, substantial crash barriers or bollards should be provided. The security fence is unlikely to provide adequate protection on its own, nor is the restriction of traffic by marking of the ground, warning notices, etc.

110   Underground vessels should be protected from the effects of ground loading by traffic either by fencing off the area above the vessels or by the provision of load-bearing covers. Underground pipework should be similarly protected where necessary.

111   Petrol driven cars and other vehicles which are under the control of the site occupier should be parked at least 6m, or the separation distance given in Table 2, column (a) whichever is the smaller, from LPG vessels. Diesel powered vehicles under the control of the occupier may be parked to within 3m of the vessels providing they do not hinder ventilation. Vehicles not under site control eg those belonging to members of the public, should be parked no closer than the separation distances given in Table 2 column (a).

Marking and identification of the installation and its contents

112   The purpose of any marking and identification is to:

(a)   draw attention to the hazardous nature of the contents;

(b)   avoid confusion, whether during normal operations or in an emergency, which might lead to incorrect actions likely to cause an incident or make it worse.

Such marking is in addition to that in paragraphs 57 and 93.

113   All markings and identifications should be both clear and durable. The information should either be on plates or tags etc securely attached to the part to which it relates, or directly marked onto it. Paper labels are not satisfactory.

114   The direct stamping of information onto any part should only be carried out if this does not impair the integrity of that part and is capable of withstanding wear and possible over-painting without becoming illegible.

115   The vessel should be clearly marked with the words 'Liquefied Petroleum Gas' or the name of the material stored where confusion could arise. The words 'Highly Flammable' should be added or a pictorial sign conforming to the Safety Signs Regulations 1980.

116   Piping should be marked or colour-coded, or both, to indicate the contents conveyed, and whether the contents are liquid or vapour. Colour coding, where appropriate, should be in accordance with BS 1710.

Valves and connections

117   The operation of all manual isolation valves should be clear. The operating points for remotely operated isolation valves and manually operated fixed water-drench systems should be clearly identified and the mode of operation marked.

118   Where butane and propane loading/unloading connections are adjacent they should be clearly identified.

Hazardous area classification for electrical equipment

119 Electrical equipment should only be installed in a safe area away from LPG vessels and equipment. Where this is not reasonably practicable the area around an LPG vessel and equipment can be subdivided according to the degree of probability that flammable concentrations of vapour may arise and the electrical equipment suitably protected depending on its location. Those subdivision are defined as:

Zone 0 An area in which a flammable gas/air mixture is continuously present, or present for long periods.

Zone 1 An area in which a flammable gas/air mixture is likely to occur in normal operation.

Zone 2 An area in which a flammable gas/air mixture can only occur in abnormal conditions and not in normal operation.

A more complete explanation of the method of classification can be found in BS 5345 and guidance in choosing suitable electrical equipment for those zones in Health and Safety booklet HS(G)22.

120 If electrical equipment has to be installed near LPG vessels etc, it should meet the standards and separation distances in Table 5.

121 LPG vessels do not normally require lightning protection.

Fire precautions

General

122 The possiblity of a major fire outbreak can be minimised by good plant design and layout, sound engineering, good operating practice and proper instruction and training of personnel in routine operations and action to be taken in an emergency. Good plant design and layout should include consideration of water supplies, fire protection equipment, fire fighting, means of access for fire brigade appliances, protection of fire brigade personnel and arrangements to ensure an early call out to the fire brigade in the event of fire.

123 Under the Fire Services Act 1947 it is the responsibility of the local fire authority to make provision for fire fighting purposes, and to equip and maintain a fire brigade accordingly to meet all normal requirements. The local fire authority may make arrangements with works fire teams to provide assistance but the local authority brigade will assume control of fire fighting operations upon arrival at a fire. The fire brigade should be called out whenever a fire occurs which may threaten the LPG storage.

124 The fire service will wish to be consulted at an early stage where LPG storage is planned. The enforcing authority (see glossary) should be consulted where additional guidance on fire fighting and protection facilities is required which is not to be found in this document.

Fire protection

125 LPG storage vessels threatened by fire should be kept sufficiently cool to prevent vessel failure. This protection can be achieved by the discharge of water onto the vessels at a rate sufficient to maintain an adequate film of water over the surface of the vessels and supports.

126 Vessels may also be protected from radiant heat by burial, mounding or other methods, such as insulating coatings, providing an equivalent standard of protection to adequate water drench systems (ie monitors or fixed sprays) can be achieved. Where these methods are used, water for fire protection need not be provided except for unprotected manholes on underground or mounded vessels. Water protection for the tanker offloading bay and any process plant containing LPG may still be required.

Water supplies

127 At all installations there should be an adequate supply of water for fire protection for use in an emergency. To provide adequate protection for a vessel threatened by fire an application rate of 9.8 litres/m^2/min over the whole surface of the vessel for at least 60 minutes is required*. The capacity of the supply may need to be increased where there are no

*The use of water sprays to protect fire engulfed LPG storage tanks. Billinge, Moodie and Beckett. 5th International symposium. Loss Prevention and Safety Promotion in the Process Industries. 1986.

Table 7 Summary of fire precaution requirements

Installation capacity		Fire precautions	Paragraph
Litres	Tonnes		
150 - 2500 Domestic	< 1.1	Water supply for fire brigade use 100m away	127 131
150 - 2500 Commercial and industrial	< 1.1	Water supply for fire brigade use 100m away 19mm hose reel or 2 x 9 litre water extinguishers 2 x 9kg dry powder extinguishers (not commercial sites)	127,131 143 144
>2500 - <56250	>1.1- <25	Water supply for fire brigade use 100m away 19mm hose reel 2 x 9kg dry powder extinguisher	127, 133 143 144
Liquid Offtake vessel capacity >15750	>7	Water supply Consideration should be given to providing a means of applying cooling water to vessels 19mm hose reel 2 x 9kg dry powder extinguishers	127 134 143 144
56250 - <112 500	25te- <50te	Water supply Fixed and/or portable monitors 19mm hose reel 2 x 9kg dry powder extinguishers	127 135 143 144
≥112500 (50te)	≥50te	Water supply Automatic fixed sprays 19mm hose reel 2 x 9kg dry powder extinguishers	127 136 143 144
Cylinder filling		Water supply Automatic fixed sprays 19mm hose reel 2 x 9kg dry powder extinguishers	127 137 143 144
Road tanker filling/delivers more than twice a week		Water supply Additional fire protection 19mm hose reel 2 x 9kg dry powder extinguishers	127 139 143 144

additional water supplies available near the premises. If water is supplied via a recirculating system the storage reservoir should hold 30 mins supply without recirculation. Special consideration should be given to the possibility that there could be a loss of power on the site and the consequences this would have for the fire protection arrangements provided.

128   On-site hydrants and fixed drench systems should be designed so that the water flow can be controlled from a safe position beyond the separation distances set out in Table 2 column (a). Connections for fire brigade use should be provided on the water supply to fixed drench systems. The connections should be located in a safe place agreed with the fire brigade.

129   There should be adequate drainage to deal with water used for fire protection and firefighting purposes. Water sealed interceptors should be fitted, where necessary, to prevent LPG entering the storm drains and sewers.

Fire protection equipment

130   The provision for fire protection at fixed installations depends on a number of considerations. These include the maximum storage capacity of the installation, individual vessel sizes, the number of tanker deliveries and whether there is an increased risk of fire on site which may affect the vessels eg at LPG cylinder filling plants. Paragraphs 131 to 141 provide guidance on the standards for fire protection which will be required by the enforcing authority. This guidance is summarised in Table 7. Higher standards of fire protection may be required by the enforcing authority where other factors prevail such as increased off-site risks and hazards, location of the nearest water supply and the time for the fire brigade to reach the site.

Domestic and small installations

131   Domestic installations and those small commercial or industrial installations with vessels, where the capacity of each vessel does not exceed 2500 litres (1.1 te), should be provided with an adequate water supply for fire brigade use. For these premises an adequate water supply may consist of hydrants, ponds, canals or rivers. The supply should be readily accessible

and usually no further than 100m from the vessels.

132   At remote installations where the population near the vessels is low, making it easy to evacuate the area, it may be acceptable for the water supply to be more than 100m from the vessels. In these cases the fire brigade should be consulted. A comprehensive evacuation plan should be available which the residents in the vicinity of the installation are familiar with.

Installations with a total inventory in vessels greater than 2500 litres (1.1 te) but less than 56 250 litres (25 te)

133   For installations in this inventory range fire protection may consist solely of an adequate water supply for fire brigade use except for vessels exceeding 15 750 litres capacity (7 te) with liquid outlets. The level of fire protection would depend on the installation meeting the other provisions of this guidance note. When deciding on the level of protection consideration should also be given to the ease of evacuation of the surrounding area and the attendance time of the fire brigade.

134   For vessels with liquid outlets, where the vessel size exceeds 15 750 litres (7 te) and remotely operated emergency valves are not fitted to the liquid outlets, consideration should be given to providing a means for applying cooling water to the vessels. This may be fixed or portable monitors or other suitable means.

Installations with a total inventory in vessels of 56 250 litres (25 te) but less than 112 500 litres (50 te)

135   At bulk installations with inventories from 56 250 litres (25 te) but less than 112 500 litres (50 te) means should be provided to apply cooling water to the vessels. Portable or fixed monitors or other suitable means may be used for this purpose.

Installations with a total inventory in vessels of 112 500 litres (50 te) and greater

136   At bulk installations with inventories of 112 500 litres (50 te) and greater, the vessels should be provided with fixed fully automatic water spray systems capable of detecting a fire threatening the vessels and operating the sprays without manual intervention. A fire detection

system dependent solely on the sensing of excess vessel pressure is not adequate for this purpose. At refineries and similar large installations where continuous supervision is available, manually operated water sprays may be sufficient. At these installations it may not be necessary to simultaneously drench all storage vessels and means may be provided to allow drenching of individual vessels or groups of vessels. A remote manual operating point should be provided in a safe place (see paragraph 128).

Other installations where fire protection is required

137   Fixed water spray systems should be fitted to bulk vessels at cylinder filling installations. A similar level of protection may be necessary at some aerosol filling plants where the vessels could be threatened by a fire involving the filling installation or the aerosol store. Fixed spray systems are not necessary where automative LPG is dispensed and paragraph 71 applies or where only a small number of cylinders are filled eg for fork lift trucks.

138   At installations with a total inventory in vessels of 56 250 litre (25 te) or greater, the road tanker bay should be provided with the same level of fire protection as the fixed vessels.

139   At installations where an average of more than two road tanker deliveries a week take place, or where more than two road tankers a week are filled with LPG, based on the consumption over six months including the winter period, consideration should be given to the provision of additional fire protection at the tanker bay.

140   Rail loading and unloading gantries should be provided with fixed water sprays or an equivalent form of fire protection.

141   For the purposes of the paragraphs 131 to 138 individual vessels may be considered in isolation where they are the sum of the separation distances given in Table 2, column (a) apart.

Portable fire fighting equipment

142   There should be sufficient and suitable portable fire fighting equipment on the premises.

This equipment should be selected and located to enable fires adjacent to the vessels to be extinguished and so prevent fire spreading to or jeopardising the LPG installation. Fire extinguishers or hose reels or an equivalent combination of the two types of equipment may be provided. Fire extinguishers should be selected, sized, located and maintained in accordance with BS 5306: Part 3: 1980, and hose reels should be selected and installed in accordance with BS 5306: Part 1: 1976.

143   All fixed LPG installations should be provided with at least one 19mm hose reel. At small installations with vessels up to 2500 litres (1.1 te), two 9 litre water extinguishers may be provided as an alternative. Hose reels and extinguishers need not be provided at domestic premises because of the lack of trained people to operate them.

144   In addition to the requirements in paragraphs 142 and 143, at least two fire extinguishers suitable for extinguishing an LPG fire should be provided (see paragraph 146). Powder extinguishers rated at least 223B (eg a capacity of 9kg) would normally be suitable. Powder extinguishers need not be provided at domestic and small commercial installations where it is unlikely that anyone will be available who has been trained to fight LPG fires.

Access

145   Access to and around the installation should be provided for fire fighting and should be kept free at all times.

Fire instruction and training

146   People on premises where LPG is stored should recieve adequate instructions with training as appropriate to enable them to understand the fire precautions and action to be taken in the event of fire or leakage of LPG. They should receive instruction and training appropriate to their responsibilities in the event of an emergency. Those trained to fight LPG fires should be aware that these fires should not normally be extinguished unless the source of LPG can be isolated. At commercial and industrial sites notices setting out the emergency procedures should be prominently displayed near the LPG storage area. At domestic

installations the user should be provided with full instructions which include the action to be taken in an emergency.

Loading and unloading facilities

General

147 Written instructions should be given which clearly define responsibilities for all personnel involved in loading/unloading operations.

148 Manning levels for LPG transfer operations will be dictated by the size and complexity of a particular installation. As a general safety rule the number should not be less than two. For many installations, this would normally be the road tanker driver and an employee from the site. In some cases, particularly at domestic and small installations, this may be impractical, as only the driver will be present.

149 Except in those cases mentioned in paragraph 148, a responsible person on site should check that the quantity and type of LPG being transferred is suitable for the receiving vessel. Vessels should be checked to see how full they are before filling, and also during filling using the contents gauge where fitted. The maximum level device should be used to ensure overfilling does not occur. Road and rail tankers should preferably be check weighed prior to leaving the depot to ensure they have not been overfilled. Specifications for filling ratios for LPG can be found in BS 5355: 1976.

150 **Overfilling can have extremely serious consequences and any overfilled tanker or vessel should have the excess LPG removed immediately in a safe manner.**

151 The point of transfer, where connections and disconnections are made should be sited in a well ventilated position.

152 Flexible hoses used for conveying LPG to and from road and rail tankers into fixed piping or vessels should:

(a) be designed and constructed to an appropriate standard eg BS 4089;

(b) have a means of identification;

(c) be examined for kinks and wear on every occasion prior to use. Hose fittings should be similarly examined;

(d) be hydraulically tested every year;

(e) be periodically checked for electrical continuity;

(f) have written records of the tests in (d) and (e);

(g) be kept so that the hose will not be physically damaged or adversely affected by the weather when not in use or when being conveyed;

(h) have means for protecting their end fittings against damage or ingress of foreign material;

(i) where appropriate, be protected by a procoil or similar device to protect against external damage;

(j) be replaced or repaired when damaged or worn.

153 Loading arms or flexible hoses in which liquid could be trapped between shut-off valves should be protected against excess pressure caused by the thermal expansion of the contents, eg by hydrostatic relief valves or by their design.

Loading/unloading of road tankers

154 In order to minimise the risk of accidental movement, the tanker should stand on an essentially level site during loading or unloading. Chocks should be placed against the vehicle's wheels or other means provided to prevent vehicle movement prior to loading/unloading. These should only be removed when transfer is complete. The ground beneath the tanker should be drained, cambered or have a shallow gradient to a safe place to prevent any spillage from remaining under the vehicle or from flowing under any vessels or piping in the fixed installation.

155 The loading/unloading operation should only be carried out when it is safe to do so and where practical be separated from other traffic movement. Where vehicles or pedestrians are likely to pass by, physical barriers may be needed to deter them approaching the transfer operation.

156 Consideration should be given to the provision of a driveway protection device on all installations with vessels of 9000 litres capacity (4 te) or above. Examples of such devices are:

(a) a self-sealing breakaway coupling connected to the flexible hose;

(b) means to shut emergency isolation valves on both the fixed plant and the tanker automatically

(c) an interlocked physical barrier or similar system on either the vehicle or static installation;

(d) a means to automatically actuate the vehicle braking system to lock immediately the delivery hose is taken from its normal transit stowage position until it is restored to that position;

(e) a brake flap arrangement which must be moved aside to gain access to the filling branch, the action of which actuates the braking system.

157 When a vehicle's engine is used during loading/unloading, usually to drive a pump, an emergency engine cut-off device should be installed so that the engine can be switched off from outside the cab.

158 The road tanker should stand off the highway while unloading and be positioned so that it can be readily driven away in the event of an emergency, if it is safe to do so. The location of the tanker should permit the driver to see the tanker when standing at the storage vessel. While the driver is at the vessel he should be able to stop filling immediately the vessel is full.

159 At some installations, eg at domestic premises it may not be possible to park the tanker off the road during unloading. Where this is so the tanker should not cause an obstruction to others and the Highway Code should be observed.

160 Hoses should not be run across a public footpath or pavement during unloading unless there is no alternative and where consideration of the safety of the public indicates that it will not constitute a significant hazard. In such cases, before and during unloading, warning notices, readable from 6m, should be set up on both sides of the hose stating:

(a) **Warning - LP Gas Transfer Taking Place**; and

(b) **No Smoking or Naked Flames,**
or words to that effect.

161 Any accumulated static electricity on a road tanker should be discharged to earth. The tank of the road tanker should be electrically bonded to the fixed installation before any LPG transfer operation is carried out. The electrical bonding connection should be broken only after the liquid and, where used, the vapour balance connection have been disconnected.

Loading/unloading rail tankers

162 The rail loading/off-loading operation should be separated from other rail traffic, eg on a siding. The transfer point should be sited in a well ventilated position at least 15m from buildings, boundaries, sources of ignition and any storage vessel forming part of the fixed installation.

163 In order to minimise the risk of accidental movement, the track should be laid essentially level. A slight downward gradient of less than 1:250 is acceptable, provided that this is away from the main line track, or in the case of a siding ending at buffers, towards the buffers.

164 Rail tankers containing LPG should not be loose shunted.

165 Physical barriers should be provided where there is a possibility that a tanker could be damaged by road vehicles, eg where a road and a rail siding are sited beside each other.

166 A barrier gate and other means of positive isolation should be provided to prevent a train from being accidentally pulled away while the tankers are connected to the fixed installation. Suitable means include:

(a) removal of the locomotive;

(b) removal of the towing cable or isolation of the capstan motor;

(c) locked points;

(d) application of wagon handbrakes.

Interlocks may be provided with product transfer pumps, isolation valves, etc to ensure that the train has been correctly positioned before transfer begins. Signals may be provided for additional security.

167 A system of work should be provided to ensure the tankers are not moved without the knowledge and approval of the plant personnel in charge of the LPG transfer operations. Traffic

movements to and from the transfer point should be controlled, where appropriate, by a written procedure. Where tankers are shunted, the closest cooperation is necessary between the locomotive driver and plant personnel. When British Rail drivers are used, BR provide and require the use of a permit system before their personnel will move any wagons. A similar system should be used when shunting is carried out by a firm's own locomotive.

168 The ground beneath a tanker should be drained, cambered or sloped to one side to prevent any spillage from remaining under the vehicle or from flowing and collecting under any vessel or piping in the fixed installation or other rail vehicle.

169 Remotely operated emergency isolation valves should be provided on the loading bay. In addition, manual shut-off valves should be provided for each loading/unloading liquid LPG branch pipe. Each manual valve should be fitted with its own key or operating handle with which it can be operated quickly in an emergency. Safeguards, such as remotely operated valves etc should also be considered for vapour lines. Where a common manifold is used, non-return valves should be fitted to prevent backflow of liquid into rail tankers during unloading.

170 Additional protection against pullaway incidents should be provided. This may be in the form of self-sealing breakaway couplings, isolation valves interlocked with the movement of the rail wagons or other equipment providing equivalent protection.

171 Care should be taken to prevent overfilling. To do this it may be necessary to limit the number of tankers being controlled by a single operator and to meter the delivery. A positive way of preventing overfilling is to continuously weigh the vehicle being filled on a weighing machine with an automatic shut-off set at the predetermined quantity.

Commissioning and de-commmissioning

172 Commissioning and de-commissioning of LPG vessels should only be undertaken by people familiar with the procedures and aware of the hazards of LPG.

Commissioning

173 Before filling with LPG, the vessel and its fittings should be tested, proved free of leaks and fit for use. A method of leak testing is to pressurise the vessel with air or inert gas and check for any pressure drop. Further information on safe methods of pressure testing can be found in Guidance Note GS4.

174 Care should be taken that, during leak testing and purging, the vessel is not subject to pressures, vacuum or temperature conditions outside it's design criteria.

175 Before commissioning, vessels and their ancillary equipment should be purged until the oxygen content is reduced to a level which will not support combustion. Air in the vessels should be removed by replacement with water, inert gas, LPG or by evacuation.

176 If water is used to remove the air from the vessel, the vessel and its supports should be able to withstand the weight when full of water. Care should be taken to remove all the water after purging.

177 Where inert gas is used for purging the vessel it is necessary to remove the purge gas with LPG. The purge gas/LPG mixture should be vented either to a safe place well away from LPG vessels, boundaries, buildings, places to which the public have access and sources of ignition or to a flare stack. The separation from boundaries, LPG vessels etc, depends upon the rate of purging. The basis for separation should be:

(a) that if the LPG mixture caught fire, the heat flux at the boundary or LPG vessel would not exceed $12.6kW/m^2$;

(b) when not ignited would be safely diluted to less than the lower flammable limit before reaching boundaries, buildings and sources of ignition.

178 If LPG vapour is used to replace air then the vessel and system will, for a period, contain a flammable mixture which should be vented to atmosphere in a safe manner. A suitable flame arrestor should be fitted in the vent line to prevent flashback should ignition of the vented gases occur. This operation should only be carried out under the supervision of a competent person.

179 Evacuation is only suitable for vessels designed to full vacuum conditions.

De-commissioning

180 The installation to be de-commissioned and purged free of LPG should be isolated from any process, plant or vessels containing LPG. Normally, this is achieved by removing pieces of piping or by fitting blanks or spades in the pipes. The closure of shut-off valves is not a suitable means of isolation.

181 Before opening, an LPG vessel should be:

(a) emptied of liquid LPG as far as possible, by normal use or transfer to another suitable vessel, flaring or venting. Where a drainline is used for emptying the vessel it should comply with paragraph 66. If it is necessary to vent LPG to atmosphere, only the minimum quantity of material should be vented;

(b) purged with an inert gas until it contains less than 4% LPG and remains at or near that concentration of LPG, ie there are not heavy ends still gassing off flammable vapours;

(c) purged by displacement with water or another suitable method. Care should be taken to ensure no heavy ends remain which could lead to the formation of a flammable atmosphere when air is introduced into the vessel

Maintenance and examination

182 The installation should be properly maintained to acceptable standards determined and overseen by a competent engineer of appropriate discipline with the objective of maintaining the established safe operating limits. Emphasis should be placed on features affecting the integrity of the installation or the ability to take emergency action. For installations rented from the gas suppliers this work may be carried out by the company owning the vessel.

183 A maintenance scheme should be prepared which includes protective devices and instruments, the form and detail of which should reflect the needs of the particular installation. Servicing and maintenance handbooks may be adequate for simple installations.

184 Suitable records should be kept so that all maintenance schemes are properly monitored. All significant repairs or replacements should be recorded.

185 A scheme for examining the installation should be drawn up by or be endorsed by a competent person and reviewed after each examination. Vessels should be examined at intervals as required by a competent person. Direct heated vaporisers should be thoroughly examined at intervals not exceeding one year.

186 The scope of any particular examination and the inspection techniques to be used should be decided by the competent person. Examination of pressure vessels should include support structure, holding down arrangements and foundations.

187 Examination of underground or mounded vessels should include tests for corrosion eg detailed ultrasonic thickness checks. If internal access is not possible the external surface of the vessel will need to be exposed to enable examination to take place.

188 Underground piping carrying liquid which is laid in a backfilled trench should be examined for corrosion, or tested in such a way as to establish continuing integrity, at least once every ten years.

189 Any significant deterioration or defects found and any remedial work undertaken, should be recorded on the examination report with particulars of the inspection techniques used. The effect of such deterioration, defect or repair should be assessed by the competent person and the safe working limits endorsed or modified accordingly.

190 The examination report should specify:

(a) the maximum safe operating pressure;

(b) the minimum safe operating pressure;

(c) the minimum safe operating temperature;

(d) the maximum permissible load (on supports);

(e) the date of next examination.

191 Any repair or modifications undertaken should be to a standard which is at least equal to the original design and construction code. Where such work may affect the integrity of the

installation it should be overseen and certified by a competent person who should endorse or modify the safe operation limits accordingly.

Operational procedures

192 Written operating procedures should be prepared which clearly define the actions or functions required of people involved. These should cover both normal and emergency operations and be regularly reviewed to ensure that they are appropriate at all times. They should be amended to take into account any alterations or modifications to the installation. The procedures should be readily available and preferably clearly displayed. Where appropriate, copies or relevant abstracts should be issued to people on site, including contractors entering or working at the site.

193 Procedures should include:

(a) the transfer of LPG to or from the installation (for which check lists may prove a useful supplement);

(b) the transfer of LPG at other sites when delivery tankers operate from the site;

(c) permit-to-work systems;

(d) plant maintenance and modification including the maintenance of protected electrical equipment;

(e) emergency procedures.

194 Employees and self employed people should only act within their sphere of responsibility. Any deviation from the written procedures should only be undertaken with the written authority of the appropriate responsible person on site.

194 Particular care should be taken when draining storage vessels in service in order to minimise the escape of LPG. Of the two drain valves, that nearer to the vessel should be fully opened first and draining then controlled by gradually opening the second valve. If, on opening the second valve, no flow occurs, both valves should be closed immediately to allow subsequent investigation. On completion of the draining operation, the valve furthest from the storage vessel should be closed first, then the other valve.

Training

196 Employers should ensure that employees concerned with LPG are familiar with its properties and hazards. Employees should be instructed on normal operations, including loading and off-loading procedures and emergency operations, fire-fighting and emergency shut-down. This instruction should be followed by appropriate practical training sessions designed to ensure that each employee is competent to carry out their duties and also to ensure that they are familiar with the installation and its operating procedures. Training should be a continuous commitment and include refresher courses, where appropriate. The emergency procedures should be practiced at least once a year, except at domestic installations.

197 All operations at LPG installations should be performed by properly trained personnel. A sufficient number of people should be appointed and trained to supervise procedures and operations at the installation.

198 The operator should be made aware of any plant alterations, and any change in operating procedures and should receive additional training to ensure safe operation of the installation.

Bibliography

Legal

The Health and Safety at Work etc Act 1974,
ISBN 0 10 543774 3 HMSO

The Highly Flammable Liquids and Liquefied
Petroleum Gases Regulations 1972 (SI 1972 No 917)
ISBN 0 11 020917 6 HMSO.

Health and Safety (Enforcing Authority)
Regulations 1977 (SI 1977 No 746)
ISBN 0 11 070746 X HMSO.

The Control of Industrial Major Hazards
Regulations 1984 (SI 1984 No 1902)
ISBN 0 11 047902 5 HMSO.

The Notification of Installations Handling
Hazardous Substances Regulations 1982 (SI 1982
No 1357) ISBN 0 11 027357 5 HMSO.

The Safety Signs Regulations 1980 (SI 1980
No 1471) ISBN 0 11 007471 8 HMSO.

Fire Certificates (Special Premises) Regulations
1976 (SI 1976 No 2003) ISBN 0 11 062003 8 HMSO.

Dangerous Substances (Conveyance by Road
Tankers and Tank Containers) Regulations 1981
(SI 1981 No 1059) ISBN 0 11 017059 8 HMSO.

Approved Code of Practice. Operational
provisions of the Dangerous Substances
(Conveyance by Road Tankers and Tank
Containers) Regulations 1983 ISBN 0 11 883728 1
HMSO.

The Classification, Packaging and Labelling of
Dangerous Substances Regulations 1984 (SI 1984
No 1244) ISBN 0 11 047244 6 HMSO.

Gas Act 1986 ISBN 0 10 544486 3 HMSO.

Pipelines Act 1962, ISBN 0 10 850098 5 HMSO.

Petroleum (Consolidation Act) 1928
ISBN 0 10 850212 0 HMSO.

LPGITA Codes

LPGITA (UK) Code of Practice No 1 March 1978.
*Installation and maintenance of bulk LPG storage
at consumers' premises.* ISBN 0 900323 9.

LPGITA (UK) Code of Practice No 22 LPG Piping
- System design and installation.

Health and Safety Executive Guidance

Health and Safety Series Booklet HS(R)16. *A
Guide to the Notification of Installations Handling
Hazardous Substances Regulations 1982*
ISBN 0 11 883675 7 HMSO.

Health and Safety Series Booklet HS(R)21. *A
Guide to the Control of Industrial Major
Accident Hazard Regulations 1984*
ISBN 0 11 883767 2 HMSO.

Health and Safety Series Booklet HS(G)22
*Electrical apparatus for use in potentially
explosive atmospheres* ISBN 0 11 883746 X. HMSO

Health and Safety Series Booklet HS(G)25 *The
Control of Industrial Major Accident Hazards
Regulations 1984 (CIMAH): further guidance on
emergency plans* ISBN 0 11 883831 8 HMSO.

HSE Guidance Note CS4 (June 1986) *The keeping
of LPG in cylinders and similar containers*
ISBN 0 11 883539 4 HMSO.

HSE Guidance Note CS8 (May 1985) *Small scale
storage and display of LPG at retail premises*
ISBN 0 11 883614 5. HMSO.

HSE Guidance Note GS4 *Safety in Pressure
Testing.* HMSO 0 11 883043 0. HMSO.

British Standards

BS 476 Fire Tests on building materials and
structures.

Part 1: 1953 Fire tests on building materials and
structures (superseded by Parts 7 and 8).

Part 4: 1970 Non combustibility test for materials.

Part 8: 1972 Test methods and criteria for the fire
resistance of elements of building construction

BS 1710:1984. Specification for identification of
pipelines and services.

BS 3351:1971. Piping systems for petroleum
refineries and petrochemical plants.

BS 4089:1966. Rubber hose and hose assemblies
for liquefied petroleum gas lines.

BS 4250:1975. Specification for Commercial Butane
and Propane.

BS 5146: Inspection and test of valves. Part 1:1974:
Steel valves for petroleum, petrochemical and
allied industries.

BS 5306 Code of Practice for fire extinguishing installations and equipment on premises.

Part 1: 1976 Hydrant systems, hose reels and foam inlets.

Part 3: 1985 Code of Practice for the selection, installation and maintenance of portable fire extinguishers.

BS 5345: Code of Practice for the selection, installation and maintenance of electrical apparatus for use in potentially explosive atmospheres (other than mining applications or explosive processing and manufacture).

Part 1: 1976 Basic requirements for all parts of the Code.

BS 5355: 1976 Specification for filling ratios and developed pressures for liquefiable and permanent gases.

BS 5423: 1980 Specification for portable fire extinguishers.

BS 5499: Fire safety signs, notices and graphic symbols. Part 1: 1984: Specification for fire safety signs.
BS 5500: 1985 Unfired fusion welded pressure vessels.

BS 5958: Code of Practice for the control of undesirable static electricity. Part 1: 1980: General considerations.

BS 6651: 1985 Code of Practice for protection of structures against lightning.

BS 6759: Part 3: 1984 Specification for safety valves for process fluids.

Note: British Standards are obtainable from the British Standards Institution, Sales Department, Linford Wood, Milton Keynes, MK14 6LE.
Tel (0908) 32006 (call queuing system *operates*)

American Petroleum Institute Standards

API 520 Recommended Practice for the Design and Installation of Pressure. Relieving Systems in Refineries.
Part 1: Design
Part 2: Installation

API 607 Fire tests for soft seated quarter turn valves.

API 6FA Specification for fire tests for valves.

API 2000 Venting atmospheric and low pressure storage tanks (non-refrigerated and refrigerated).

American National Standards

ANSI B31.3 Chemical Plant and Petroleum Refinery Piping.

1: 1981 addenda to ANSI/ASME B31. 3 - 1980 edition (ANSI/ASME B31.3a-1980).

2: 1982 addenda to ANSI/ASME B31.3 - 1980 edition (ANSI/ASME B31.3b - 1982).

Appendix: Protection of vessels against vacuum conditions

General

1 During prolonged periods of cold weather it is possible for the temperature of the contents of a vessel to fall below 0°C. For some product compositions, particularly commercial butane, this will lead to the vapour pressure in the vessel falling below atmospheric pressure. Unless the vessel has been designed for operation under vacuum conditions this could lead to vessel failure.

Vessel design

2 As stated in paragraph 38 of the main document the design of butane vessels should meet the following criteria:

Maximum safe operating pressure	4.83 bar gauge (70psig)
Minimum safe operating pressure	480mbar absolute (7psi absolute)
Minimum safe operating temperature	-18°C

A vessel should therefore be designed to withstand a vacuum or a system should be incorporated which provides a positive means for preventing a vacuum. If it can be shown that local meteorological conditions are such that prolonged cold spells do not occur precautions against vacuum may not be necessary.

Preventing a vacuum

3 A vacuum can be prevented by:

(a) **Hot vapour return.** Warm LPG vapour can be recycled from a vaporiser to the vapour space of the vessel to maintain the required pressure providing:

(i) the vaporiser has sufficient capacity to maintain the vessel above its safe minimum operating pressure while supplying vapour to the process at its maximum demand rate;

(ii) a means is provided to regulate the flow of vapour to the vessel to maintain the necessary pressure. This may be a self-operating regulator of sufficient capacity to govern the flow of vapour or, where there is

constant supervision, a manually operated flow valve. A manual by-pass valve should be provided around the regulator to allow manual operation of the system if the regulator fails.

(iii) an automatic high and low pressure alarm is fitted;

(b) **Propane vapour pressurisation.** The vapour space of the vessel can be interconnected with the vapour space of a propane vessel or cylinders containing propane, providing:

(i) the propane vessel or cylinders are sited in accordance with the advice in this guidance booklet;

(ii) a propane pressure regulator of sufficient capacity is provided to govern the flow of vapour to maintain a safe pressure;

(iii) the pipework and fittings between the two vessels or vessel and cylinders is permanent, designed to propane standards and adequately supported. Flexible hoses should not be used except with cylinders where short metallic hoses may be used in the cylinder-to-manifold connection;

(iv) the pipework is installed so that there is no possibility of liquid propane entering the receiving vessel;

(v) an automatic high and low pressure alarm is fitted;

(vi) the quantity of propane in the propane vessel is checked regularly to ensure an adequate supply. Where cylinders are used it is not always practical to check their contents and an automatic changeover system should be incorporated.

(c) **Product composition** In special cases the composition of butane to BS 4250: 1975 may, by agreement with the supplier, be controlled so that the vapour pressure under the lowest operating temperature will be above the minimum safe operating pressure of the vessel. The supplier and user should agree the standard in writing. The installation should be able to withstand the maximum vapour pressure of the LPG mixture at the reference temperature of the vessel.

(d) **Vacuum breakers** Vacuum breakers will prevent a vacuum from occurring but can introduce many operating and safety problems and should normally only be used in an emergency. Specialist advice should be obtained from the LPG supplier.

(e) **Inert gas pressurisation** An inert gas can be fed into the vessel vapour space but may introduce operating problems because of the non-condensible nature of the gas. Specialist advice should be obtained from the LPG supplier.

High and low pressure alarms

4   The pressure sensors for the high and low pressure alarms should monitor the vapour pressure in the vessel. Pressure sensors in the pipework between the vaporiser or propane vapour source and the vessel may not give a true indication of the pressure in the vessel.

(a) **High pressure alarm** This should be set below the vessel relief valve setting and should warn of an abnormally high vessel pressure. Water sprays fitted to the vessel which are operated automatically by high vessel pressure and which sound an alarm are suitable.

(b) **Low pressure alarm** This should warn of an abnormally low pressure indicating a fault in the pressure control equipment. It should be set above the minimum safe operating pressure of the vessel.

Appendix 5 (b)

Safety advice for bulk chlorine installations

(Reproduced from Health and Safety Executive : *Safety advice for bulk chlorine installations,* Health and Safety series booklet HS(G) 28 (London, HMSO, 1986).)

Contents

Foreword

Introduction

Siting of installations

Unloading area

Design and location
Potential incidents
Deliveries of liquid chlorine by road tanker
Deliveries of liquid chlorine by rail tanker
Interlocks
Design considerations for the access structure at
the unloading point

**Connections between the tanker and the fixed
lines to the storage installation**

Design and maintenance
Types of connection
Flexible couplings
Flexible hoses
Articulated arms
Operating and maintenance procedures

Pipework for liquid chlorine

Permanent pipework at the unloading point
Pipelines for liquid chlorine
Design criteria for pipelines transferring liquid
chlorine to storage tanks or from storage to point
of use.
Protection of pipework

**Protection of liquid chlorine pipelines against
over pressure**

Provision of relief systems
Relief systems
Bursting discs to relieve line
Expansion tanks to relieve line

Valves

Types of valve
Vertical globe valves
Conical plug valves (PTFE sleeved)
Ball valves
Remotely controlled valves

Storage vessels

Design criteria
Connecting pipework and means for isolation of
storage tanks
Liquid chlorine inlet
Liquid chlorine outlet
Vent and compressed dry gas lines
Relief system
Instrumentation

Protection of storage vessels against over-pressure

Relief system
Bursting discs
Arrangements for relief systems
System of maintenance
Expansion vessels
Pressure alarms

Inspection and commissioning of chlorine tank installations

General
Inspection procedure
Testing

Unloading of liquid chlorine from tankers to storage

Unloading using dry compressed air or dry
nitrogen
Compressed nitrogen
Compressed air
Supply to the system
Unloading using chlorine gas pressure
Use of re-compressed chlorine vapour
Use of vaporised chlorine

Transfer of chlorine to the consuming units

Transfer of liquid chlorine
Transfer of gaseous chlorine
Precautions
Transfer of liquid chlorine using vapour
pressure
Transfer of liquid chlorine by padding with dry
compressed gas
Transfer of liquid chlorine using a separate
pumping tank
Transfer of liquid chlorine using a submerged
pump

Chlorine vaporisers

Methods of heating
Types
Regulation of throughput
General installation
Safety
Hazards
Routine and emergency isolation
Pressure control valve
Corrosion

Chlorine absorption system

Vent collection system
Absorption equipment
Instrumentation
Disposal of effluent from the chlorine absorption plant

Protective and emergency equipment

Respiratory protective equipment for routine use
Respiratory protective equipment for emergencies
Protective clothing for emergencies
Emergency tool kits
Containment of chlorine leakage

Operator selection and training and operating instructions

Operator selection and training
Operating instructions

Maintenance

Clearance procedures
Modifications of the chlorine systems

Emergency procedures

Chlorine detector alarms
Local alarm stations
Works emergency plan
Emergency control centres
Site emergency team
Emergency assembly areas
Attention to casualties

Appendices

1 Properties of chlorine
2 Outside installations and inside installations
3 Publications and standards
4 Procedures for discharging road tanks of chlorine
5 Summary : Types of vaporiser

Foreword

This advice was prepared by a Working Party which met under the auspices of HSE's Chemical National Industry Group and is based on the *Guidelines for Bulk Handling of Chlorine at Customers Installations* published by the Chemical Industries Association Ltd in 1980. As knowledge develops, the advice may need to be updated again in the future.

Membership of the Working Party consisted of representatives from the four UK producers of chlorine, a representative of the Transport and General Workers Union, and staff from HSE working under an HSE chairman.

The guidelines may be applied to any bulk chlorine installation but they are not intended to be a detailed design code. Some existing installations may not at present meet all the recommendations and, in some cases, not all the recommendations may be appropriate. It is for the occupier, usually in consultation with the chlorine supplier and/or specialist advisers, to judge the need in any particular case. If modifications are shown to be needed, a responsible decision is required on the nature and timing of changes to be made. The final responsibility remains with the company operating the plant to do so safely.

A CIA publication *Inter-Company Collaboration for Chlorine Emergencies* published in 1978 is relevant. It gives advice to chlorine users faced with emergencies and gives details of the immediate assistance which is available under the Chlor-Aid scheme.

The HSE is grateful to representatives of the chlorine industry for their assistance and co-operation in preparing this advice, and to the Chemical Industries Association Ltd for permission to reproduce substantial portions of the 1980 *Guidelines*.

Introduction

1 This publication gives guidance on safe handling of bulk liquid chlorine. Its aim is to provide advice for those who receive liquid chlorine by road or rail tanker so that the unloading and storage, and the subsequent transfer, vaporisation and use, may be carried out in such a way that the possibility of incidents giving rise to danger to operators, the public or to plant, is minimised. The recommendations are based on the combined experience of the four UK manufacturers of chlorine, their customers, and HSE, supplemented by other recommendations published internationally.

2 The advice covers the requirements at all stages, from the receipt of the liquid chlorine to the point of use, including the location, design, testing, operation and maintenance of equipment. Procedures for dealing with emergencies are also outlined.

3 Experience has shown that each installation requires individual consideration and that there are many aspects of detailed design which necessitate full discussion between the consuming company operating the plant and the supplier of the chlorine.

4 'Chlorine works', i.e. works in which chlorine is made or used in any manufacturing process, are listed as Scheduled Works under the Alkali etc Works Regulation Act 1906 as amended by the Health and Safety (Emissions into the Atmosphere) Regulations 1983, and must be registered annually with the Health and Safety Executive's Industrial Air Pollution Inspectorate, or the Scottish Development Department, HM Industrial Pollution Inspectorate for Scotland.

5 The Notification of Installations Handling Hazardous Substances Regulations 1982 (SI 1982 No 1357) require that all installations where more than 10 tonnes of chlorine is liable to be kept must be notified to the Health and Safety Executive. Changes in the notified activity must also be notified. New installations over 10 tonnes chlorine capacity, or proposals to increase the notified capacity to more than three times the original capacity, must be notified three months in advance. The form of the notification is in the Regulations.

6 The Control of Industrial Major Accident Hazards Regulations 1984 (SI 1984 No. 1902) also apply to sites storing or processing chlorine. These regulations apply at two levels. There are two general requirements: to demonstrate to HSE, at any time, that major accident hazards have been recognised, and to report major accidents. In the case of the 'isolated storage' of chlorine, they apply at a threshold quantity of 10 tonnes. For process sites, no threshold quantity is specified, but HSE will initially give priority to sites notifiable under the NIHHS Regulations. The specific requirements of the Regulations are for the preparation of a safety case, the preparation of on-site and off-site emergency plans and the provision of information to members of the public likely to be affected by a major accident. In the case of chlorine, the specific requirements apply to process sites at a threshold quantity of 50 tonnes and to 'isolated storage' at a threshold of 200 tonnes.

7 Planning permission for new installations must be obtained in the usual way from the Local Authority, who will usually refer for advice to the HSE. Technical submissions in respect of the installation will usually be required by the HSE in such cases.

Siting of installations

8 The following observations relate to general features affecting the location of the installation. Other, more specific, factors which may be considered are reviewed in the detailed sections dealing with off-loading and emergency procedures, where ease of access is of great importance.

9 Full account will have to be taken of the requirements imposed by the Planning Authorities when giving planning permission. For a new installation, the local Planning Authority needs to ensure that the overall plan will avoid problems arising in the future from developments leading to a high density population in the vicinity of the installation, or from the introduction of other potential hazards in an adjacent area. For sites which may present such hazards the HSE may recommend that the highest standards be applied.

10 For existing installations, control of present population density is not posible. However, developments nearby which would increase the number of people are controllable and would be permitted by the local Planning Authority only after detailed consideration, which will normally include the use of advice received on request from the HSE.

11 The location of new chlorine installations within a site has to be such as to take into account possible damage from flooding or subsidence, and the possible damage they might receive should neighbouring plant or factories suffer a catastrophe by fire or explosion. Installations should be sited at a sufficient distance (25m minimum) from public roads or main railway lines to reduce the risk of damage to the chlorine installation in the event of an accident. Protective barriers should be installed where necessary.

12 In all cases, suitable fences, together with adequate security supervision, should be provided to minimise the possibility of unauthorised access.

13 Hazards arising from aircraft may normally be regarded as minimal with probabilities below the level of significance required for any special consideration. However, attention may be necessary in exceptional circumstances, for example if the installation is at the end of an airport runway or close to an airfield which is used for training.

14 The installation is preferably located in the open air; under some circumstances installation in a building may, however, be appropriate. In formulating a decision on this matter, it is important that a full review be made, taking into account the factors listed in Appendix 2.

Unloading area

Design and location

15 To minimise the possibility of chlorine escape during transfer of the liquid chlorine from the transport vehicles to the storage installation, detailed attention to the siting, design and layout of the unloading equipment and operating procedure is essential.

16 The unloading area should be on reasonably level ground with adequate surrounding space providing good access from different directions. Adequate lighting covering all escape routes should be provided and the provision of emergency lighting may be advisable.

17 Sufficient manually operated alarm stations need to be provided to enable warning to be given in the event of a chlorine escape. Further details on emergency procedures will be found in paras 247 to 263.

18 The unloading point should preferably be reasonably close to, but not less than 5m from, the storage installation. However, if there is a physical impact barrier between the tanker and the storage installation, this distance can be reduced. The unloading point should also be sited at a safe distance from any plant or equipment which might give rise to fire or explosion.

19 It may be desirable to install a remotely controlled valve on the discharge line to the storage tanks.

20 The possible effect on the locality of the escape of chlorine should be considered, taking note of the prevailing wind direction, ventilation intake, the location of control rooms and presence of the general public.

Potential incidents

21 The following potential incidents which could result in chlorine escape need to be considered.

(a) Damage to chlorine lines by the tanker while it is moving to or from the unloading point; allowance has to be made for adequate clearance from the valve dome when it is open.

(b) Movement of the tanker during the transfer operation, eg. the normal upward movement of the tank on its suspension, can cause damage if there is inadequate flexibility in the connection.

(c) Damage to the liquid chlorine tanker, storage tank or connecting pipework caused by impact from other vehicles, by movement caused by inadequate braking or chocking or careless operation by the driver.

(d) Errors in operating procedures.

(e) Equipment failure due to corrosion.

(f) Damage caused by fire or explosion.

Deliveries of liquid chlorine by road tanker

22 It is strongly recommended that the following means of minimising potential risks are adopted wherever possible.

(a) Provision of a separate unloading area for the sole use of chlorine tankers. This could be a lay-by with adequate side protection (such as a motorway-type crash barrier) or a cul-de-sac.

(b) Restriction by suitable means of the speed of traffic on adjacent roads.

(c) The placing of warning barriers, notices, moveable barriers or road cones, and the closure of gates when the chlorine tankers are in position.

(d) Provision of an interlock (see para 25) system to prevent coupling of liquid chlorine lines to the tankers unless barriers are in position.

(e) A system of work whereby one person (the driver) is present throughout the unloading, and a second is present during connection and disconnection. The second man should be in the vicinity and available throughout the unloading. A typical procedure is set out in Appendix 4.

(f) Routing of chlorine pipelines in the area to minimise the risk of damage from collision by the tanker, other vehicles or mobile equipment.

23 Where a separate unloading area cannot be provided and the unloading point is on a factory through road, such roads should be closed to other vehicle traffic during the transfer of liquid chlorine.

Deliveries of liquid chlorine by rail tanker

24 It is strongly recommended that the following means of minimising potential risks are adopted.

(a) Closure of the sidings to other traffic during transfer of chlorine from tankers to storage, by locking the points.

(b) Control by suitable means of the volume and speed of adjacent traffic.

(c) The closure of warning barriers and/or the placing of warning notices when the chlorine tankers are in position.

(d) Provision of an interlock (see para 25) system to prevent coupling or uncoupling of the liquid chlorine lines unless barriers or warning notices are in position. It is recommended that the interlock system extends to ensuring that appropriate points on the rail sidings are locked and wheel stops raised before transfer of liquid chlorine can start.

(e) A system of work whereby one person is responsible for the whole operation of unloading, and a second is within call during connection and disconnection. The second man should be in the area and available throughout unloading.

(f) Routing of chlorine pipelines in the area to minimise the risk of damage from collision by the tanker, other vehicles or mobile equipment.

Interlocks

25 As indicated in paras 22 to 24, interlocks have value in preventing approach by other tankers and may also be made part of a system to prevent inadvertent movement of a tanker still connected up. For example, interlocks can be devised to ensure that the vehicle brakes are fully applied before the unloading pipe is finally connected up, or the pressure in the unloading pipe activates a flashing sign to remind the driver that he is connected (the latter system may be appropriate at a producer plant or a consumer plant with a large throughput). The manoeuvring necessary to locate a road tanker precisely in relation to a solid pipe connector may make it more difficult to devise an interlock to the highest standard of security. In such cases, an interlock to prevent access of other tankers is strongly recommended, and special attention must be paid to the system of work which effectively prevents accidental movement of the tanker, and to driver training.

Design considerations for the access structure at the unloading point

26 Satisfactory access should be provided to the permanent pipework for discharge of the chlorine tankers and to ensure that connections to the tankers can be made with minimum risk. Where this involves working from a place above ground level, a permanent structure should be provided, designed so that, in case of emergency, escape is possible with minimum risk.

27 A substantial and non-flammable (e.g. steel) structure should be provided and platforms should be free of obstructions and have non-slip surfaces, adequate toe-boards and guard-rails. Alternative escape ways should be provided with stairways of standard slope; vertical ladders or steep stairways should be avoided. If vertical ladders are unavoidable, ensure that safety hoops, etc, do not impede access by people wearing breathing apparatus. The design of moveable platforms giving access to the top of the tankers should be such as to minimise the possibility of accidents due to collision with tankers. Interlock systems may be used for this purpose.

28 It may be useful to provide protection against the weather on fixed gantries at unloading points, for example by windbreaks or overhead canopy.

29 Adequate storage space for emergency equipment (e.g. gas masks, air sets, protective clothing and spare equipment) should be provided in a safe location to be readily available in an emergency.

Connections between the tanker and the fixed lines to the storage installation

30 Operations of road loading and unloading are subject to the Dangerous Substances (Conveyance by Road in Road Tankers and Tank Containers) Regulations 1981. Connections for the transfer of liquid chlorine require very careful consideration, as they are the most likely source of problems which could lead to a release of chlorine to the environment. Pipework should be as simple as possible.

31 For transfer to storage, it is necessary to couple the liquid chlorine outlet line on the tanker to the inlet line to storage and also to connect a supply of dry compressed air, nitrogen or chlorine vapour to the tanker.

Design and maintenance

32 Failure of the unloading connections can result from inadequate design, incorrect materials or construction, improper use or inadequate inspection and maintenance. It is, therefore, essential to ensure that the design standards are adequate, that testing and inspection procedures are regularly carried out and that the equipment is satisfactorily maintained.

Types of connection

33 Three types of connection are available.

(a) Flexible couplings which give a solid connection but with a degree of flexibility when coupled.

(b) Flexible hoses.

(c) Articulated arms.

Flexible couplings are normally used but flexible hoses or articulated arms may be used by agreement with the chlorine supplier.

Flexible couplings

34 Flexible couplings are normally constructed from steel pipe. Flexibility is provided by cranking of a free length of pipe (less usually by a coil) to allow for vertical movement of the tanker during discharge. Screwed connections are used for the connections to the tanker; screwed connections are commonly used at either end of the flexible coupling.

35 Piping local to the tanker berth should not be fixed for the first 5-7m (15-20 ft) but it needs to be supported. The system of support used should ensure that the pipework is kept above the headroom required by the tanker when it is being put in position. The support should also allow the pipework the necessary vertical movement of 150mm (6 in). A minimum pipe diameter of 20mm (¾in) is recommended.

36 The design criteria for flexible couplings constructed from pipework are similar to those

for fixed pipework (see paras 41 to 46). Where the connections are screwed connections, the gasket should be a trapped joint ring.

Flexible hoses

37 Flexible hoses, the design of which should be agreed with the chlorine supplier, require more frequent testing than do the flexible couplings described in the previous section. The life of flexible hoses is shorter than that of flexible steel pipes but positioning of tankers is easier. Flexible Monel braided hose connections are normally constructed up to 50mm (2 in) size for the liquid chlorine discharge, and 25mm (1 in) size for the compressed gas connection to the tanker.

38 The operating instructions covering unloading should ensure that visual inspection and leak testing of the flexible hoses is carried out before the introduction of liquid chlorine.

Articulated arms

39 Articulated arms, with swivelled joints, are occasionally used on manufacturing installations with high output which are outside the scope of the present guide.

Operating and maintenance procedures

40 Operating procedures for unloading should specify requirements for inspection and testing of couplings before use; maintenance procedures should lay down requirements for engineering inspection and renewal. Details are summarised below:

(a) *Operating*

(i) Visual inspection, before use, with particular attention to threads.

(ii) Use of new gaskets (CAF) each time connections are made to the tanker. The discarded gaskets should be collected and disposed of safely, bearing in mind that they contain asbestos.

(iii) Proving of connection tightness before introduction of liquid chlorine.

(iv) Capping of pipes after use and protection of pipes to reduce the possibility of accidental damage to threads and ingress of moisture.

Refer to Appendix 4 for a typical procedure.

(b) *Maintenance*

(i) Engineering inspection to be carried out at least once per year, or per 1000 operations; a record to be kept of these inspections.

(ii) Renewals to be carried out at regular intervals, or as required as a consequence of the engineering inspection.

(iii) Replacement flexible connections to be dried out, after testing, with dry air to dew point −40°C.

Pipework for liquid chlorine

Permanent pipework at the unloading point

41 The permanent pipework at the unloading point consists of the following lines.

(a) Pipework for pressurising the tanker with dry air, nitrogen or chlorine.

(b) Pipework for the transfer of liquid chlorine to storage.

(c) Pipework for compressed air supplies that operate remotely controlled valves on the tanker if these are installed.

Lines should be colour-coded and/or labelled; detailed design requirements for the pipelines and fittings are described below. The system for off-loading of liquid chlorine is described in paras 134 to 156.

Pipelines for liquid chlorine

42 Routing of pipelines for liquid chlorine should normally be above ground and should be such as to maximise protection from mechanical damage, corrosion and fire. A minimum diameter of 20mm (¾ in) is recommended to ensure adequate mechanical strength and lines should be clearly labelled and painted yellow (e.g. to 08E51-BS 4800).

Design criteria for pipelines transferring liquid chlorine to storage tanks or from storage to point of use

43 Pipework should be designed, fabricated, inspected and tested in accordance with a recognised Code, eg BS 3351 or ANSI B31.3 and any additional requirements of this section.

Design pressure Should be in accordance with design codes but no less than 12 barg (174 psig), corresponding to a design temperature of +45°C. Any part of the system which may operate at a higher temperature should be designed to withstand the corresponding vapour pressure.

Pipework should also be adequately strong and robust for all foreseeable conditions of work.

Design temperature Should be less than the minimum at which the pipe is intended to operate, or the temperature to which it will be cooled if liquid chlorine boils off at atmospheric pressure (−35°C). The normal design range is −35°C to +45°C.

Materials of construction Seamless carbon steel tubing is preferred, but resistance seam welded tubing, which is welded and stress relieved automatically during manufacture, is acceptable.

Elbows, tees and reducing pieces should be forged or hot-formed without reduction in wall thickness.

Corrosion allowance 1mm

Radius of curvature of any formed bends 3 pipe diameters minimum (weld elbows must be used where tighter bends are necessary).

Bolting Should be to requirements of BS 4882.

Flanges The number of flanges should be limited as far as possible and those used should be to the requirements of a recognised design code eg BS 1560 or ANSI B16-5. Steel used for fabrication of flanges or welded connections to the pipe must be compatible with that of the pipe itself.

Gaskets Gaskets should be compressed asbestos fibre (CAF) to the requirements of BS 2815 Grade A, and should be tabbed for easy identification on installations where a variety of jointing materials are in use.

The use of incorrect materials for gaskets can be dangerous. The industry should continue to search for a satisfactory jointing material which does not contain asbestos.

44 The following controls should be applied during construction.

Stress relief All fabricated items and butt welds should be stress relieved before final inspection and testing.

Inspection and pressure testing All butt welds should be fully radiographed or ultrasonically examined.

All pipework should be pressure tested in accordance with the design code. Where hydrostatic tests are made it is essential that the complete piping system is thoroughly cleaned and dried prior to the introduction of chlorine.

All oil, grease, weld spatter, scale and other foreign matter should be removed. If a hydrostatic test is made after installation it will be necessary to change all gaskets to ensure dryness. Appropriate leak tests will then be required to check the newly made joints.

Modifications Any extension, modification or repairs to pipework should be carried out to a standard at least equivalent to the original design and construction code including stress relief, inspection and testing.

Protection of pipework

Note the important topic of protection against overpressure is dealt with in paras 47 to 53.

45 Failure of pipework may result from

(a) impact;

(b) fire (resulting in a reaction between the steel and chlorine);

(c) severe internal or external corrosion.

46 Pipelines conveying chlorine should be installed so that they are

(a) safe from impact from vehicles by distance or with barriers;

(b) protected from falling objects (e.g. no overhead hoists, roofs constructed of light weight materials,

(c) separated from pipelines carrying corrosive or flammable materials or other sources of heat. The separation will depend on the nature of the other material and an estimate of the hazard;

(d) adequately supported;

(e) accessible for maintenance and inspection;

(f) preferably unlagged, and regularly inspected under any lagging to detect corrosion due to failure of weather-sealing.

Protection of liquid chlorine pipelines against over-pressure

47 The possibility of pressure build-up in liquid chlorine pipeline systems due to thermal expansion of the liquid chlorine must be considered in all cases where liquid chlorine might be trapped between closed valves. Operating procedures should allow for such a possibility and appropriate instructions should be laid down to minimise the risks.

48 The risk of liquid chlorine being trapped between closed valves is increased by the following factors.

(a) Isolation valves that are controlled by different operators. This may be a special risk where there are long lines or complex pipework between units.

(b) The simultaneous closure of remotely operated valves that have been installed for plant isolation. It is important not to have too many automatic valves which could lead to trapping. It is preferable to employ manually initiated remote control valves.

Trapping of liquid chlorine followed by a rise in temperature increases the risk of over-pressure. Even a small temperature rise can cause a very high hydraulic pressure, because of the high coefficient of expansion of liquid chlorine.

Provision of relief systems

49 Relief systems complicate pipework and introduce other potential hazards, and should in general be avoided. However, if the capacity of the system is such that release of the chlorine present could lead to a serious incident, automatic means of releasing excessive pressure in the pipeline needs to be provided. It follows that the configuration of the pipeline, positioning of valves, and valve closing methods (see para 48) have to be studied to see whether the hazard can occur.

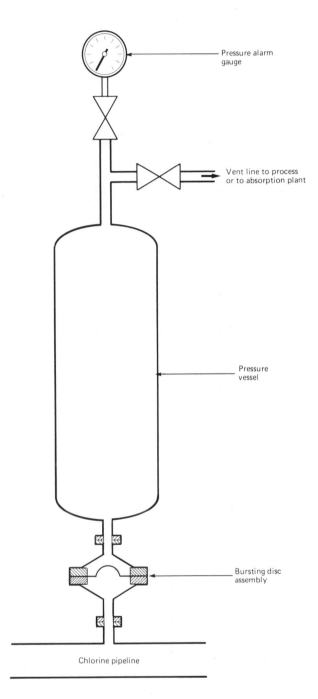

Fig 1 Pressure relief system for chlorine pipelines (para 52)

50 It is recommended that provision of relief systems is fully discussed with the chlorine suppliers. Reliance on the springing of flanged joints for relief of thermal expansion is not acceptable.

Relief systems

51 Relief systems available for protection of liquid chlorine lines are:

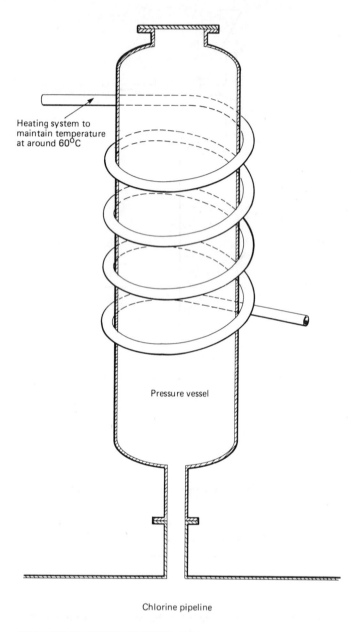

Heating system to maintain temperature at around 60°C

Pressure vessel

Chlorine pipeline

Fig 2 Pressure relief system for chlorine pipelines (not recommended) (para 53)

(a) Installation of a bursting disc on the pipeline, discharging to a suitable collecting system (see para 52).

(b) Installation of an expansion tank designed to provide and accommodate a gaseous phase

(see para 53). This system is now considered undesirable due to difficulties in determining whether the gas space contains chlorine or inert gases and it is therefore not recommended for new installations.

In either case the relief volume should be at least 20% of the line volume. Any expansion vessel should be registered as a pressure vessel for examination and recording purposes.

Bursting discs to relieve line

52 The requirement for this type of relief system may be met by installation of a bursting disc at a vertical tee on the line discharging to a pressure vessel (Fig 1). The pressure vessel should be fitted with a suitable alarm which operates as a result of the rise in pressure in the vessel if the bursting disc leaks or ruptures. The vessel and line can then be vented to process or to the chlorine absorption system.

Expansion tank to relieve line

53 A vertical pressure vessel may be connected to a tee on the pipeline as indicated in Fig 2. The vessel needs to be thoroughly dried out before installation. Its upper section should be maintained at a temperature of around 60°C by a thermostatically controlled system designed to avoid the possibility of hot spots. Electrical heating tapes should not be used unless they are of the thermal compensating type. A temperature alarm should be provided to give warning of high or low temperature. There should be no isolation valves between the vessel and the liquid chlorine pipeline, and the vessel design needs to meet the requirements for chlorine pressure vessels. The design temperature range should, however, be amended to meet the higher temperatures expected, and the system's pressure rating should be sufficient to withstand the vapour pressure of chlorine at the vessel temperature. This system is not recommended for new installations (see para 51(b)).

Valves

54 Care is essential in the choice of valves for use on installations handling liquid chlorine. For all types of valves the materials used have to be

resistant to chlorine and able to cope with the stresses to which they may be subjected. The valve body should preferably be fabricated of forged steel; cast iron is not acceptable. If the valve design is such that liquid chlorine could be trapped within the body when the valve is closed, provision should be made to avoid excess pressure which may develop with temperature rise.

55 Owing to evaporation of liquid chlorine, operating temperatures may fall to $-35°C$; the valves should be selected not to fail if this occurs. Problems which are specific to cold or to liquid chlorine limit the application of certain designs of valve.

56 The selection of the appropriate type of valve for each application should be reviewed with the suppliers of the liquid chlorine who will be able to suggest manufacturers of valves whose equipment has given satisfactory service with liquid chlorine. This will reduce the possibility of unsatisfactory valves being used which will require replacement after a short period and could be a potential source of hazard.

57 It is emphasised that, during maintenance operations, reliance on valves of whatever type for isolation is insufficient. The design of the system should be such that complete isolation of the section concerned is possible. Suitable methods for achieving this include the installation of spool pieces in the lines which can be removed and substituted by blanks, or the insertion of slip plates.

Types of valve

58 Valves of the following types have been developed for use with liquid chlorine or dry chlorine gas under pressure.

(a) Vertical globe valves

(b) Conical plug valves

(c) Ball valves

59 Valves have to be degreased before use and should be completely dry. It is recommended that after this treatment the valves should be stored in individual gas-tight plastic bags ready for installation when required.

Vertical globe valves

60 This type of valve is preferably used for isolation of liquid chlorine stock tanks or for large flows of chlorine, while the billet-globe valve is particularly recommended for installation on the liquid chlorine outlet line from chlorine storage tanks (see para 88). The gas seal around the valve spindle in globe valves may be formed by a packed gland (preferably using rings or chevrons of PTFE) or by a bellows seal. The bellows should be backed up by a secondary seal. Globe valves may, with advantage, be fitted with a back seating arrangement which isolates the gland from line pressure when the valve is fully open.

Conical plug valves (PTFE sleeved)

61 Conical plug valves, PTFE sleeved, are satisfactory for isolation of liquid chlorine lines, particularly when quick isolation may be required, but the primary valve on the storage tank is preferably a globe valve.

62 Conical plug valves for use with liquid chlorine require provision for the avoidance of problems arising from liquid chlorine trapped in the bore when the valve is closed. If this makes the valves uni-directional, they need to be marked with an indication of the required direction of liquid flow to ensure correct installation. Gas-tightness is provided by a PTFE sleeve inserted into the body of the valve and by a supplementary seal along the length of the spindle between the valve body and head. Care should be taken to avoid the application of side thrust to the spindles of plug valves.

Ball valves

63 This type of valve can be used for isolation in liquid chlorine lines and should incorporate the following.

(a) spherical turning limited to a quarter-turn;

(b) straight-through flanging;

(c) PTFE seals.

64 Ball valves should be avoided when operating conditions involve large and frequent temperature changes.

65 Ball valves for use with liquid chlorine should make provision for the avoidance of problems

arising from liquid chlorine trapped in the bore when the valve is closed. If this makes the valve uni-directional they need to be marked with an indication of the required direction of liquid flow to ensure correct installation.

Remotely controlled valves

66 The rate of closure of any actuated valve should not be so rapid as to cause undue pressure surges in the system.

Storage vessels

67 In this advice, storage of liquid chlorine under pressure only is considered. Storage of liquid chlorine at low temperatures and low pressure is sometimes used on chlorine producing plants but is not appropriate for consuming installations.

68 The capacity of a chlorine storage tank should be significantly greater than the capacity of a full load of liquid chlorine from a road or rail tanker. To minimise the danger of over-filling, an installation consisting of smaller tanks which would require split loads is not recommended.

69 Installation of bulk storage facilities should be considered only if the annual consumption of chlorine is sufficient to justify bulk supplies rather than purchase of liquid chlorine in drums.

70 In considering the number of individual storage tanks for a required total storage capacity, the following points should be taken into account.

(a) The minimum size of tank should be adequate to accommodate the maximum foreseen unit delivery.

(b) If continuity of supply is essential, at least two tanks will be required to allow time for necessary inspections and to facilitate maintenance. This also provides greater flexibility of operation.

(c) Increasing the number of storage tanks leads to an increase in the ancillary plant and equipment with a corresponding increase in complexity of operation.

71 The distance between adjacent storage tanks should be adequate to provide good access to

the tanks under all circumstances, including those in which bulky protective equipment (such as self-contained breathing apparatus) is being used.

72 All chlorine storage tanks should be installed in a bund which is impervious to liquid chlorine. The bund should be capable of taking the contents of the largest storage tank with adequate freeboard and a sump. If there is a sub-division to give a separate section under each tank, each section should have a sloping floor leading to a sump, which may serve more than one tank. Sumps should not be connected to drain. Provision should be included for removal of rain water over the bund wall, not via drain or through valves in the bund.

73 As leaks of liquid chlorine are potentially more dangerous than leaks of gaseous chlorine, the system needs to be so designed that sources of leakage of liquid are reduced to a minimum. A major contribution to this will be the avoidance of joints which are continuously exposed to liquid chlorine (for example, bottom outlets should not usually be fitted, see para 78); thus, any leakage will be only as gas.

74 The severity of a leak is reduced by lowering the pressure within the system and therefore it is important that facilities for transferring gaseous chlorine to a consuming process or to a waste-chlorine absorption plant are available when chlorine is being transferred.

75 Chlorine storage tanks should be erected above ground level. Installation in deep pits is not recommended because it increases the difficulties of treatment and dispersal of a chlorine escape and of access for maintenance or repair.

76 Layout for the area should be planned to provide all facilities necessary for good housekeeping; ample storage space is needed for maintenance and safety equipment, which has to be readily accessible in the event of an emergency.

77 Thermal insulation of the storage tanks is not normally required. However, if the vessel operates at low temperature and lagging is required, the material should be fire-resistant, chemically inert to liquid or gaseous chlorine and resistant to ingress of atmospheric moisture.

Design criteria

78 Design criteria for new liquid chlorine storage and expansion vessels are outlined below.

Design pressure 12 barg (174 psig) minimum

Design temperature When liquid chlorine evaporates at atmospheric pressure its temperature falls to −35°C and therefore the minimum design temperature should not be any higher. Normal design range is −35°C to +45°C.

Filling ratio Filling ratios for transportable liquid chlorine containers are detailed in BS 5355:1976 for various size ranges of containers and for different temperatures. Although there is no equivalent standard for fixed tanks, for simplicity a figure of 1.25 kg of liquid chlorine/litre capacity is normally used. This ensures that the volume of liquid chlorine does not exceed 95% of the total volume of the vessel, even for a maximum temperature of 50°C.

Design code New vessels should be designed and manufactured to BS 5500 Category 1 (or equivalent standard).

Corrosion allowance Minimum 1mm.

Supports The vessel supports should be designed in accordance with the design code to permit thermal expansion or contraction over the design temperature range. Special consideration may be necessary where load cells are used for determining the contents of the tank.

Branches Dimensions should be limited to the minimum required, particularly for the liquid lines. All branches should, where possible, be mounted on the manhole cover or covers. Manhole access should be provided on the top of the vessel. The opening should preferably be 600mm diameter, but in no case should it be less than 460mm diameter.

Bottom outlets should not be provided except where required for chlorine transfer by pumping. Any bottom outlet should have an internal valve, preferably remotely-operable, plus a back-up isolating valve (see para 89).

Bolting Should be to requirements of BS 4882.

Gaskets Should be of compressed asbestos fibre (CAF) to the requirements of BS 2815 Grade A and should be tabbed for easy identification on installations where a variety of jointing materials are in use.

Use of incorrect materials for gaskets can be dangerous.

Documentation The BS 5500 Certificate of Compliance (or similar documentation if other standards are being used) should be retained for reference, together with other documents pertaining to mechanical integrity.

79 Paragraph 78 applies to new systems designed and constructed in accordance with a current standard. Where an existing tank has been provided in accordance with a different standard, the systems should be assessed according to the requirements of those original standards. In particular, if the vessel's safe working pressure is less than 12 barg (174 psig), then the air system pressure, relief devices etc all have to be altered to suit, and the delivery system has to be arranged so as to be capable of working within the storage tank conditions.

Connecting pipework and means for isolation of storage tanks

80 Connections to the storage tanks are:

(a) liquid chlorine inlet;
(b) liquid chlorine outlet;
(c) vent lines and compressed dry gas lines;
(d) relief system;
(e) instrumentation and pressure gauges;

81 The number of connections should be kept to a minimum to reduce the potential sources of leakage. The arrangements of valves and pipework should be made as simple as possible to minimise errors in operation. Isolation valves should be fitted directly to the branches on the manlid or the tank so that any pipework with branches or tee connections can be isolated. The system should be so designed that, if the joints between the valves and the storage tanks fail, gaseous chlorine only will be released. For example, any line ending below the liquid surface should emerge through valves mounted in the tank wall above the liquid level, and the line should be fitted into the body of the valve inside the tank (see para 88).

82 All valves and pipework associated with chlorine storage tanks should be labelled and colour coded.

83 Whenever two valves are installed in series for isolation, it is recommended that the system of operation is planned so that each valve is used exclusively for a defined period during normal operation. This ensures that both valves are kept in operable condition at all times.

84 An application of the principles in this section is shown diagrammatically in Fig 3. Not all installations will be to this pattern, and variations (some of which are described in the text) may be appropriate.

Liquid chlorine inlet

85 The liquid chlorine inlet should not normally extend further into the tank than the maximum liquid level. The use of a dip-pipe on the inlet line could result in liquid chlorine flowing back if the filling line failed: this possibility is avoided by use of a short inlet line at the top of the tank or, alternatively, by drilling holes in the top of the dip-pipe so that liquid will not siphon back. A full dip-pipe may be provided as an inlet to a vessel for importation and exportation, but in such a case it should be fitted with the additional controls appropriate to a liquid chlorine outlet.

86 The isolation valve on the chlorine inlet line, directly bolted to the flange on the storage tank, should preferably be a globe valve.

87 A back-up valve should be provided, which may be remotely operated. Alternatively, both a remotely-operated valve and a back-up isolation valve may be installed.

Liquid chlorine outlet

88 The removal of liquid chlorine from the storage tank is by means of a dip-pipe, the arrangements for which should ensure that liquid chlorine cannot be released if the joint between the isolation valve and storage tank fails. This is most satisfactorily achieved on new plant by use of a billet-type globe valve, bolted to the flanged branch on the storage tank, the dip-pipe being screwed into the bottom of the valve.

89 The main isolation valve should be backed up by an additional valve to enable isolation to be achieved if one valve fails to seat effectively. Depending on local piping arrangement, provision of one or more remotely controlled valves is recommended for emergency control. A remotely

operated valve which is designed to give positive isolation and which is suitably positioned may also serve as one of the two isolation valves required above.

90 In addition, it is strongly recommended that flow in the line to the consuming plant should be limited to the maximum required by the process; this may be achieved by the incorporation in the line of an excess flow valve or an orifice. The object of this flow-restricting device is to reduce the size of a release from a major failure to less than the full-bore flow through the pipe. It is not necessarily set to control the flow to as little as the maximum process demand, where this maximum would be so small as to lead to other problems of maintenance, such as proneness of the orifice to blocking, etc. It is not recommended that the excess flow valve or orifice be located within the tank in the dip-pipe itself because of the problem of removing the liquid chlorine from the tank in the event of the ball sticking or blockage of the orifice. In some plants, the flow restrictor can be replaced by a suitable flow or pressure sensor operating the remotely-operable shut off valves (see para 104). Excess flow valves may be advisable for lines normally taking a flow of chlorine much less than the flow which could pass through in fault conditions. They are not suitable for lines in which the normal flow rate is high, and for which other means of fault detection and flow isolation should be used.

Vent and compressed dry gas lines

91 Vent lines and compressed dry gas lines can be connected to the storage tank either through separate inlets or through a combined single inlet. In either case, the valve directly connected to the storage tank should be backed up by a second valve.

92 To limit the liquid volume in the storage tank to that permitted by the filling ratio, an ullage pipe can be screwed into the bottom of the valve on the vent line. The length of this ullage pipe is such that, if liquid chlorine rises above the correct level, it will flow through the ullage pipe. The ullage pipe should be checked when the routine inspection of the storage installation is made. A low temperature or other alarm can be fitted on the vent line from the storage tanks to

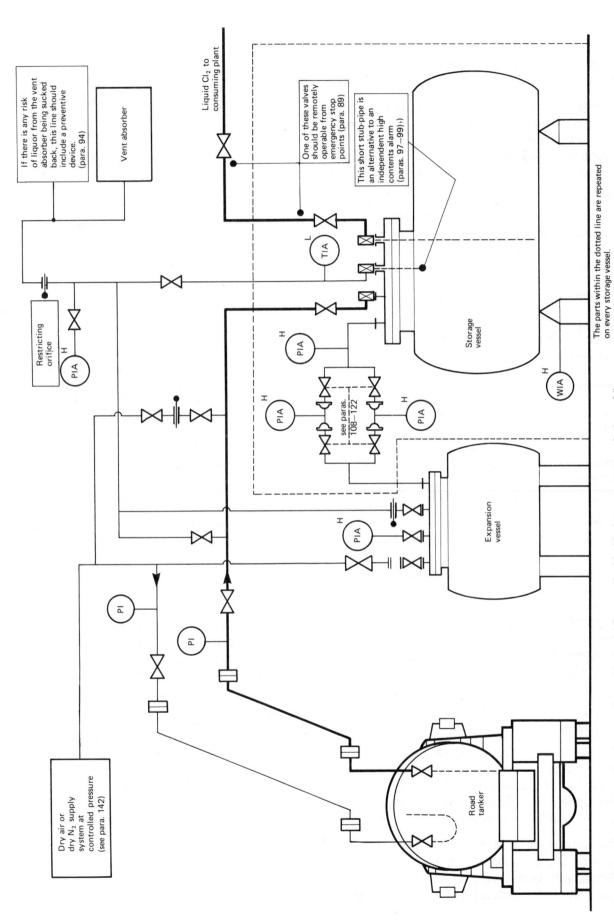

Fig 3 An example of the arrangements from chlorine tankers to liquid chlorine storage vessels (para 84)

Note: Not all installations will be to this pattern.

give warning if liquid chlorine is entering the ullage pipe on the vent line.

93   The procedure for transferring liquid chlorine to the storage tanks should provide for the vent valve to be opened slightly at the end of discharge to check that the tank has not been over-filled (see typical procedure in Appendix 4).

94   The prevention of suck-back of aqueous liquor into the vent line requires similar precautions to those described for vaporisers (see paras 184 to 186). The prevention of back-diffusion of moisture is described in paras 205 to 207.

Relief system

95   The special requirements for the isolation valves on the pressure relief system on the storage tanks are covered in paras 111 to 115.

Instrumentation

96   Control instrumentation on storage tanks and elsewhere in the installation should, wherever possible, be designed to fail safe. Electrical and electronic equipment, unless specially protected against corrosion, should not be placed in areas where it could be affected by gas leaks.

97   The quantity of liquid chlorine in each storage tank is preferably determined by installing the tank on load cells or on a weighbridge. The weight of liquid chlorine in each tank should be indicated locally and may be repeated in the plant control room. Alarms are required on the contents measuring device. A high-contents alarm in the control room (and on complex plants, possibly an extra-high contents alarm) is required for safety reasons.

Note   There is little safety value in the optional extra-high alarm unless it is run independently of the system giving the high-contents alarm.

98   A low contents alarm may be useful for operational reasons and may have safety implications if, for example, there could be process upsets on failure of chlorine supply or passage of padding air into a downstream vessel.

99   The independent contents indicators would normally be instruments, but on a simple installation, with good manning and attendance at the tanks, the extra high-level alarm may consist

of a short ullage pipe on the vapour vent. If a high contents alarm is ignored during filling of the tank, the liquid reaches the bottom of the ullage pipe and evaporates in the vent-line above the vent control valve, producing frosting of the pipe.

100   Regular checking and inspection procedures need to be planned and appropriate records need to be kept of the results.

101   As an alternative to the measurement of the quantity of liquid chlorine by weight, measurement by liquid level in the tanks is also acceptable. However, selection of suitable equipment is difficult and should be discussed with the chlorine supplier.

102   The pressure in the chlorine storage tanks is measured by gauges specially developed for use with liquid chlorine; these have silver or tantalum diaphragms. The gauges need to be completely degreased before use and subsequently tested using only clean, dry, oil-free compressed air. The pressure gauges may be fitted with switches to give an alarm if pressure exceeds, or falls below, a pre-set value. Alternatively, pressure switches may be used to give an independent signal for the high and low pressure alarms.

103   The air in a building housing chlorine storage tanks may be continuously monitored to give warning of chlorine leakage, particularly for plants which are normally unattended (see para 251). Regular and efficient maintenance is essential to keep such monitoring equipment in effective operation especially in plants such as certain water treatment plants which are routinely unattended but monitored by telemetry. The detectors should be set at about the recommended exposure limit of 1 ppm.

104   Where reference is made to flow or pressure sensors 'operating' valves (para 90 above) the choice remains whether the operation is automatic or via manual intervention. At the extremes, operation should be automatic in an unmanned plant, and may be indirect in a well-instrumented plant with a continuously manned control room.

105   Instrumentation associated with the automatic pressure relief system is included in paras 108 and 116 to 122.

Protection of storage vessels against over-pressure

106 The adoption of recommendations already given in these guidelines will reduce to a minimum the risk of over-pressure in the liquid chlorine storage tanks. Over-filling with liquid chlorine is indicated by alarms on the weigh system used to determine the liquid chlorine content of the storage tanks (paras 97 to 101) or by use of an ullage pipe in the vent line with provision of an alarm to warn of entry of liquid chlorine into the vent system (para 92). Over-pressure on the compressed air or nitrogen supply to the storage tank is prevented by the installation of a relief valve on the storage vessel for the compressed gas (para 142). High pressure on the liquid chlorine storage tank is indicated by a high pressure alarm (para 102).

107 As an ultimate safeguard, the storage tanks need to be protected by a suitable automatic relief system limiting the pressure to the design value.

Relief system

108 The preferred pressure relief system to protect liquid chlorine storage tanks consists of two bursting discs placed back to back. A bursting disc followed by a relief valve may be used but is always subject to the risk of corrosion of the relief valve. Protection of the relief valve from corrosion must be carefully considered if the bursting disc — relief valve system is used. The use of relief valves alone is not recommended because of the corrosion or blockage which could occur if a relief valve were to be left continuously exposed to chlorine. Whichever system is used there should always be a pressure alarm and indication between the two discs or between the disc and relief valve (see para 122). In the latter system the relief valve has to be removed and overhauled whenever the bursting disc is replaced.

109 The discharge line from the pressure relief system enters a closed expansion vessel (except in a few specialised arrangements). Any pressure in the expansion vessel or between components in the relief system reduces the protection given to the storage vessel (see paras 119 to 120).

Bursting discs

110 Bursting discs (which are designed to fail at or below the design pressure of storage tanks) are commonly made of nickel, although tantalum, silver or other compatible materials may be used. Uncoated graphite is not recommended. Discs should be carefully selected for the operating temperature range, bearing in mind that the rupture pressure is temperature-dependent, and should comply with BS 2915 (or equivalent standard).

Arrangements for relief system

111 On very simple installations (usually those with a single storage vessel and associated expansion vessel) a single bursting disc system without any isolating valves may be used, installed directly on the storage vessel. In practice it is more convenient to install a valved system so as to allow replacement of discs under a controlled system of work without the necessity of completely emptying and purging the system. Where two or more storage vessels share an expansion vessel arrangements must be made to allow prompt replacement of discs and venting of all excess pressure out of the expansion vessel.

112 The preferred arrangements are shown in Figs 4 and 5. The isolating valves may be mechanically interlocked so that one pair of discs is always operative, or the isolating valves may be individually locked. The bursting discs should be of the simple domed unsupported type with the concave side facing the source of pressure. The identifying tags should be left attached to each disc so that they can be identified as having been installed correctly. On existing older installations the arrangement shown in Fig 6 may often be found. The arrangement in Fig 4 or Fig 5 should be used on all new installations and should be considered on existing installations when major modifications are in hand.

113 The valves which remain open must permit the operational devices to discharge at the required rate to an expansion vessel. Pipework before the isolating valves should be as short and simple as possible to minimise the risk of chlorine leakage from joints and pipework; the isolation valves before the bursting discs should preferably be fitted directly on flanged connections on the manlid of the storage tanks.

114 Procedures to be followed in the event of the failure of a bursting disc should be clearly defined and based on the principle that at no time should a vessel be boxed up so that unacceptable pressure may be developed. Procedures may vary with plant design but they should be in written form and include safe working practices for removing the vessel from normal service, stabilising the pressure, changing the bursting disc, venting the expanse tank, and returning the vessel to normal use.

System of maintenance

115 At any installation where a locked-open isolating valve precedes a bursting disc, a safe system of work should be defined which will ensure so far as is reasonably practicable that no unacceptable pressure from any source can occur in the vessel whilst the isolating valve is closed. Such safe systems will vary with plant design but should:

(a) be in a written form, unambiguous and readily available;

(b) include a permit-to-work system;

(c) be included in plant personnel training programmes;

(d) be properly supervised with responsibilities clearly allocated;

(e) be regularly updated particularly when plant design, operating procedures or management systems are modified, and

(f) be rigidly adhered to.

Expansion vessels

116 The design requirements for the construction of the expansion vessel are similar to those for the storage tanks; the capacity should be about 10% of the largest storage vessel.

117 The expansion vessel should be capable of being vented manually to an absorption system.

118 The storage installation needs to be emptied of liquid chlorine during inspection and maintenance of the expansion vessel unless provision has been made for alternative means of release of pressure.

119 The expansion vessel should be provided with a pressure sensing device to give an alarm if pressure builds up in the vessel. The alarm system needs to be capable of being tested regularly to ensure that it is operable. (See para 122).

120 The compressed air or nitrogen connection to the expansion vessel should be arranged to avoid the possibility of inadvertently pressurising the vessel. This may be achieved by physical disconnection, isolating blanking plates, or by double block valves supported by safe systems of work. If an expansion vessel serves more than one storage vessel, arrangements should be made for prompt response to a pressure alarm signal from it.

121 While the risk of the expansion vessel itself being over-pressurised with chlorine is minimal because of the precautions described above, procedural or mechanical means to ensure that this cannot occur should be agreed with the chlorine supplier and the Health and Safety Executive (Industrial Air Pollution Inspectorate and Factory Inspectorate).

Pressure alarms

122 There should be a high-pressure alarm on every storage vessel, and an additional pressure indicator/alarm at each important safety location on the relief arrangement. This means that one additional pressure alarm may suffice on an installation where each storage vessel has its own expansion vessel, and that alarm may be either in the relief line (if there is a single bursting disc) or on the expansion vessel. When one expansion vessel serves several storage vessels, there should be an additional pressure alarm within each relief assembly and also one on the expansion vessel.

Inspection and commissioning of chlorine tank installations

General

123 Inspection, testing and commissioning is the chlorine consumer's responsibility and will be organised and controlled by him. UK chlorine suppliers as a matter of policy give advice if requested to do so and visit the plant before it is commissioned, since they deliver chlorine only if

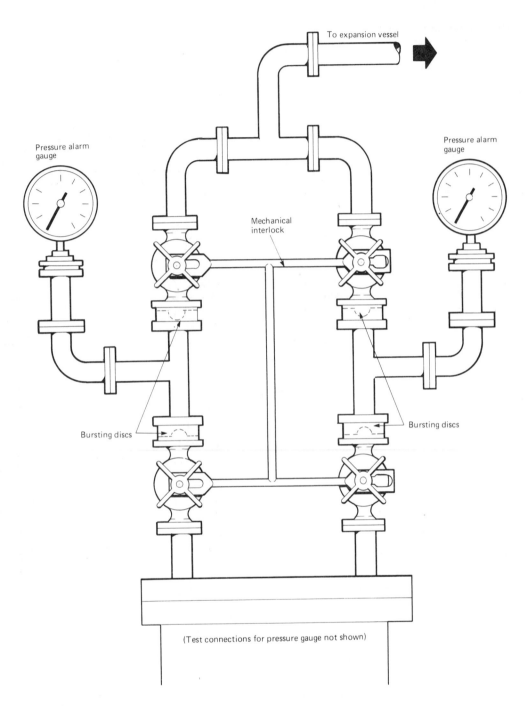

Fig 4 Pressure relief system (preferred arrangement). Double stream with interlocked valves

they consider the installation to be satisfactory. The installer of the equipment also has responsibilities under Section 6 of the Health and Safety at Work etc Act.

124 Initial inspection and testing should be carried out in accordance with the design code (see para 78). The first thorough service examination of a vessel specified for liquid chlorine duty should be made by a competent inspecting authority within five years of commissioning. Thereafter the frequency of further thorough examinations should be determined by the inspecting authority and noted on the thorough examination certificate. The interval should not normally exceed five years. A competent person to carry out such examination should have the knowledge, experience and

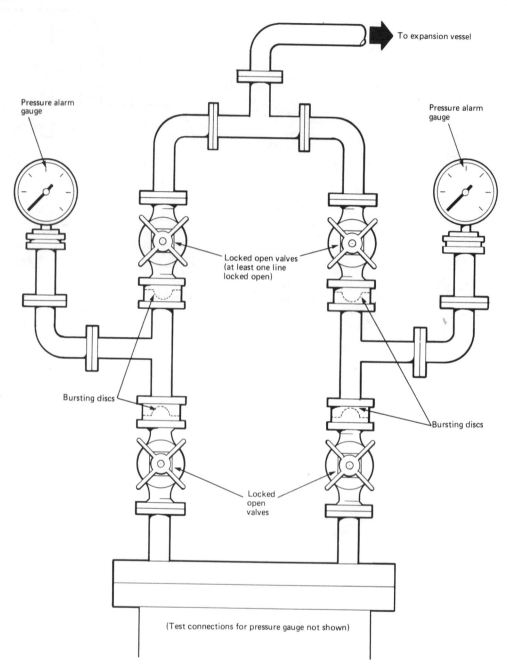

Fig 5 Pressure relief system. Double stream with locked-open valves

To expansion vessel

Pressure alarm gauge

Pressure alarm gauge

Locked open valves (at least one line locked open)

Bursting discs

Bursting discs

Locked open valves

(Test connections for pressure gauge not shown)

resources to search for, detect and assess particular defects associated with systems containing chlorine. Resources should include access to appropriate non-destructive testing and laboratory facilities, together with professional technical ability to relate inspection findings to appraisal of vessel integrity, safe working parameters and future use.

125   The scope of the thorough examination should be determined by the inspecting authority who will include any non-destructive testing considered appropriate. The thorough examination certificate should specify all inspection and testing techniques employed and contain specific details of any deterioration found in the vessel or vessel ancillaries.

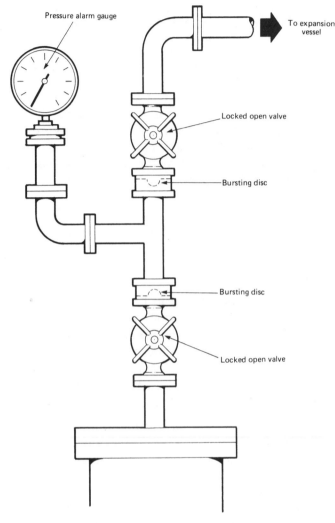

Pressure alarm gauge

To expansion vessel

Locked open valve

Bursting disc

Bursting disc

Locked open valve

Fig 6 Pressure relief system. Single stream with locked-open valves.

126 For lagged tanks, sufficient lagging should be removed to enable the condition of the external surface of the tank to be assessed.

127 Routine hydrostatic testing is not normally recommended. It is, however, essential if any modifications are made to the storage vessels. Such modifications require approval by an inspecting authority.

128 The inspecting authority should assess the vessel for continued use with chlorine with respect to:

maximum and minimum safe working pressures;
maximum and minimum safe working temperatures;

and safe working loads at supports and foundations.

Such information should be noted on the thorough examination certificate, together with the latest date for the next examination.

Inspection procedure

Preparation for internal inspection

129 Prior to opening the storage vessel for inspection, the vessel needs to be emptied of liquid chlorine and purged to remove all traces of chlorine. Procedures for this should be covered by precise operating instructions and normally include:

(a) breaking of all pipework connections to the vessel by removal of spools or by blanking off;

(b) removal of manlid and filling of the vessel with water to which soda ash has been added;

(c) siphoning off the water and checking the atmosphere in the vessel for chlorine and oxygen content;

(d) internal inspection of the vessel controlled in accordance with the conditions set out in HSE Guidance Note GS 5, *Entry into confined spaces*.

Re-assembly after inspection

130 Procedures for this include:

(a) thorough drying of the vessel by dry air or nitrogen and removal and replacement of joints on all connections to the vessel;

(b) re-fitting of the manlid;

(c) pressurisation of the vessel with dry air and measurement of the dew point of the air released;

(d) successive pressurisation with dry air and release until the dew point of the air leaving the vessel reaches −40°C. (Moisture content below 80 ppm/w).

131 All valves on the vessel should be overhauled at the time of inspection, dried out and stored in individual plastic bags pending re-installation. Ancillary equipment should be overhauled at each inspection; bursting discs should always be renewed.

Testing (See HSE Guidance Note GS 4 *Safety in pressure testing*)

132 On completion of re-assembly of the equipment and drying out to the required level, the following procedure is employed;

(a) Pressure testing with dry compressed air or nitrogen at around 120 psig;

(b) Introduction of a small quantity of chlorine to the storage vessel and pressurisation with compressed air or nitrogen to around 120 psig;

(c) Checking of all joints for leakage using an ammonia bottle.

If there is no sign of leakage, the tank is left under pressure for about 12 hours and the check is repeated.

133 All associated pipelines, which need to have been dried out, are then gas tested before introducing liquid chlorine into the system.

Unloading of liquid chlorine from tankers to storage

General

134 Transfer of liquid chlorine from tankers to liquid chlorine storage may be effected either by use of dry compressed air or dry nitrogen or by use of chlorine gas pressure. The methods employing dry compressed air or nitrogen are simpler and the use of chlorine gas pressure is normally encountered only in special circumstances.

Unloading using dry compressed air or dry nitrogen

135 The recommended system for transfer of liquid chlorine from chlorine tankers to the storage vessels, by 'padding' with dry air or dry nitrogen, is outlined in Fig 3. Detailed requirements, which supplement information given in previous sections, are reviewed below. However, for each installation the system used must minimise the risk of excessive pressure and should be agreed between the supplier and customer.

136 A separate and independent dry compressed air or nitrogen system should be used for chlorine duty, to minimise the possibility of back-diffusion of chlorine which could lead to dangerous conditions in other air-consuming units, particularly instrumentation.

137 It is important to vent gas to an absorption system (see paras 198-211) from a 'padded' tank after the transfer operation is complete, in order to restore the pressure in the tank to about the vapour pressure of chlorine at the temperature of the tank contents. If this is not done, the tank may over-pressurise as it warms up, and cause the relief system to operate.

Compressed nitrogen

138 Compressed nitrogen may be produced in a liquid nitrogen evaporation unit.

Compressed air

139 The compressed air to be used needs to be oil-free and have a dew point below −40°C. Normally, air should be compressed to around 150 psig using a truly oil-free compressor (50 ft³/min free air capacity); if an oil-lubricated compressor is used it should be fitted with an oil filter which must be regularly maintained.

140 The compressed air is cooled to remove part of the moisture content and finally dried, using a regenerative-type drying system, to a dew point below −40°C. The dew point should preferably be monitored continuously using a monitor provided with an alarm that gives warning if the dew point exceeds a pre-set figure. It is important to recharge or regenerate drying agents according to the advice of the suppliers of the equipment and of the chlorine.

141 A guard tower, filled with anhydrous calcium chloride, may be installed after the regenerative system as a further safeguard. For small installations a drier using anhydrous calcium chloride only may be adequate. Proper checks on the condition of the drying agent are essential.

Supply to the system

142 The compressed dry air or dry nitrogen should be stored in a pressure receiver fitted with a relief valve set to operate at the chlorine storage plant's safe working pressure or 150 psig, whichever is the less. From the receiver the gas should pass through a non-return valve, or pressure-actuated shut-off valve, followed by a

reducing valve to give a supply at the pressure required for unloading the tankers. This supply will also be suitable for other purposes on the chlorine plant such as drying out or purging of pipelines and vessels provided precautions are taken to prevent backflow of chlorine into the air system. Pressure gauges should be installed upstream and downstream of the pressure reducing valve so that checks can be made that the padding gas pressure is greater than the chlorine pressure. It is important to provide safeguards and alarms to ensure that excessive gas pressures cannot be applied to the chlorine system. This may be particularly important if the padding gas is supplied from high pressure cylinders.

143 The liquid chlorine discharge line on the chlorine tanker should be connected to the permanent pipework at the unloading point (see paras 30 to 41).

144 A pressure gauge, a vent line to the absorber and a connection for dry compressed gas should be installed close to the end of the permanent pipework at the unloading point, with the necessary isolation valves, as detailed in Fig 3.

145 The liquid chlorine line from the unloading point to the liquid chlorine storage vessels should be reasonably short. If it is necessary to use a long liquid chlorine line to storage, the need to protect this line against over-pressure must be considered (see paras 47 to 53).

Unloading using chlorine gas pressure

146 Liquid chlorine may be transferred from the chlorine tankers to the storage vessels by padding with dry chlorine gas. The gas is normally taken from one of the stock tanks but this should preferably not be the one into which the tanker is being unloaded. The supply of dry chlorine gas at the required pressure may be obtained by re-compressing chlorine vapour from a storage tank or by vaporisation of liquid chlorine.

147 A source of dry, compressed, oil-free air or nitrogen is still required, for drying out and purging the system (see above).

Use of re-compressed chlorine vapour

148 Selection of the appropriate compressor for re-compression of chlorine vapour requires careful consideration to ensure that the equipment can

operate satisfactorily on an intermittent basis. Diaphragm compressors or dry carbon ring reciprocating compressors are suitable for this duty provided that maintenance is carried out on a regular basis.

149 *Diaphragm* compressors for this purpose use stainless steel double diaphragms with inert fluid between them.

150 *Dry carbon ring* compressors should preferably be purged with dry air after use, to avoid problems resulting from residual chlorine in the compressor leaking from shaft glands. During operation of the compressor, the shaft glands should be pressurised with dry, compressed, inert gas.

151 If cooling of the compressor body is required, this should preferably be accomplished by air cooling. If jacket cooling is necessary, this should be achieved by circulation through an external heat exchanger with provision to detect leakage of chlorine into the heat exchange fluid. Direct water cooling should be avoided.

152 The compressor needs to be fitted with a by-pass so that the chlorine can be re-cycled until its temperature is raised sufficiently to prevent liquefaction in the delivery lines. The temperature of the chlorine should be monitored using an indicator which is fitted with an alarm set to sound if it exceeds 90°C.

153 A pressure relief system on the compressor delivery line should also be provided to prevent the delivery pressure exceeding a pre-set figure.

Use of vaporised chlorine

154 As an alternative to the use of a compressor, the pressurised chlorine vapour may be produced from a vaporiser as outlined below.

155 Liquid chlorine is transferred from the chlorine storage tanks to a chlorine pumping tank. The pumping tank need only be of relatively small capacity and should have a bottom run-off which is connected to the suction of the chlorine pump (see para 164). The liquid chlorine is then pumped to a vaporiser operating at the required pressure from where it can be used to transfer liquid chlorine to the storage tanks by pressurising the chlorine road tankers.

156 In case of an emergency resulting from failure of the joint at the bottom of the pumping tank, discharge of chlorine to the environment has to be minimised. This can be done by installing an internal valve within the tank or alternatively by dumping the contents to an empty receiver.

Transfer of chlorine to the consuming units

Transfer of liquid chlorine

157 Transfer of liquid chlorine from the storage tanks to the consuming units may be achieved by

(a) using the vapour pressure of the liquid chlorine alone;

(b) padding the chlorine storage tank with dry, compressed gas;

(c) transfer of the liquid chlorine to a separate tank from which it is pumped using a pump specially designed for use with liquid chlorine;

(d) a submerged liquid chlorine pump installed inside the liquid chlorine tank.

Methods (a) and (b) are normally the most satisfactory for customer installations.

158 Under special circumstances and by agreement with the chlorine suppliers, liquid chlorine from the tankers may be transferred direct to process or to a chlorine vaporiser; this is a special and unusual arrangement.

Transfer of gaseous chlorine

159 Apart from venting, safety considerations do not permit the discharge of *gaseous* chlorine from tankers directly to process at customer premises. Such a procedure could cause potential hazard by concentrating the small traces of explosive nitrogen trichloride present in the chlorine; there could in addition be a risk of suck-back of moisture or other materials into the tanker under abnormal circumstances, outside the control of the suppliers of the chlorine.

Precautions

160 Arrangements should be made so that the flow of liquid chlorine from the storage vessel may be stopped rapidly in the event of failure at the chlorine consuming plant (see para 89). Long liquid chlorine pipelines to consuming units may need to be protected against over-pressure (see paras 47 to 53).

161 The possibility of suck-back of aqueous solutions from an absorption system, or of process liquids, needs to be strictly minimised. This requires detailed consideration at the design stage.

Transfer of liquid chlorine using vapour pressure

162 For many applications the vapour presure of the liquid chlorine in the storage tank is adequate to transfer the liquid chlorine to the consuming unit although there may be problems in cold weather with outdoor installations. When the liquid has been removed from the tank, it may also be acceptable for part of the remaining gas to be used on process. However, a minimum positive pressure should always be maintained in the storage vessels; this should be defined for each system.

Transfer of liquid chlorine by padding with dry compressed gas

163 Transfer by padding the storage tanks with dry compressed gas is straightforward; the action and precautions which will be required are similar to those detailed in paras 135-142.

Transfer of liquid chlorine using a separate pumping tank

164 Completely enclosed pumps have been developed for transfer of liquid chlorine: these are used when the chlorine is required at higher pressure (above say 100 psig) or when the use of dry inert compressed gas is not acceptable. The liquid chlorine is first transferred from storage to a separate pumping tank which usually consists of a pressure vessel with a bottom connection. The liquid chlorine is withdrawn from the bottom of the pumping tank to the suction of the pump. A remotely operated valve is preferably installed inside the tank or between the pumping tank and the pump for isolation in emergency. In design of this system, care must be taken to ensure that the nett positive suction head (NPSH) is adequate to meet the minimum requirements for the pump used.

Transfer of liquid chlorine using a submerged pump

165 Submerged liquid chlorine pumps are also used for transfer of liquid chlorine from storage to the consuming units. If this procedure is adopted, detailed discussion will be required with both the chlorine supplier and the equipment supplier to check that the system is satisfactory.

Chlorine vaporisers

166 Vaporisers (also known as evaporators) are used to convert liquid chlorine into gas.

167 A plant with a low rate of use of chlorine can draw the gas straight from cylinders or drums arranged to deliver gas, but higher rates require a vaporiser. Vaporisers are always required when the storage is a fixed or demountable bulk tank, in order to obtain a regular, steady supply of gas to process. The alternative procedure (drawing gas from the vapour space of a bulk tank) is unsatisfactory. There is the risk of process liquids passing back into the tank, irregularity of supply and the possible accumulation of less volatile dangerous impurities such as nitrogen trichloride in the tank.

168 A major use of chlorine vaporisers is in the treatment of water, for weed and algae control in cooling water and for sterilisation of drinking water. These units are frequently supplied as part of a package with other dosing or analytical equipment. There are four UK suppliers of standard water treatment systems, though other chemical contractors can supply a package. On water treatment plants, the usual vaporiser is a self-regulating type, with an electrically heated water bath. The greater flexibility of steam heating is useful on plants using chlorine gas at high or at very variable rates.

Methods of heating

169 The methods of heating the vaporiser should be such as to minimise both the risk of corrosion and the resultant problems that could arise if the vaporiser should fail. Systems now in use include: heating with hot water; heating with steam; and use of closed circuit heating with heat transfer fluids other than water. Direct electrical heating

should not be used because of the risk of local overheating.

Heating with hot water

This is the most frequently used method; the normal working temperature (60-70°C) is well below that at which any significant reaction of carbon steel occurs with dry chlorine.

Heating with steam

The steam should be saturated and its pressure should be limited to avoid over-heating, particularly if the vaporiser is fabricated of mild steel. Any small leaks of chlorine to the water side of hot water or steam types lead to very rapid corrosion of the steel by moist chlorine.

Heat transfer fluids (other than water)

Electrical or steam heat can be applied to a heat transfer fluid which is relatively unreactive towards chlorine. The available fluids (e.g. hexachlorobutadiene) are themselves hazardous, so that the hazards of using water as heat transfer medium are in practice accepted, with suitable safeguards.

Types

170 There are four main types of vaporiser. (Further descriptions will be found in Appendix 5).

Vertical tube bundle

These resemble ordinary heat exchanges, usually with the chlorine in the tubes. The alternative formats include the common vaporiser in water treatment (a cylinder with a dip pipe liquid chlorine inlet immersed in the heating bath) or a shell and tube heat exchanger with the chlorine on the shell side.

Coil

The chlorine is evaporated in a coil of steel tubing running inside a wet steambath or a water bath heated by steam or electricity.

Concentric tube

The heat exchange surface is a tube, typically 4 inches in diameter, surrounded by a heating jacket.

Kettle

These contain a heater system (steam or heated fluid) passing through a pot containing liquid chlorine.

Regulation of throughput

Self-regulating vaporisers

171 In some types of vaporiser the liquid chlorine is fed in at the bottom and gas is drawn off via a control valve at the top. When demand is high, the liquid chlorine level rises in the container, and a greater heat exchange surface area is presented to the liquid. When demand is low, the greater vapour pressure at the temperature of the heating medium drives the liquid chlorine out of the vaporiser back into the storage vessel and the evaporation rate falls. This system is usually applicable to vaporisers with a relatively small chlorine capacity, i.e. vertical tube bundles, coil types and concentric tube types.

Constant level vaporisers

172 Other types of vaporisers, usually found only in large-capacity plants, sacrifice certain advantages of the self-regulating types noted above in order to achieve much larger vaporisation rates. These types require a separate instrumentation and control arrangement to provide a constant level of liquid chlorine in the kettle or shell with high and low level alarms. In such types (where there can be parts of the liquid chlorine pool which are not well-mixed), there is a greater tendency to concentrate the less volatile impurities than in a self-regulating vaporiser, and a separate purge and vaporiser circuit may be required to deal periodically with the residues. The design and operation of these larger-capacity vaporisers is a specialised topic, and requires consultation between the user, the designer, and the chlorine supplier.

General installation

173 The vaporiser should be installed in the storage area or in an adjacent space as close as possible to the chlorine storage tanks in order to keep pipelines carrying liquid chlorine short. Change over of liquid chlorine supply from one storage tank to another can affect operating conditions in the vaporiser system and any such

difficulties will be reduced if the spacing is not too great, e.g. less than 5 metres. Nevertheless, the space between the vaporiser and the storage system should be such as to allow adequate access for emergency action in the event of an incident at the vaporiser.

Safety

174 The quantity of chlorine in a chlorine vaporiser system is relatively small compared with that normally contained in the main chlorine storage tanks. Nevertheless, the system design should be such that failure of equipment can be detected and rectified quickly and that any consequent release of chlorine to the environment is minimised.

Hazards

175 The potential hazards with chlorine vaporisers are related to the function of the device i.e. to supply heat to a corrosive and toxic liquefied gas under pressure. They include;

(a) the risk of *pinhole leaks*, which lead to rapid corrosion and increased loss of chlorine;

(b) rapid *corrosion*, if any *moisture* is allowed into the chlorine system;

(c) *concentration of impurities* in the chlorine, such as explosive nitrogen trichloride, as the chlorine is evaporated;

(d) *reverse flow* of reaction fluids, caused by a fall in pressure in the vaporiser, or by excess pressure in the process, or by solution of chlorine gas in the fluid. The presence of the fluid (water, solvent or reagent) in the vaporiser can cause corrosion or local violent reaction;

(e) *carry-over* of liquid chlorine as bulk fluid or droplets into the gas line or into the process itself. This can (depending on the materials of construction and on the process) cause damage or hazard;

(f) overheating a vaporiser, which can apply *excessive gas pressure* to the system, since the vapour pressure of chlorine rises very steeply with temperature;

(g) the expansion of liquid chlorine which when heated, applies great *hydraulic forces* if the system is closed up and full of liquid.

176 These basic hazards are considered in more detail below, but grouped according to the remedial measure provided.

Flooding and liquid carryover

177 Flooding (filling) of the chlorine vaporiser with liquid chlorine may result from operation of the equipment above its capacity, inadequate heating, or fouling of the heat transfer surfaces. An indicator of gas flow to process may be of value to the operator for routine purposes, and will also indicate excessive withdrawal rates.

178 If the temperature of the heating medium falls too low in a self-regulating evaporator, it is possible for the outgoing gas to be inadequately superheated, or even for liquid chlorine to pass through the vaporiser. The same may happen if the level of water in a water bath falls. In the extreme, if chlorine is drawn off but no heat is supplied to the vaporiser, it is possible for ice to form on the heat exchanger surfaces and damage them severely.

179 The temperature of the heating medium is usually controlled thermostatically. If flooding occurs it can result in potential hazard (depending on the process and plant materials) due to carryover of liquid chlorine into the vapour lines. Adequate instrumentation and alarms should always be provided to give immediate warning of this condition, unless a thorough assessment of the plant and process has shown they are not necessary. Low temperature alarms may be arranged to cut off the liquid chlorine supply to the vaporiser or (in self-regulating types only) the gaseous chlorine outlet may be closed, driving the liquid chlorine back into the bulk storage.

180 A knock out pot (or spray catcher) may be fitted to prevent droplets and spray from passing into gas pipelines where they might damage the material of the pipes. There is a safety advantage in the presence of a knock out pot if the process would be unstable if supplied with some liquid chlorine. In all cases where the possibility of liquid passing to process is unacceptable, it is strongly recommended on safety grounds that a low temperature detector alarm be fitted near the knock out pot.

Accelerated corrosion and reaction (high temperature)

181 If the temperature of the steel tubes containing chlorine is too high, there is a risk of rapid chemical reaction between the chlorine and steel. The temperature should normally be restricted to a maximum of 120°C. A limit of about 70°C is applicable if the vaporiser consists of galvanised steel in a water bath, in order to avoid rapid corrosion of the water side of the heat exchange surface. If operation is required at higher temperatures, vaporisers of nickel or available nickel alloys (such as Monel 400 or Inconel) may be required. In such cases, the downstream chlorine (gas) lines may also require to be resistant at higher than usual temperatures.

182 Temperature control is usually achieved thermostatically. If the heating medium is steam, the temperature can be monitored by low pressure and high pressure alarms on the steam inlet. The pressure of steam should normally be limited to 15 psig (120°C equivalent) and the steam has to be saturated, not superheated.

High pressure

183 High pressure is usually a serious safety consideration. A high pressure alarm operated from the pressure gauge or by individual pressure switch should be fitted. The high pressure alarm has to be particularly carefully maintained and regularly tested. A common working temperature for vaporisers is 70°C. The vapour pressure of chlorine at 70°C is over 300 psi. It follows that

(a) every effort should be made to ensure that the vaporiser is not isolated full of liquid chlorine. Strict observance of written procedures for shutdown is vital;

(b) every effort should be made to avoid accidentally isolating the vaporiser on both sides. Care should be taken to ensure that the closing arrangements for the emergency valves take this into account;

(c) the vaporiser shell and pipes should be designed for a safe working pressure which operational controls ensure cannot be exceeded.

Chlorine vaporisers in the UK are usually not provided with their own pressure relief, and consequently the procedures to ensure the conditions in (a) and (b) are vital.

Reverse flow

184   A low pressure gas alarm can be fitted to the outlet gas line. This gives warning of loss of supply to the process, but the safety significance of low pressure is small, unless there is a risk of the process fluid (e.g. water from a chlorinator) sucking back into the valves, evaporator or storage with the possible consequences of local reaction. The possibility of suck-back into the vaporisers should so far as possible be eliminated. This requirement should be given very careful consideration at the design stage. Water chlorinating package systems usually incorporate a set of valves in the control system to prevent suck-back or push-back. The arrangements vary, and care needs to be taken to ensure that the system provided does give protection in the event of, for example, a leak back at the ejector non-return valve. The system needs to be checked and maintained frequently.

185   Similar precautions against suck-back and push-back of liquors will be needed on chemical plant.

186   Arrangements should be made for an alarm to operate if the gas pressure falls below a safe level; if necessary, this could be used to initiate purging of the system, using dry air or other suitable gas.

Routine and emergency isolation

187   The vaporiser has to be capable of being isolated for maintenance, etc; and also in emergencies such as a failure of the vaporiser itself through leakage or a failure of the gas line downstream. In addition to a manual valve on the liquid inlet and on the gas outlet, remotely operable valves are recommended on both inlet and outlet. A pressure reducing or flow control valve will usually be fitted on the outlet (see para 191) and it is sometimes possible for this valve to be the remotely-operable shut-off valve also.

188   As a back-up safety device in the event that automatic valves fail to operate (or are not activated) in an emergency, there is some advantage in providing a flow restrictor or excess flow valve in the liquid inlet (typically on the exit

from the storage vessel), so as to minimise the release which could occur in the event of a major plant failure. The feasibility of these additional devices will depend on the detailed design of the system.

189   The hazards of total isolation of the vaporiser are considerable (see above, para 183). If liquid chlorine is locked in, the consequences will be most severe if the evaporator is filled (e.g. if the valves close together in a condition of major gas line leak). If there is a gas space over the chlorine when the vaporiser is isolated and heated, the internal pressure will reach that of chlorine at the heating medium temperature. Consideration should be given to ensuring that vaporiser, lines and valves are designed to withstand such pressure, or incorporate arrangements to relieve it to a safe place. (Relief of the vaporiser is not found on non-chemical consumer installations in the UK, but may be found on certain high-throughput chemical plants). Automatic valves should not be arranged to close together when an alarm is raised. One approach is to arrange the gas control valve to close on alarms related to improper working of the system (e.g. low gas pressure, downstream process alarms, low temperature) and the liquid control valve at the bulk storage to close on alarms related to chlorine release (e.g. detectors local to the vaporiser and storage, manual alarms). There is some safety advantage, if the plant is continually manned, in providing for manual intervention in the system rather than providing wholly automatic operation of shut-down, but care should be taken that this does not introduce significant delays into the response to an alarm.

190   Isolation of the vaporiser is still conceivable, but interlocks between the inlet and outlet valves to prevent isolation are not usually fitted because it is occasionally necessary to close both valves during cleaning and overhaul. A safe system of work for maintenance and operation is thus a vital part of the safety arrangements.

Pressure control valve

191   All vaporiser designs incorporate an element of superheating of the vapour, either in the vaporiser itself or as a separate unit, so that the chlorine gas emerging is not liable to reliquefy into the control valves, where it could cause problems of irregular pressure in operation and local erosion.

These problems are avoided in the remaining run of the chlorine gas system by reducing the gas pressure. A suitable automatic control system to achieve this, e.g. a pressure control system, should be provided.

Corrosion

192 Regular inspection has to be carried out in accordance with the requirements of the scheme set by the engineering inspection body. The equipment should be thoroughly dried out before recommissioning. Moisture left in the system can lead to very rapid corrosion. The procedure should be covered by a written Operating Procedure.

193 The frequency of inspection and maintenance of vaporisers will need to be greater than that of fixed storage tanks because of the higher operating temperature, the conditions favouring corrosion and the possible deposition of solids. The consequence of a minor chlorine leak from the chlorine side of a vaporiser heating bath could be very serious since the mixture of chlorine and moisture is extremely corrosive. The pressure of the steam or hot water bath compared to the chlorine supply should be designed so that it is unlikely that water would actually enter the liquid chlorine line to the vaporiser, but rapid corrosion of the evaporator surfaces could occur, with a substantial release of chlorine. Corrosion of the heat exchanger surfaces is not directly monitored.

194 The inspection authority will specify inspection frequencies for a particular installation. One manufacturer of water authority chlorine plant recommends that the evaporator vessel itself should be visually examined internally and externally once a year or after 250 tonnes chlorine has passed, whichever is the more frequent. This recommendation is a reasonable guide for small evaporators given reasonably light use. Coil-in-bath evaporators are commonly given a rigorous inspection every two years, and the coils are discarded if seriously pitted.

195 The evaporator vessel or tubes are frequently protected against water corrosion by cathodic protection. Typically the anodes should be checked visually every 3-6 months. The frequency should be established by experience of the rate at which the anodes are consumed and

require replacing. If the anodes are found wholly consumed at inspection, a thorough examination of the vaporiser should be undertaken.

196 Accumulation of solid deposits reduces the effectiveness of a vaporiser and can also enhance corrosion. The vaporiser needs to be cleansed and dried again regularly. Close attention to the cleaning procedure will minimise corrosion but typically, the chlorine evaporator cylinder in a type 1c system (see illustrations) should be renewed after five years. The old one may be submitted to a competent inspection body for certification for further use if required.

197 The water bath or condensate outlet should be monitored for chlorine leaks by redox or conductivity measurements. This early warning of minor leaks is helpful in all cases, and is very strongly recommended if cathodic protection is not provided and maintained.

Chlorine absorption system

198 Detailed consideration should be given to ensuring that in all chlorine-using operations chlorine can, in an emergency, be vented to an absorber without emission to the environment.

199 Control of chlorine emissions from Scheduled Works should be the subject of consultations with HM Industrial Air Pollution Inspectorate (or HM Industrial Pollution Inspectorate for Scotland).

200 In some installations, the nature of the consuming process is such that absorption of the chlorine is possible without a special absorption unit. However, in such circumstances operators need to ensure that during maintenance periods adequate absorption capacity is always kept available to accommodate any chlorine emissions. Examples of installations where a separate absorption plant may not be essential include cooling-water treatment plants and bleach liquor production plants.

201 For most bulk storage installations, however, a separate chlorine absorption plant is required and it should always be maintained in a state of readiness. The quantity of reagents available in the absorption system needs to be adequate to deal with any foreseeable emergency.

202 The responsibility for the installation of an adequate chlorine absorption system rests with the consumer, but the chlorine supplier's advice on the proposed installation should be obtained.

203 Careful consideration should also be given to the provision of adequate instrumentation with alarms and to the disposal of effluent from the chlorine absorption plant.

204 Adequate standby equipment should be provided to cover breakdowns and routine overhauls. Essential circulating pumps, fans and instrumentation should be amongst those items which are connected both to the mains and to the factory emergency power supply if the latter is available. When the absorption facility is required to be continuously available (e.g. vents from reactors) it is essential to provide emergency power and stand-by circulating pumps or an emergency gravity-fed supply of absorbing solution.

Vent collection system

205 The pipelines for the collection of the vent gases containing dry chlorine may be fabricated of mild steel but back-diffusion of moisture from the absorption system, such as may occur if ventings are intermittent, has to be prevented.

206 Vent systems from relief systems, which are likely to operate only infrequently, may be protected from back-diffusion of moisture by the use of protective membranes. In some cases it may help to provide a controlled dry gas purge through the vent lines.

207 If there is any risk of moisture contamination, the pipework has to be fabricated of rubber-lined or plastic-lined carbon steel, or plastic resistant to wet chlorine (e.g. PVC, *Hetron* or *Atlac 382*), or glass.

208 If there is any possibility of liquid chlorine carry-over, liquid gas separators should be installed on the lines to avoid excess pressure or overloading of the absorption system; these separators are fitted with a temperature alarm to indicate the presence of liquid chlorine in the separator. Furthermore, if it is possible for liquid chlorine carry-over to take place, plastic pipework should not be used. Pipework should be sized to take into account the maximum possible flows under the most unfavourable conditions.

Absorption equipment

209 Various types of absorbers are used for treatment of vent gases; suitable absorbers may be based on the use of packed towers, vent injectors or sparge absorbers. It can be an advantage if the system selected gives a suction on the plant.

210 Caustic soda liquor is the most convenient reagent for absorption of chlorine in waste gases. The concentration of caustic soda should not exceed 21% NaOH because of the risk of salt deposition causing blockages in the absorption plant.

211 Alternatively, for installations where there is no bulk storage for caustic soda liquor and where lime or soda ash is available on the site, a lime slurry or a soda ash solution may be used.

Instrumentation

212 It is essential that faults are detected quickly and adequate instrumentation with alarms should be provided on the vent absorption plant to ensure that warning is given if equipment fails. Faults of particular significance are:

(a) loss of circulation;

(b) chemical depletion of the absorbing solution

213 Consideration should be given to the provision of a pressure indicator fitted with an alarm to show if there is excessive venting or a blockage in the absorption system.

214 A monitor to detect chlorine may be installed on the outlet from the absorber.

Disposal of effluent from the chlorine absorption plant

215 The disposal of the liquor from the chlorine absorption plant requires careful consideration, as the presence of hypochlorite may create problems. If the waste liquor is discharged without treatment, the possibility of interaction with other effluents should be investigated (for example, a mixture with acid effluent can lead to evolution of chlorine in the effluent mains, and with ammoniacal effluent can lead to formation of nitrogen trichloride).

216 Under some circumstances, it may be necessary to treat the effluent to reduce hypochlorite content to an acceptable level; this may be achieved by treatment with sodium sulphite.

Protective and emergency equipment (See paras 247 to 263 also for Emergency procedures)

Respiratory protective equipment for routine use

217 It is a frequent practice for personnel in larger chlorine installations to carry ori-nasal cartridge masks to act as escape masks against nuisance concentrations of chlorine in the event of accidental chlorine release. These masks MUST NOT be used in routine maintenance or other operations where there is the potential for a release of chlorine gas.

218 Canister type respirators are suitable for certain routine operations and they should either be worn, or available at the ready, where there is the potential for low concentrations of chlorine gas to develop. This would typically be during the connecting up or disconnecting of transport containers, or breaking into previously purged chlorine systems. They should not be used if there is any potential for escape of liquid chlorine, in which circumstances self contained breathing apparatus should be employed. Self contained (or compressed air-line) breathing apparatus to BS 4667 should also always be used where there is the potential for chlorine gas to be released in a confined space, or where the means of access or escape are physically restricted.

219 All personnel working in the above areas or circumstances need to be trained in the use of the relevant respiratory protective equipment, and in the constraints applying to its application or use. It should also be noted that in some situations covered by the Factories Act or Chemical Works Regulations, only respiratory protective equipment which has been approved by the HSE can be used. Suitable arrangements should also be made for the maintenance of the respiratory protective equipment provided.

Respiratory protective equipment for emergencies

220 Emergency equipment is needed in all chlorine plant areas where there is a possibility that gas escapes may occur. The number of items of equipment and their location should be given careful consideration. Emergency equipment should be regularly inspected and

maintained to ensure that it is in satisfactory condition.

221 Whilst canister type respirators are suitable for routine operations such as off-loading, and for use in low concentrations of chlorine gas, they are not adequate if serious chlorine escapes occur. To deal with such incidents the following breathing apparatus should be available;

(a) self-contained breathing apparatus giving the required air supply for 30-40 minutes, so that rescue work or emergency work to isolate equipment can be carried out in high concentrations of chlorine gas. This equipment is provided with an audible alarm when the pressure in the air cylinders falls below a stipulated figure, so that the operator is aware of the time available before he must leave the contaminated area.

(b) escape sets, comprising self-contained breathing apparatus which lasts for 10 minutes, for use only for emergency evacuation of the plant.

Protective clothing for emergencies

222 Protective clothing should be available for use in areas where leakages of chlorine gas are possible. There should be at least two 30 to 40 minutes self-contained breathing sets and two full sets of protective clothing (impervious suit, hood, gloves and boots) kept in lockers in the vicinity of the storage installation, accessible in the presence of a leakage.

Emergency tool kits

223 Emergency tool kits (including spare valve keys) should be provided in the chlorine storage area. The equipment supplied should be regularly inspected and maintained.

Containment of chlorine leakage

224 Materials and equipment, including plastic sheets (para 226), to contain chlorine leakages should be readily available.

225 A supply of sand may be useful for containment of liquid chlorine spillage.

226 The need for supplies of foam or water sprays to be provided should be discussed with the local Fire Service and the chlorine supplier

since the use of foam and water may in certain circumstances aggravate the problem. If the spill is indoors and contained, it will rapidly cover itself with a cold vapour layer and a coating of slushy chlorine hydrate. Application of foam would cause renewed evolution of vapour because of the heat supplied. Covering a stabilised spill with plastic sheets may often be the best action. The Fire Brigade may carry stocks of suitable foam, but the decision to use it should be taken in conjunction with the senior technical manager on site.

Operator selection and training and operating instructions

227 The main risk of chlorine escape to the environment arises from incorrect operation of the plant. Selection and training of process operators is thus extremely important for efficient and safe operation.

228 Detailed operating instructions are required for all process work and procedures involved in the unloading of liquid chlorine tankers, operation of the storage installation and utilisation of the chlorine.

229 Procedures need to be defined in detail for plant commissioning and shut-down, for periodic plant testing and inspections, and for emergency action to deal with chlorine spillages and gas escapes.

Operator selection and training

230 Careful selection of operators for bulk chlorine handling installations is necessary. It is essential that the personnel selected are of adequate physical fitness and they should pass a medical examination before engagement. The objectives of pre-employment and routine medical examination are discussed in Guidance Notes MS 18 and 20. Operators need to be capable of effective communication and be reliable under stress conditions. Previous experience in the chemical or similar industry is very desirable.

231 Operator training should comprise both off-the-job and on-the-job training instruction.

232 Off-the-job training should include basic information on the physical, chemical and toxicological properties of chlorine, as well as detailed descriptions of the process operations required of the operators. Operators should be provided with personal protection, clothing, eye protection etc, as appropriate, and be trained in its use. On-the-job training should be carried out under the guidance of an experienced operator who is familiar with the process and management and supervisory staff should also be involved in training. Emphasis must be given to safety precautions and methods of dealing with emergencies.

238 The training programme should include coverage of procedures for special operations which arise only at infrequent intervals; for example plant shut-down, isolation and preparation of equipment for maintenance and inspection and plant re-commissioning. Training and practice with breathing apparatus should also be carried out.

234 Re-training should be carried out regularly at defined intervals.

Operating instructions

235 Written operating instructions are required for all foreseeable routine and emergency operations ranging from guide cards for simple operations to complete manuals.

236 The operating instruction should cover each process operation in detail and should be formally issued by the manager responsible for the operation of the plant section concerned. He is also responsible for authorising any subsequent amendments.

237 Copies of the instructions, which should include a flowsheet and indicate valves to be closed in an emergency, should be available in the working area for operators and in the control centre for supervisors.

238 Supervisors should check regularly that operations are carried out precisely according to the written instructions.

Maintenance

239 Satisfactory maintenance of plant, equipment and instrumentation is essential to minimise hazards.

240 Schedules need to be prepared defining the required frequency for servicing, testing and inspection; these schedules should be strictly adhered to and be adequately recorded.

241 Detailed written instructions covering all routine maintenance operations should be available. These should be formally approved and issued by the responsible maintenance engineer. Supervisors should check regularly that work is carried out according to these instructions.

242 Close liaison is necessary between the maintenance engineer and the process manager, to ensure that maintenance work is started only after the equipment concerned has been adequately prepared by process personnel and is free from chlorine.

243 Adequate training is required for all maintenance personnel. This should include basic information on the properties of chlorine, safety precautions and emergency procedures.

Clearance procedures

244 Formal clearance procedures need to be established as part of a permit-to-work system for

(a) ensuring that the plant is in a satisfactory condition, appropriately isolated and free from chlorine;

(b) covering all work in the chlorine area which requires the use of cranes, mobile equipment, welding sets or other plant which could lead to accidental damage to the chlorine system. This safeguard is necessary even if the work does not directly involve the chlorine-containing lines or equipment;

(c) formal acceptance of plant back to process after the work has been completed.

Modifications of the chlorine system

245 Modifications to the chlorine system should never be carried out without specific authorisation. This ensures that approval is first given by responsible staff covering the operating and engineering sections involved, and procedures need to be laid down to deal with any alterations required. Proposed modifications should preferably be discussed with the suppliers of the liquid chlorine.

246 Written schemes of examination and maintenance, and arrangements for proper control of repairs and modifications, are provided for in the proposed Pressure Systems and Transportable Gas Containers Regulations (Consultative Document 1984). Any modifications or repairs which could affect the integrity of the system would have to be defined and overseen by a competent person.

Emergency procedures

Note Further guidance is contained in CIMAH Regulations 1984 and associated publications. The CIMAH Regulations make specific requirements for emergency procedures at some chlorine sites.

247 A works emergency plan to deal with the range of possible escapes of chlorine should be prepared and a copy of the plan should be made available to all personnel involved in its implementation.

248 Each factory should have means of warning all workers that a gas escape has occurred, and the appropriate action to be taken following a gas escape warning should be defined in written instructions.

249 For a minor gas escape, only simple actions may be necessary, but if the escape is serious, a further special warning should be given, which initiates the works emergency plan.

250 Regular practices of the Emergency Plan should be arranged in which the Police, Fire, Hospital and Ambulance Services are involved.

Chlorine detector alarms

251 Early warning of chlorine leaks, particularly in buildings which are not continuously manned, has the advantage of allowing prompt remedial action (see para 103). Chlorine detectors and alarms should be provided in buildings housing chlorine storage tanks or vaporisers. Their value outdoors depends on the size of the installation, and the manning levels and response times achievable. Recommended alarm actions are: distinct local audible alarm, warning light outside building, visual and audible warning in control room.

Local alarm stations

252 Local alarm stations to provide early warning of chlorine escapes are an essential link in the emergency procedure. Local alarm stations (push-button type preferred) should be located at strategic points near chlorine storage installations; generally two alarm stations on convenient escape routes from the chlorine unloading terminal/storage tank area are sufficient. The local alarm stations may actuate the works emergency alarm directly or indirectly by raising an alarm in the emergency control centre and the main control room. Preferably in large works the local alarm station should actuate a distinct local chlorine alarm to warn people off from the affected area.

253 The alarm stations may also actuate the remotely operated shut-off valves on the chlorine storage tanks where this is consistent with the safe operation of the user plant.

Works Emergency Plan

Note A fuller discussion of emergency plans appears in HSE booklet HS(G) 25 *Further guidance on emergency plans*

254 The works should have an emergency plan for dealing with a major chlorine release. The plan should include instructions for the emergency team and for non-essential personnel, and for liaison with the emergency services. The emergency plan may be based on the CIA publication *Recommended Procedures for Handling Major Emergencies*. Some elements of the plan are in the following paragraphs.

255 The plan may include detailed instructions for the following actions

(a) raising the alarm;

(b) investigation and assessment of the source and extent of the chlorine release;

(c) alerting all personnel on-site or in neighbouring premises and the Emergency Services. Setting up emergency control centres, and assessment by key personnel of the incident and consequential emergency measures on and off site;

(d) methods for control of the chlorine release;

(e) systems of search for casualties, and accounting for personnel on-site;

(f) methods for assessing the directional spread and concentration of the gas cloud;

(g) criteria to use to determine whether to evacuate non-essential personnel or to advise them to stay inside buildings with doors, windows and ventilation shut;

(h) methods to assess whether corresponding actions are advisable for people off site and in particular liaison with the manager at any adjacent underground workings where chlorine could enter the ventilation system. Advice to emergency services on the direction, spread and concentration of the gas cloud;

(j) first aid to on-site casualties, and arrangements for evacuation where advisable and practicable. Advice to ambulance service on routes to use.

256 Since each installation will have its own special features, a detailed plan relating to the particular plant will be required. Local management should be responsible for preparation of the plan which should be developed in collaboration with the local authority, the Police, Fire, Hospital and Ambulance Services, the local Health and Safety Executive, and the supplier of the chlorine. Specific duties are laid on some of these people by the Control of Industrial Major Accident Hazards Regulations 1984.

Emergency control centres

257 Basic requirements for a satisfactory system to deal with an emergency resulting from a serious escape of chlorine are outlined below.

(a) Two control centres should be provided so that, in the event of a gas escape, operations can be controlled from the centre which is least affected under prevailing atmospheric conditions.

(b) Each centre should be provided with a separate external telephone line, as well as with connections to the factory external and internal telephone system;

(c) Adequate emergency equipment (compressed air sets, supplies of suitable foam as agreed with the emergency services, protective clothing, etc) should be available in the centres (see paras 222-226);

(d) Emergency First Aid facilities, including equipment for administration of oxygen, need to be provided;

(e) A large scale map (1:25,000 or 1:10,000) of the surrounding area should be available to assist in determining which parts of the factory and the local neighbourhood are likely to be affected;

(f) Wind direction indicators have to be visible from or indicated in each control centre;

(g) Equipment and information are needed to assess the likely extent of the gas cloud for various sizes of release and various weather conditions.

258 The Emergency Plan has to specify in advance the individuals and deputies responsible for the action necessary to deal with the emergency.

Site emergency team

259 There should be a trained emergency team with the following key personnel

(a) *Site Incident Controller* He is the senior man on-site responsible for the initiation of the emergency plan and the direction of on-site operations;

(b) *Site Main Controller* He is normally the Works Manager or deputy and has overall responsibility for the operation of the emergency plan. He will maintain close liaison with the police and fire services and will advise them on the risk;

(c) *Other key personnel* These include:
   (i) the team responsible for the control of the chlorine release;
   (ii) the team responsible for the search for casualties, for first aid and for the control of evacuation.

260 The police will be responsible for dealing with members of the public who might be affected by the chlorine escape; they will need to be advised of the size and expected duration of the release together with the areas which

could be affected, to allow the police and the site main controller to agree whether the public should remain indoors or be evacuated.

Emergency assembly areas

261 Emergency assembly areas should be designated for use in a chlorine emergency by personnel not involved in the emergency team. The assembly areas allow for counting of personnel and for controlled evacuation if the need should arise. Preferably the assembly area should be at the periphery of the works site with good exit for evacuation. A building with upper storeys at a location upwind of the chlorine release may offer sufficient protection while the release is brought under control. Evacuation of personnel to the assembly areas should be directed by a senior member of the emergency team who would take wind direction into account. There will be occasions when evacuating off-site is not the best action, for example, when the release is sudden and of limited duration.

Attention to casualties

262 Persons who have inhaled chlorine gas should be kept at rest with the head and chest raised. They have to be kept warm. It is essential that qualified medical attention is obtained quickly, as serious symptoms may develop up to 48 hours later. All persons who have been affected by chlorine gas should be examined locally by a medically competent person or sent to hospital by ambulance.

263 First Aid attendants should be aware of the dangers arising from gassing by chlorine. The following basic rules should be observed

(a) if chlorine has affected the eyes, they should be irrigated immediately with plenty of clean water (preferably tap water);

(b) contaminated clothing should be removed and affected skin washed with plenty of water;

(c) artificial respiration should not be applied if the patient is breathing. (Oxygen may however be administered by suitably qualified personnel).

Appendix 1 Properties of chlorine

1   Chlorine is a greenish-yellow gas at ambient temperature and pressure. It is supplied commercially in steel containers as a liquid under pressure.

2   Commercial liquid chlorine conforms to BS 3947:1976. This Standard specifies a minimum limit for chlorine content and maximum levels for water content and residue on evaporation; details of the methods of analysis for gaseous impurities (carbon dioxide, oxygen and nitrogen), water content, nitrogen trichloride, and residue on evaporation are also given.

3   Traces of dissolved gaseous impurities in chlorine are not normally significant for most applications; moisture content however is extremely important because of the corrosive nature of wet chlorine.

4   Residues which are left on evaporation, usually chlorinated organic products or ferric chloride, may be troublesome since they can lead to blockage of pipelines, valves or instruments; nitrogen trichloride can be potentially dangerous if the vaporisation process leads to its concentration in residues.

5   Physical properties

Atomic weight	35.46
Molecular weight	70.91

Density

	Liquid	1561 kg/m^3 at $-35°C$
		1468 kg/m^3 at $-0°C$
		1410 kg/m^3 at $+20°C$
	Gas	3.214 kg/m^3 at 0°C/760 mmHg (relative density 2.490 at 20°C relative to air)

Boiling point at 760 mmHg	$-34.05°C$
Melting point	$-101°C$
Critical temperature	144°C
Critical pressure	77.1 bars absolute
Vapour pressure at 20°C	6.7 bars absolute

Viscosity: Liquid at 20°C 0.35 cp

1 volume of liquid chlorine = 457 volumes of chlorine gas at 0°C/760 mmHg

1 pound of liquid chlorine = 4.98 cu ft of chlorine gas at 0°C/760 mmHg
1 kg of liquid chlorine = 0.315 m^3 of chlorine gas at 0°C/760 mmHg

The vapour pressure of liquid chlorine is given in Fig 1.1.

Thermal properties

Specific heat (Liquid chlorine between 1°C and 27°C)	0.236 kcal/kg/°C
Specific heat (Gas at constant pressure at 100 psia or less and between 1°C and 27°C)	0.113 kcal/kg/°C
Ratio of specific heat at constant pressure to specific heat at constant volume	1.355
Latent heat of fusion	21.6 kcal/kg
Latent heat of vaporisation at 0°C	63.2 kcal/kg
Coefficient of cubic expansion (liquid chlorine at 20°C)	0.0021 per°C
Heat of reaction of chlorine gas with sodium hydroxide liquor	348 kcal/kg of chlorine

6   While the above data give a general summary of the physical and thermal properties of chlorine it is recommended that, for use in plant design calculations, more precise information should be obtained from the literature.

Solubility of chlorine in water

7   Chlorine dissolves slightly in water to give a solution which has oxidising, bleaching and germicidal properties. The solubility of chlorine in water increases with the partial pressure of the chlorine. The table below gives the solubility of chlorine in water for a total pressure of 760 mmHg.

Temperature °C	10	15	20	25
grams of chlorine per litre of water	9.97	8.5	7.29	6.41

hydrochloric acid and hypochlorous acid:

$$Cl_2 + H_2O \rightarrow HCl + HOCl.$$

Chemical properties

10 Dry chlorine at ambient temperatures reacts directly with many of the elements producing chlorides both of non-metals (e.g. sulphur or phosphorus) and of metals (e.g. iron in a finely divided form, aluminium or titanium). Dry chlorine at ambient temperature does not attack steel, copper or nickel in the massive form, but these metals are attacked at higher temperatures. Steel combines with dry chlorine above 200°C, and, since the reaction is exothermic, the rate of reaction may increase rapidly. Reaction with nickel does not take place until the temperature exceeds 500°C.

11 Traces of moisture in chlorine lead to rapid corrosion of steel, copper and nickel.

12 Titanium is resistant to wet chlorine up to around 100°C but not to dry chlorine.

13 Chlorine dissolves in cool aqueous solutions of alkalis to produce solutions of hypochlorites; in hot or boiling aqueous alkalis, chlorates can be produced.

14 Chlorine reacts vigorously with many organic compounds including mineral oils and greases, producing chlorinated products. The mechanism is either that of direct addition to unsaturated bonds or of substitution of hydrogen. In the latter case hydrogen chloride is formed as a by-product.

15 Mixtures of chlorine and hydrogen are explosive over a large range of concentrations; the explosion may be initiated by a spark, by photochemical action or by a catalyst. Under certain conditions reaction of chlorine with ammonia may produce nitrogen trichloride which is spontaneously explosive.

Selection of materials of construction

16 The choice of appropriate materials of construction for chlorine systems should be discussed with the supplier of liquid chlorine and be confirmed only after a detailed survey of all possible variations in operating conditions.

17 A system constructed of steel, which is appropriate for dry chlorine, must itself be dried

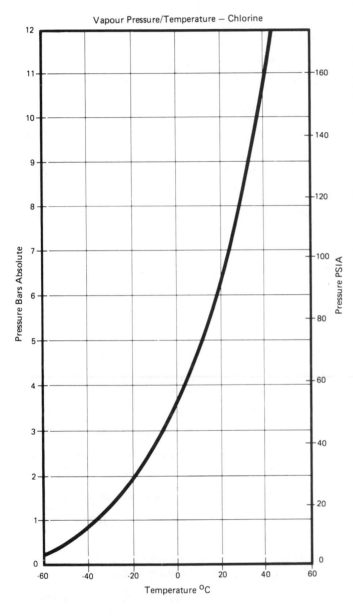

Fig 1.1 Vapour pressure/temperature — Chlorine

8 On cooling below 9.6°C, crystals of chlorine hydrate ($Cl_2.8H_2O$) are deposited. For this reason wet chlorine in process must always be kept above this temperature to avoid the blockages which would otherwise occur as a result of the formation of solid chlorine hydrate.

9 A solution of chlorine in water forms

adequately before commissioning. This may be done by purging with dry air or inert gas until the exit purge has a dew point below −40°C. However, the upper operating temperature must be limited.

18 The use of titanium metal for wet chlorine is satisfactory, provided that the moisture level is always kept high and that control is exercised over the upper operating temperature limit. Maintenance and inspection procedures must include awareness of the possibility of crevice corrosion. However, where titanium is used in plants containing wet chlorine (gas or liquid) consideration should be given to the possibility of a fault condition giving rise to contact between titanium and dry chlorine gas or liquid. If such a fault could possibly arise it may be best to consider alternative construction materials.

19 Materials which are resistant to attack by both wet or dry *gaseous* chlorine at ambient temperatures include glass, stoneware, porcelain, tantalum, ebonite and certain plastics. The use of plastic materials (other than PTFE or related materials) with *liquid* chlorine is generally unsatisfactory.

Toxicological properties

20 The Recommended Exposure Limit for exposure to chlorine is 1ppm (v/v), a concentration which is just detectable by smell. The Short Term Exposure Limit (STEL) is 3 ppm.

21 Irritation of the mucous membranes of the eye and nose, and especially of the throat and lungs, is caused by exposure to chlorine at levels of around 15 ppm. Concentrations of 50 ppm or more are dangerous even for short exposures; they may cause inflammation of the lungs with accumulation of fluid. Such symptoms may not appear immediately, but may occur suddenly up to two days after the exposure of the gas. Contact of liquid chlorine with the skin or mucous membranes can produce burns.

Appendix 2 Outside installations and inside installations (para 14)

1 A chlorine installation is preferably located in the open air; under some circumstances

installation in a building may, however, be appropriate.

2 A building may enclose the entire installation or may only enclose the manlids, valves, associated pipework, gauges and other equipment, leaving the tank itself outside.

3 The advantages, disadvantages and consequent requirements of either choice are listed below.

Outside installations

4 The advantages of outside installation are that:

(a) leakages are not confined and hence the source of leakage is more safely accessible from upwind;

(b) identification of the point of leakage is easier and immediate local corrective action is facilitated;

(c) access for installation and for major maintenance is simpler;

(d) building costs are lower;

5 The disadvantages of outside installation are that:

(a) only from downwind positions may leakages be detected at an early stage;

(b) small leaks particularly those arising from corrosion can develop unnoticed;

(c) maintenance and repair work may have to be carried out in adverse weather conditions;

6 It follows that outdoor installations require

(a) strict vigilance and protection against corrosion;

(b) protection against possible mechanical damage and unauthorised access;

(c) an appropriate emergency system possibly including procedures for the use of water sprays for gas clouds and foam application for liquid chlorine spillage;

(d) consideration of the provision of weather protection of critical areas for maintenance; this could be either a permanent canopy or temporary sheeting;

(e) continuous manning on the site if a release of chlorine could present serious consequences on or off site.

Inside installations

7 The advantages of inside installations are that:

(a) valves and other equipment are protected from rain and snow and provided the building is kept dry, there will be less risk of corrosion;

(b) background heating is possible to help provide dry surroundings and increased chlorine vapour pressure for processes where inert gas/air padding is not acceptable;

(c) controlled ventilation is possible, limiting the external effects if the leak is fairly small;

(d) there is greater likelihood of a monitoring device detecting a leak; this is a particular advantage on unattended plant;

(e) the installation is protected from accidental mechanical damage, explosion or fire in adjacent plant or interference by unauthorised persons.

8 The disadvantages of inside installations are that:

(a) a medium or major leak will result in a high local concentration of gas and therefore emergency access has to be made to a confined toxic atmosphere;

(b) the point of leakage may be difficult to identify owing to lack of dispersion and mist formation;

(c) if the building is heated, there will be greater ground evaporation and flash from a liquid leak;

(d) access for maintenance is likely to be more difficult.

9 It follows that indoor installations require:

(a) adequate forced ventilation systems, including initiation from operating points outside as well as inside the building;

(b) careful consideration of plant layout and provision of adequate escape routes and escape respiratory equipment;

(c) appropriate emergency systems, including provision of self-contained breathing apparatus in addition to normal canister respirators, and protective clothing.

Appendix 3 Publications and standards

Legislation, and publications of the Health and Safety Executive and the Health and Safety Commission.

Advisory Committee on Major Hazards

First report 1976
Second report 1979
Third report 1984

Legislation

Factories Act 1961
Chemical Works Regulations 1922
Alkali &c Works Regulation Act 1906
   (as amended by the Health & Safety (Emissions into the Atmosphere) Regulations 1983)
Health and Safety at Work etc Act 1974
Dangerous Substances (Conveyance by Road in Road Tankers and Tank Containers) Regulations 1981.

Notification of Installations Handling Hazardous Substances Regulations 1982.

Reporting of Injuries, Diseases and Dangerous Occurrences Regulations 1985.

Control of Industrial Major Accident Hazards Regulations (CIMAH Regulations) 1984.

Proposed legislation (Publication of consultative document)

Control of Substances Hazardous to Health Regulations.

Pressure Systems and Transportable Gas Containers Regulations (1984).

Advisory Codes, Guidance Notes, Approved Codes

Guidance Note EH 40, *Occupational exposure limits* 1985
Guidance Note GS 4, *Safety in pressure testing*.
Proposed Approved Codes of Practice for the Pressure Systems and Transportable Gas Containers Regulations
Approved Code of Practice for the Operational Provisions of the Dangerous Substances

(Conveyance by Road in Road Tankers and Tank Containers) Regulations 1981
Guidance Note GS 5 *Entry into confined spaces*
Guidance Note MS 18 *Health surveillance by routine procedures*
Guidance Note MS 20 *Pre-employment health screening.*
Booklet HS(G)25 *Further guidance on emergency plans*
Notes on Best Practicable Means, BPM 18, *Chlorine works.*

Chemical Industries Association

Codes of Practice for Chemicals with Major Hazards — Chlorine.
Major Hazards-Memorandum of Guidance on Extensions to Existing Chemical Plant Introducing a Major Hazard.
Inter-Company Collaboration for Chlorine Emergencies.
Safety Audits – A Guide for the Chemical Industry.
Is it Toxic?
A Guide to Hazard and Operability Studies.
Recommended Procedures for Handling Major Emergencies.

Chlorine Institute, Inc.
70 W40 Street, New York, NY 10018, USA.

Chlorine Manual (4th Edition, 1969).

National Institute for Occupational Safety and Health (NIOSH)

US Department of Health, Education and Welfare
Public Health Service
Centre for Disease Control
NIOSH
Cincinnati
OHIO 45226 USA.

Criteria for a Recommended Standard: Occupational Exposure to Chlorine

British Standards Specifications

BS 3947: 1976	*Specification for Liquid Chlorine*
BS 5355: 1976	*Specification for Filling Ratios and Developed Pressures for Liquefiable and Permanent Gases.*
BS 5500: 1982	*Unfired Fusion Welded Pressure Vessels.*
BS 3351: 1971	*Piping Systems for Petroleum Refineries and Petrochemical Plants.*
BS 1560:	*Steel Pipe Flanges and Flanged Fittings (Nominal Size ½ in to 24 in) for the Petroleum Industry.*
BS 1560: Part 2:	*1970 Metric Dimensions.*
BS 4882: 1973	*Bolting for Flanges and Pressure Containing Purposes*
BS 2815: 1973	*Compressed Asbestos Fibre Jointing.*
BS 2915:	*Bursting Discs and Bursting Disc Assemblies.*
BS 1501:	*Steels for Fired and Unfired Pressure Vessels. Plates.*
BS 1501: Part 1:	*1980 Carbon and Carbon Manganese Steels.* Imperial Units.
BS 1501: Part 2:	1970 *Alloy Steels.* Imperial Units.
Addendum No. 1	(1973) to BS 1501: Part 2: 1970.
Addendum No. 2	(1975) to BS 1501: Part 2: 1970.
BS 1501: Part 3:	*1973 Corrosion and Heat Resisting Steel.* Imperial Units.
BS 1501-1:	*1958 Steels for use in the Chemical Petrochemical and Allied Industries.*

Chlorine — Its Manufacture, Properties and Uses ACS Monograph Series J S Sconce (1962).

Le Chlore, Institut National de Recherche et de Sécurité, Paris 1978.

Bureau International Technique du Chlore, Avenue Louise 250, Bte 72, 1050 Brussels Belgium.

Reports covering recommendations by the Chloprine Storage and Transport Sub-Committee

Addresses of chlorine producers

Hays Chemicals Ltd, Murgatroyd Division, Sandbach, Cheshire CW11 9PZ, United Kingdom.

Imperial Chemical Industries PLC, Mond Division, P O Box No 13, The Heath, Runcorn, Cheshire WA7 4QF, United Kingdom.

Staveley Chemicals Ltd, Staveley Works, Chesterfield S43 2PB, United Kingdom.

The Associated Octel Company Ltd, P O Box 17, Ellesmere Port, Wirral, Cheshire L65 4HF, United Kingdom.

Appendix 4 Procedures for discharging road tanks of chlorine (see para 40).

NOTE This typical procedure assumes that the storage tanks and associated items of equipment have a safe working pressure of at least 175 psig. If this is not the case then the air system pressure, relief devices etc will have to be altered to suit and delivery systems arranged so as to be capable of working within the limits of all the components.

Action 1 Safety. The procedures are designed to minimise potential leaks by ensuring that all newly made joints are tested by gas pressure with at most only a small amount of liquid. During these test operations a gas mask must be worn. Similarly a gas mask must be worn during the disconnecting operation when there is a possibility of the escape of a small quantity of residual vapour. During the rest of the operations it should be kept readily available.

Customer 2 Will operate all valves on the bulk storage installation including the filling pipe.

Driver 3 On arrival at the works will weigh off on the site weighbridge and proceed to the discharge berth.

Driver 4 Will position the tanker at the · discharge berth and place the chocks in position to prevent movement.

Driver 5 Will present his notes to a responsible official.

In signing these notes the customer accepts the responsibility that there is sufficient space available in the storage tank to receive the full load from the road tank and that the installation is fit and ready for the discharge to proceed.

Driver 6 Will tell the *plant operator* the weight of chlorine in the tanker so that he can determine where the final reading will be on the weighing machine dial or load cell indicator.

Customer 7 Will ensure that any warning notices are displayed and barriers are erected, and will operate any safety interlocks associated with the road vehicle berth.

Customer 8 Where there are two or more tanks the customer will determine which tank is to receive and check that the storage tank cannot be overfilled. The pressure on the tank before commencing discharge should not normally be greater than 85 psig but in very hot weather it may be higher.

Customer 9 Will ensure *before* discharge that the vent valve on the stock tank filling pipe is CLOSED.

Driver 10 Will (wearing a gas mask) remove both caps from the road tank valves and the customers filling arms and test for leaks. Using new CAF joint rings connect both air supply and liquid discharge arms to the appropriate valves on the tanker.

Joint 11 Wearing a gas mask, apply pressure to the discharge connection, preferably by briefly opening the valve to the stock tank. An alternative, less desirable, method is to open the tanker discharge valve *momentarily*. The driver (wearing a gas mask) test joints on the discharge pipe using ammonia water. If satisfactory, the driver can remove his gas mask and then request the plant operator to open the valve on the stock filling line after the drop arm. The liquid valve on the tanker can be *slowly opened* to fill the delivery line: the pressure observed will be the pressure on the road tanker.

Joint 12 Start the air compressor and when the line pressure is 120 psig open to the road tanker. When the road tanker pressure (as indicated on the filling pipe to the stock tank) is 25 psig above that of the stock tank request the *plant operator* to open the valve to the appropriate stock tank and commence discharge of the road tank.

Joint 13 Observe the discharge of the road tanker is proceeding satisfactorily by reference to the weighing machine dial or load cell indicator.

Joint 14 Observe the stock tank pressure as the discharge is proceeding. Should this rise to 90 psi request the customer to crack open the vent valve on the tank to reduce the pressure.

Joint 15 Indication that the road tanker has been completely discharged is:

(a) fluctuation of pressure gauge on the liquid chlorine delivery line;

(b) equalisation of tanker and line pressure readings.

Joint 16 Close the liquid valve and the air valve on the road tanker. Shut down the air compressor. Ask the *plant operator* to close the storage tank valve and vent valve on the stock tank if this has been opened. Ask the *operator* to crack open the vent valve on the stock tank filling pipe. When the hoar-frost begins to disappear and the pressure gauge indicates zero ask the operator to close the valve at the end of the liquid discharge pipe. Close filling line vent valve.

Customer 17 Crack open the vent valve on the stock tank for about one minute in order to check that the level of liquid chlorine in the tank is below the bottom of the vent dip pipe. This operation also vents non-condensable gases. Check that the pressure in the tank is reasonable for the temperature of the chlorine.

Driver 18 Wearing a gas mask, disconnect the liquid discharge pipe from the tanker, replace the sealing plug and swivel back to the staging. Tell the *plant operator* that the vent can be closed. The short connecting pipes from the liquid and air valves can be disconnected, both valves sealed and the tanker dome securely fastened.

Customer 19 *Under no circumstances allow any section of the pipeline to be left unvented with liquid chlorine trapped betwen closed valves.*

Driver 20 Before leaving the storage plant ask the designated responsible person to sign the advice note and consignment note after the words "all operations connected with the discharge of the road tank have been completed satisfactorily". Hand one copy to the responsible person. On leaving the works weigh again on the site weighbridge.

Appendix 5 Summary: Types of vaporiser (See paras 170 to 172)

Chlorine vaporisers may be divided into four basic types:

1 Vertical tube bundle
2 Coiled tube immersed in a heating bath
3 Concentric tube
4 Kettle-type evaporator

Vertical tube bundle (Type 1)

Advantages of this type of system are

(a) small overall size for relatively large heat transfer surfaces;

(b) easy maintenance;

(c) for the mode of operation in which the chlorine is in tubes, the liquid chlorine is automatically displaced by over-pressure when the vapour supply to the consuming plant is shut off.

Disadvantages of this type of system are

(a) for the mode of operation in which the chlorine is in the tubes, there is a risk of instability at high throughput owing to variation of liquid levels and a possibility of corrosion in the region of the liquid surface;

(b) for the mode of operation in which the chlorine is in the shell, it is difficult to dry out the shell.

Coiled tube immersed in a heating bath (Type 2)

Advantages of this type of vaporiser are

(a) it is simple to maintain and operate;

(b) the long coil generally ensures adequate superheating;

(c) there are no problems with differential thermal expansion;

(d) plug flow operation avoids concentration of high boiling impurities;

(e) drying out of equipment before use is relatively easy;

(f) liquid chlorine is automatically displaced when the vapour supply to the consuming plant is shut off.

Disadvantages of this type of vaporiser are

(a) low throughput;

(b) external corrosion of the tube can easily occur, especially near the liquid surface;

(c) irregular internal erosion of the coil may occur;

(d) internal inspection and cleaning of the coil is difficult.

Concentric tube units (Type 3)

Advantages of this type of system are

(a) simple construction with minimum welding requirements;

(b) ease of maintenance and operation;

(c) easy provision of adequate corrosion allowance;

(d) automatic displacement of liquid chlorine when the vapour supply to the consuming plant is shut off;

(e) plug-flow operation above a certain minimum flow avoids concentration of high boiling impurities.

Disadvantages of this type of system are

(a) potential instability of operation at high and low throughput;

(b) limitation of unit capacity owing to relatively small heat transfer surface area;

(c) greater difficulty in obtaining adequate superheating of the chlorine.

Kettle-type evaporator (Type 4)

Advantages of this type of system are

(a) It can be designed for large throughput;

(b) allowance for thermal expansion can easily be made;

(c) operation is stable provided that either the level of chlorine in the kettle is controlled or the pressure of chlorine fed to the vaporiser is controlled.

Disadvantages of this type of system are

(a) since the vessel contains a relatively large amount of liquid chlorine, the occurrence of leakage or the development of excess pressure in the vessel poses a greater potential hazard;

(b) a relief system with a large capacity is required unless the vaporiser is designed for high pressure;

(c) operation can result in concentration of nitrogen trichloride; the purging process required to reduce this hazard may be difficult to carry out on consumer premises;

(d) drying of the equipment on the chlorine side is difficult;

(e) dismantling of the tubes is difficult and requires a large space.

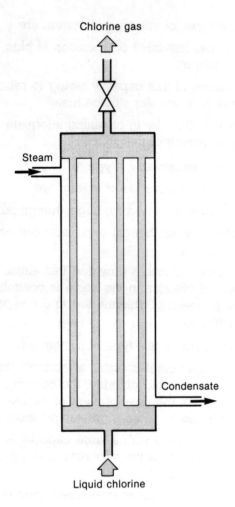

Type 1a   Shell and tube

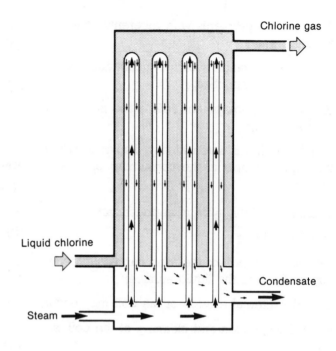

Type 1b   Steam bayonet

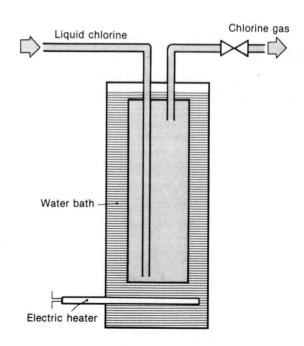

Type 1c   Hot water bath

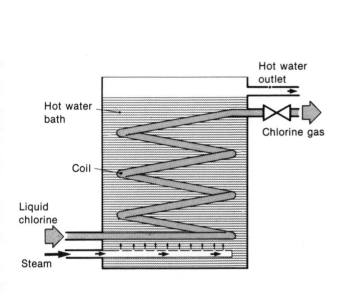

Type 2. Coil tube immersed in heating bath

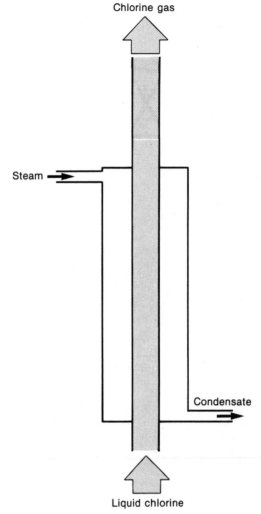

Type 3 Concentric tube unit

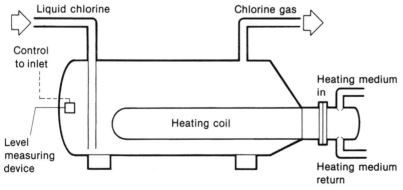

Type 4 Kettle type evaporator

Appendix 5 (c)

Storage of anhydrous ammonia under pressure in the United Kingdom

(Reproduced from Health and Safety Executive: *Storage of anhydrous ammonia under pressure in the United Kingdom,* Health and Safety series booklet HS(G) 30 (London, HMSO, 1986).)

Contents

Foreword

A code of practice for the storage of anhydrous ammonia under pressure in the United Kingdom was issued by the Chemical Industries Association (CIA) in 1980. The code covered storage in spherical and cylindrical vessels. Since that time there has been continuing development of the knowledge within the industry, particularly with respect to the measures required to avoid stress corrosion cracking in spherical vessels. It has therefore been decided to update Part 1 of the 1980 CIA code to incorporate this improved knowledge. The opportunity has also been taken to update Part 2.

This guidance was prepared jointly by the HSE, the Ammonia Product Group of the Chemical Industries Association and ICI PLC. It is based on development of the 1980 CIA code which it now supersedes. It is not intended to constitute a design code.

Grateful acknowledgement is made to those who contributed.

General information

Scope

1 This guidance covers basic requirements for the design of spherical and cylindrical pressure vessels and essential fittings for safe operation and certain operational matters.
Recommendations are made regarding siting, bunding, training, safety equipment, inspection and emergency procedures.

Security

2 In addition to observing safe standards for the construction and operation of an ammonia storage installation, close attention shall be paid to overall site security arrangements. (See para 88).

3 Anhydrous (water free) ammonia is a gas at ordinary temperatures and pressures. The term 'anhydrous ammonia' as used here refers to ammonia in gaseous or liquefied form; it is not to be confused with 'aqueous ammonia' which is a solution of ammonia in water. Throughout this document anhydrous ammonia is referred to simply as ammonia.

4 It may be liquefied by reducing its temperatures to minus 33°C, or by moderately increasing its pressure. These properties allow it to be stored as a liquid in various types of container. Three methods of storage are currently used, the choice primarily depending on the quantity to be stored.

(a) *Storage at ambient temperature and equivalent pressure in cylindrical vessels.* This method is used when relatively small quantities are involved as practical manufacturing and transport considerations limit the size of the vessel.

(b) *Storage under pressure in spherical vessels.* Spherical vessels can be constructed on site to hold several thousand tonnes of ammonia. However, very large spheres are uncommon, and most vessels are in the range 500 to 3000 tonnes. Refrigeration equipment may be used to lower the temperature of the ammonia and in such cases the vessels operate at a lower temperature than ambient temperature vessels; this type of storage is often referred to as 'semi-pressure' or 'semi-refrigerated.'

(c) *Storage at atmospheric pressure.* Ammonia may be stored at atmospheric pressure by reducing the temperature to -33°C. In this condition it may be contained in cylindrical flat-bottomed tanks, since the pressure of the tank must withstand is only that imposed by the head of liquid. In practice, a slight positive pressure is maintained, to simplify the operation of the refrigeration system. This method of storage is generally considered economical when quantities in excess of 5000 tonnes are involved. Many tanks have been built in the 20000-35000 tonnes range with a few in excess of 35000 tonnes.

5 Ammonia stored at pressure has considerable potential energy and should a rupture of the primary container occur, liquid will flash into a vapour spontaneously as the thermodynamic state

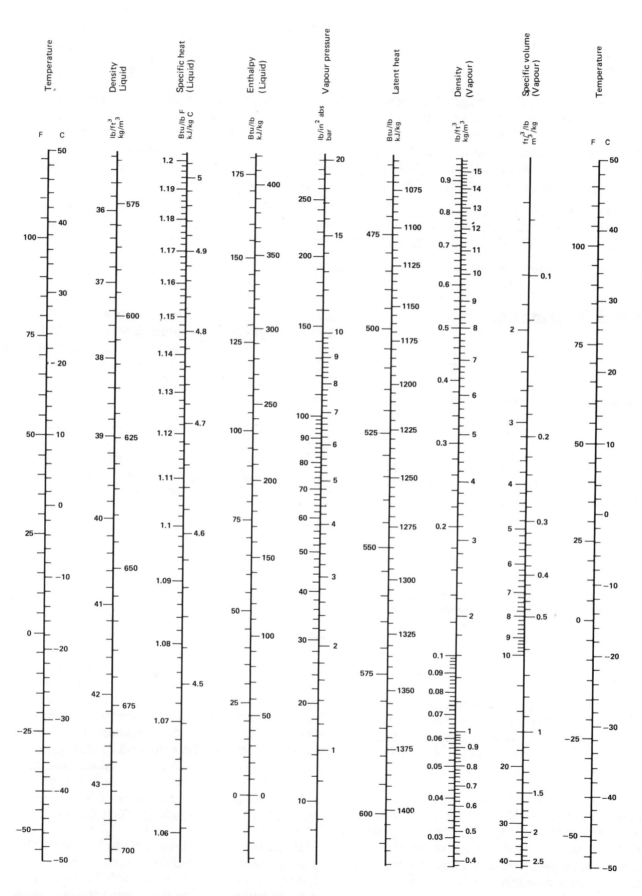

Nomograph to show some properties of ammonia

of the ammonia adjusts itself to the diminished pressure. Since this adiabatic flash evaporation takes place almost instantaneously throughout the bulk of the liquid most of the contents of a ruptured pressure vessel will enter the atmosphere either as a vapour or as a fine liquid aerosol. For this reason the design of the primary container should be of a standard which virtually eliminates the possibility of a major failure; this guidance has been written on that premise. The design of equipment for storing and handling substances such as ammonia under pressure are well understood and the chance of a major escape is very remote. However, when ammonia is in association with certain other materials the possibility of stress corrosion cracking presents particular problems.

6 As ammonia is a hazardous chemical in both liquid and gaseous forms, even in small quantities safety is a prime consideration in any storage installation.

7 Everyone concerned with the storage of ammonia should be familiar with the following:

(a) At ordinary temperatures and atmospheric pressure anhydrous ammonia is a gas, but it may be stored in liquid form under pressure. the pressure will depend on the storage temperature. For example, at an ambient temperature of 20°C the pressure will be approximately 7.5 bar gauge; at a typical semi-refrigerated storage temperature of 0°C the pressure will be approximately 3 bar gauge. It may also be stored at atmospheric pressure in liquid form by reducing the temperature to its atmospheric boiling point of -33°C.

(b) Ammonia gas is pungent and colourless, and serves as its own warning agent. Normally it is lighter than air and in the open will disperse by virtue of its own buoyancy. Gas produced from liquid may mix with air, however, to produce heavier-than-air mixtures which will stay close to the ground.

(c) Ammonia will not readily attack carbon steels, but reacts strongly with copper and alloys containing copper. The reaction is accelerated if water is present, even in minute quantities. Only those steel and non-ferrous alloys proved to be

suitable for ammonia service may be used for fittings and ancillary or adjacent equipment. The use of copper and alloy containing copper in any equipment in other plant located in the vicinity of the ammonia storage installation should be carefully considered.

(d) Ammonia combines with mercury to form explosive compounds, so instruments containing mercury must not be used if ammonia can come into contact with the mercury.

(e) The flammable limits of ammonia are from 16 to 25% by volume in air with an ignition temperature of 651°C. Ignition of such mixtures is difficult, but if it occurs in a confined space an explosion may result. The risk of this happening is low, therefore ammonia installations are not regarded as significant fire hazards.

8 Ammonia is extremely soluble in water and some organic solvents, heat being liberated during solution. The main physical constants are as follows:

Atmospheric boiling point	- 33.35°C
Freezing point	- 77.70°C
Critical temperature	132.40°C
Critical pressure	114.25 bar absolute
Latent heat (1 atm, minus 33°C)	1370.76 kj/kg
Liquid density See Appendix 1	
Vapour pressure See Appendix 1	
Vapour density See Appendix 1	
Flammable limits (% by volume in air)	16 to 25%
Auto ignition temperature	651°C

Health hazards

9 At low concentrations in air, ammonia vapour irritates the eyes, nose and throat. Inhalation of high concentrations produces a sensation of suffocation, quickly causes burning of the respiratory tract and may be fatal. Liquid ammonia causes severe burns on contact with the skin. Severe damage can be caused by exposure to high gas concentrations or direct contact with the liquid. A summary of symptoms and exposure periods associated with specific ammonia vapour concentrations is given in Table 1.

Table 1 Health hazards

Vapour concentration (ppm v/v)	General effect	Exposure period
5	Odour detectable by most persons.	
25		Recommended exposure Limit - Long term - 8h TWA.
35		Recommended Exposure Limit - Short term 10 minutes TWA.
50	Irritation just detectable by most persons but not persistent.	
70	No prolonged effect for average worker	Maximum exposure for long periods not permitted.
400-700	Immediate nose and throat irritation.	½-1h exposure causes no serious effect.
1700	Severe coughing, severe eye, nose and throat irritation.	Could be fatal after ½ hour.
2000-5000	Severe coughing, severe eye, nose and throat irritation.	Could be fatal after ¼ hour.
5000-10000	Respiratory spasm. Rapid asphyxia.	Fatal within minutes.

10 Attention is drawn to the requirements of the Health and Safety at Work etc Act 1974 (HSW Act), and associated regulations particularly with reference to paras 89 to 97 of this guidance*.

11 It is recommended that this guidance should apply to all new installations designed after 1 January 1987 and to all other installations as far as is reasonably practicable, although it is recognised that existing installations may not meet all the recommendations. Any required modifications will depend on individual circumstances and a responsible decision will be needed on the nature and timing of the changes to be made to equipment or procedures. Consideration should be given to further developments which may have taken place since the preparation of this guidance.

Spherical vessels

Siting

12 Spheres should be sited as far away as possible from residential areas, public buildings,

*Health and Safety at Work Act, 1974. HMSO.

roads, railways and airports, taking due account of the direction of the prevailing wind.

13 The choice of site should take into account existing plans for future development in the area.

14 In many cases the siting of spheres will require planning permission, so local authorities should consult The Health and Safety Executive (HSE) about the safety aspects of the siting in relation to people in neighbouring land uses. The HSE advice will take account of the details of the installation and the size of the neighbouring population. It is unlikely that HSE would advise favourably for a proposal which places a sphere within a few hundred metres of land uses where there are likely to be substantial concentrations of housing. It is therefore recommended that manufacturers consult the HSE at the earliest opportunity.

15 The proximity of roads and railways carrying fast traffic should be taken into account. Suitable crash barriers should be erected, where necessary, to avoid the risk of damage in the event of vehicle collision. In any case, spheres should not be less than 25 metres from busy site roads or through railways.

16 It is not practicable to guard against the risk of crashing aircraft but it should be noted that most major crashes occur during landing or take-off. Spheres should therefore not be sited near airports.

17 Recognition should be given to the presence of, or proposals for, plant or processes involving flammable and explosive materials. The ammonia sphere should be located so that radiation from a fire, or debris from an explosion, involving such plant or processes, should not cause damage to the sphere.

18 The storage area should be located so that it is possible for road vehicles to reach it from two directions.

Sphere design

Design code

19 The sphere should, as a minimum requirement, be designed, fabricated, erected, inspected and tested in accordance with at least the equivalent standard to BS 5500*, for a Category 1 vessel, with due regard to Appendix D of that standard, including 100% magnetic particle inspection of all internal welds and any additional requirements of this part of this booklet.

Design conditions

20 The sphere should be designed to sustain stresses imposed when it is filled to the maximum permitted level and a pressure superimposed equal to the vapour pressure of the ammonia at the maximum design temperature together with any additional pressures which may result from the presence of inert gases, and external loads etc generally as defined in Appendix A of BS 5500*.

21 The minimum design temperature should be the lowest temperature the sphere can achieve in service. Preferably this should be taken as -33°C but in no case should it be taken as warmer than -10°C.

22 Full thermal stress relief should be applied to all new spheres after construction and to existing

* BS 5500 *Specifications for unfired fusion welded pressure vessels.*

spheres which have previously not been used for ammonia. This procedure should take due recognition of the present state of knowledge and should ensure that any doubts concerning the stress relief of complete very large spheres have been resolved.

Materials of construction

23 To minimise the risk of stress corrosion cracking the welding consumables should overmatch the tensile properties of the plates by the smallest practicable amount. Furthermore, the tensile strength of the plates should not be allowed to exceed the maximum detailed in the plate specifications. The minimum specified yield strength of the steel from which the vessel is made should not exceed 350 N/mm^2. The individual plates for use in the sphere construction should be identified during the manufacture and testing and marked accordingly.

24 Hard stamping of the plate material should not be allowed.

25 Copper and copper-bearing alloys should *not* be used. (See para 7(c)).

Sphere supports

26 Most existing spheres are supported on legs but other methods are possible including circumferential ring supports or part of a spherical concrete dish or 'egg cup'. The supports should be designed to withstand the weight of the vessel when filled with water. Hollow tubular supports should be completely sealed against water and air which would lead to progressive internal corrosion. Particular care should be taken to ensure that water is not trapped in the supports during construction. The height above ground chosen for the sphere will depend partly on the ease of access required to the bottom fittings and partly on the type of pump to be used for discharging the ammonia. The sphere will need to be high enough to provide adequate nett positive suction head (NPSH) for satisfactory operation of the pump, although the height may be reduced by putting the pump in a pit.

Sphere attachments

27 *Openings - general* Openings should be in the form of flanged nozzles or pads provided with studs or bolts. The welds of adjacent openings should not be closer than 50 mm. Screwed connections should not be used nor should nozzles smaller than 50 NS.

28 All nozzles should be grouped together in the top and bottom crown plates. All nozzles to which pipes are connected, including spare nozzles, should have isolating valves mounted directly on the nozzle and bottom outlets should have two such valves closer together.

29 *Access openings* Any access openings should be in the top crown plate of the sphere. It is recommended that the covers for access openings be hinged or fitted with davits to avoid the need for lifting tackle. The minimum inside diameter of any access opening should be 600 mm.*

30 *Relief valves* At least two pressure relief valves should be fitted, which should meet the requirements of BS 6759 Part 3†. If the sphere is not capable of withstanding full vacuum, a vacuum break valve should be fitted. Separate pressure and vacuum valves may be used or, alternatively, they may be of the combined pressure/vacuum type. There should be enough relief valves so that any one valve can be removed for examination or maintenance without losing protection of the sphere. An isolation valve should be fitted between the sphere and each relief valve, and a system should be incorporated so that only one valve can be isolated at any one time.

31 The pressure relief valves should be provided with outlet pipes independently extended to such a point that the discharge will not be hazardous to a person standing on the top platform. The pipework downstream of the relief valve should be designed so that a relief valve can be removed in a safe manner. The outlet

pipes should be designed to prevent the ingress of rain water and should have drain holes.

32 The inlet to the relief valve should be so designed or protected as to prevent the blockage of the inlet by internal fittings, for example level floats, which may become accidentally detached.

33 *Level indicators* At least two independent level indicating devices shall be fitted, at least one of which is accurate to within 12 mm. For this, a float-and-tape type (preferably with a stilling tube) or a float guided on a stainless steel tube containing a magnetic follower, is acceptable. As a back-up gauge, a device actuated by the differential pressure of the hydrostatic head of liquid in the sphere is acceptable, but this needs care in design and positioning to ensure that the 'liquid leg' remains full at all times.

34 *High level alarm* A separate high level alarm, independent of any level indicator, should be fitted. It should be set to operate at a level which gives time for effective action.

35 *Filling nozzle* It is recommended that the filling nozzle be provided with an internal deflector to ensure, as far as possible, that the incoming flow does not impinge on the level float nor cause droplets of liquid to be drawn into the vapour take-off to the refrigeration plant.

36 *Earthing bosses* Spheres should be provided with two earthing bosses in accordance with Fig 22 of BS 4741* except that austenitic steel should be used instead of brass for the studs and washers, and the copper conductor should be wrapped to prevent contact with ammonia. On spheres supported on legs the bosses should be on two legs as nearly diametrically opposite as possible.

37 *Other nozzles* Consideration should be given to the provision of a suitable number of spare nozzles to cover future requirements.

38 *Valves on outlet nozzles* All bottom outlet nozzles should be provided with internal valves which can be remotely operated and which

*Section 30 Factories Act 1961, and Regulation 7, Chemical Works Regulations 1922.

† BS 6759: Part 3: *Specification for Safety Valves for Process Fluids.*

* BS 4741: 1971 *Vertical cylindrical welded steel storage tanks for low temperature service - single wall tanks for temperatures down to - 50°C.* British Standards Institution.

close on failure of operating power or any other fault in the operating system. Alternatively, external remote operated valves may be used provided they are made of austenitic stainless steel and bolted directly to the outlet nozzle.

39   If there is a single bottom outlet fitted with an internal valve, consideration should be given to the provision of a manually operated means of releasing a seized valve to restore normal operation.

Constructional requirements

40   *Preparation and protection of plates*   Before being despatched to site, all materials should be appropriately prepared and protected against corrosion.

41   *Welding procedures - procedure and welder qualification*   These should be the subject of agreement between the purchaser and supplier but should, as a minimum, meet the requirements of BS 5500, Appendix E.

42   *Stress relief of plates with welded mountings*   The top and bottom crown plates shall be stress-relieved after completion of all nozzle and attachment welds, before despatch to site. Plates having leg connections or other support brackets and any other plate with a welded connection, must be similarly stress-relieved. In the case of leg connections the part heat treated shall include, as a minimum, a length of leg outside any lagging equal to its diameter.

43   *Nozzle welding details*   All shell nozzle welds should be full penetration welds to BS 5500. Figures E.2(3)a and b, (10)b and c, (11), (12), (20)b, (21), (22), (23)b, (24)e, f and g, (25)a, b and c, should not be used. Welding neck flanges, Figure E.2 (27)a, are preferred to the slip-on types.

44   *Temporary attachments*   All temporary attachments should be carefully removed after use, ie *not* knocked-off, and scars made good and ground smooth. Such scars should be tested by magnetic particle crack detection methods after grinding. This work should be done before stress relieving.

45   *Permanent attachments*   A central platform

should be provided on the top of the sphere, big enough to give convenient access to all the top mountings. This platform should be carried on brackets which are welded to the crown plate before it is stress-relieved; attachments should have full penetration welds.

46   Access stairs should not be welded to the sphere.

47   *Access stairs*   A stairway should be provided to give access to the top of the sphere and it is preferable that this is independent of the sphere. Alternatively, the stairs may be fixed to the sphere support legs, but no part of them should be welded to the pressure-containing shell. Where appropriate, allowance should be made for possible differential settlement between the sphere and the stairs.

48   The stairway should have intermediate landings every 16 treads and should be at least 750 mm wide, complete with handrails and toeboards.

Sphere testing and examination

49   The testing of the sphere should include filling with water and testing in accordance with Clause 5.8.3 of BS 5500. All spheres should be thoroughly inspected during construction in accordance with the fabrication code requirements. In addition:

(a)   100% magnetic particle crack detection examination should be carried out on all internal welds and at the location of removed toggle cleats, temporary attachments and scars before commissioning (see footnote to para 125 for preferred method). This will provide base data for subsequent examinations;

(b)   full visual inspection and magnetic particle crack detection examination along at least 10% of each butt weld should be made on the external surface of the sphere.

(c)   ultrasonic testing: The wall thickness of the shell and nozzles shall be measured ultrasonically and the nozzle-to-shell attachment welds flaw detected.

(d)   if it is intended to use acoustic emission testing at a later stage, a reference base should be taken during hydrotesting of new spheres.

Foundations

Design code

50 The foundations for an ammonia sphere and stairway should be designed to comply with accepted good practice and generally conform to the requirements of BS Code of Practice for Foundations CP2004:1972. The foundations should be designed to withstand the weight of the sphere when filled with water.

Settlement

51 The design should take into account the characteristics and allowable bearing pressures of various types of ground, particular attention being directed to likely settlement. It is important to ensure that the difference in settlement between the empty and the loaded sphere is small enough to be acceptable to pipework connections, so that no significant loads (particularly cyclic loads) are transmitted to the sphere nozzles.

Testing

52 When the sphere is being tested hydraulically it is strongly recommended that deflection measurements are taken at four points during the filling and emptying procedures to check that the settlement is acceptable.

Bunding

53 A bund wall should be provided, not less than one metre high, positioned outside the sphere radius and sphere support structure. The capacity of the bund should, as a minimum, be 20% of the capacity of the sphere*.

54 The sphere support structure should be protected against vehicle collision by trapping barriers of adequate strength or by the bund wall.

* The possibility of retaining liquid ammonia escaping from a sphere in a bund depends on the storage pressure and the circumstances of the incident. If a leak occurs where the ammonia is contained in a sphere under pressure, some of the contents will escape into the atmosphere but some liquid may collect on the ground. The bund wall should preferably be situated approximately one sphere radius outside the sphere equator.

55 The floor of the bund should be of impermeable material. Provision should be made for the collection of liquid in a low point drain pit discharging via a flanged valve which should normally be closed. Water may then be drained as required and other material removed by means of a temporary pumping system.

56 Normal access to equipment mounted on the sphere should be from outside the bund.

Ancillary equipment

General

57 Detailed recommendations for pumping and refrigeration equipment associated with an ammonia storage facility are outside the scope of this guidance. The techniques used are well established and there are many reputable manufacturers who will supply suitable equipment. In this section, therefore, attention is drawn only to details of particular significance.

Pressure vessels and heat exchangers

58 Pressure vessels and heat exchangers should, as a minimum, meet the requirements of at least equivalent to the relevant British Standard, eg, BS 5500 and BS 3274*. In both cases materials should be in accordance with Section 2 of BS 5500.

59 All dished ends should be provided in the normalised condition.

60 Pressure vessels and heat exchanges should be designed to withstand the most arduous combination of pressure and temperature which may be encountered during normal or emergency circumstances, with regard, where necessary, to the special requirements of sub-zero temperature design.

61 There should be no copper or copper bearing alloys, either in the vessels or in fittings.

62 Only steels having minimum specified yield strengths up to 350 N/mm^2 should be used. Welds in fabricated items including pipework, which come into contact with liquid ammonia,

* BS3274:1960 *Tubular heat exchanges for general purposes.* British Standards Institution.

should be stress relieved*. Items in contact with ammonia gas should be stress relieved if required by the notes to Table 3 para 2.

63 Compressors may be of the reciprocating or rotary type, and both may be lubricated or oil-free†. Oil lubricated compressors will result in some contamination of the ammonia, and the level which can be tolerated will influence the choice of compressor.

Pumps

64 The most frequently used type is the centrifugal horizontal multi-stage pump fitted with a mechanical seal followed by a conventional gland with soft packing.

65 A glandless canned motor pump is equally acceptable‡.

---

* Some steels, but not austenitics, are prone to stress corrosion cracking in the presence of liquid ammonia contaminated with oxygen. As ammonia gas is drawn off the sphere and re-liquefied, non-condensibles (including oxygen) are inevitably concentrated in the liquid in the pipework and vessels of the refrigerated plant. Since thermal stress relief inhibits the process of stress corrosion cracking, stress relief is applied to these items.

† Rotary compressors normally use oil for sealing and cooling, and not primarily for lubrication.

‡ Pumps will only work satisfactorily, particularly when the sphere liquid level is low, if adequate Net Positive Suction Head is available. The NPSH requirements of the pump selected should be ascertained at the design stage and the sphere raised sufficiently above the ground to provide the necessary head to enable the sphere to be completely emptied. It should be noted that long suction lines effectively reduce NPSH. Inadequate insulation and/or poor means of venting the suction lines leads to vapour formation and may result in vapour locking of the pump. If, for some reason, insufficient head can be provided for a pump mounted at ground level, additional effective head can be achieved by either putting the pump in a pit or by using a vertical canned pump in a borehole. In the latter case the pump must be protected against possible damage from frost heave. (Frost Heaves and Storage Vessel Foundation. CEP Technical Manual - Safety in ammonia plants and related facilities, Volume 12.)

The advantage of a glandless canned motor pump is that it is a completely sealed unit and therefore never gives rise to unpleasant working conditions due to minor gland leaks, which frequently occur with conventionally glanded pumps. This type of pump, is therefore, particularly appropriate when men are working continuously in the area, ie, road and rail loading stations.

---

66 The liquid outlet line from the sphere to the pump should slope uniformly, be well insulated and kept as short as possible consistent with sphere foundation movements, and movements caused by thermal cycling, not causing excessive stresses in the pipework.

67 A bypass line should be arranged to return part of the pump's output to the sphere to cool the pump, should the delivery valve be closed while the pump is still running. The orifice plate or valve which controls the return flow should be as close to the sphere as possible and the return line should discharge into the sphere vapour space*.

68 A device should be fitted to indicate loss of flow through the pump, due to vapour locking or any other cause. This may be a differential pressure or a low flow trip.

69 Materials of construction should be suitable for sub-zero temperatures. (see para 80). Exposed copper or copper-bearing alloys should not be used anywhere on the pump (see para 7c).

Piping: Design

70 (a) Pipework should be designed in accordance with BS 3351† or ANSI B31.3‡, and any additional requirements of this section of this guidance.

(b) Piping, valves and other fittings should be designed for the most arduous foreseeable combination of pressure and temperature conditions.

(c) Any increase in metal strength which occurs at temperatures below 0°C should be ignored when determining design stress values.

---

* When an orifice is used to reduce flow, flashing will take place downstream of the orifice. This will result in two-phase flow, which may cause vibrations in the pipework, leading to subsequent fatigue failure. It is, therefore, preferable to place the orifice close the the sphere, thus ensuring that the liquid phase is maintained in the pipework.

† BS 3351: 1971 Piping systems for petroleum refeineries and petro-chemical plants. British Standard Institution.

‡ ANSI B31.3 Code for pressure piping - Chemical plant and petroleum refinery piping. American National Standard 1976.

(d) Piping should be correctly aligned to avoid the imposition of stresses on bolting up but this is not intended to prevent the application of the correct initial preset designed to reduce stresses due to thermal contraction. The design code allowance for short-term variations from normal operating conditions should not be claimed.

(e) The 'allowable stress range', defined in the design code and used for thermal analysis, should be taken as half that permitted by the code.

(f) The number of joints should be kept to a minimum. Welded joints are preferred. Flanged joints should only be used when connecting to flanged equipment (eg, valves, pumps, etc).

(g) Spiral wound gaskets are recommended; gaskets of compressed asbestos fibre (CAF) or aluminium may be used, but only with tongue and groove type joints.

(h) Liquid ammonia has a high thermal coefficient of expansion and, therefore, some means of safe venting should be provided on pipelines in which liquid can be trapped between valves, etc.

(j) Since liquid ammonia in a pipeline may be near or at its boiling point, the possibility and effect of two phase flow occurring should be taken into account at the design stage.

(k) Over-design resulting in an increase of thickness should be avoided, because the risk of brittle facture increases with thickness.

(l) Welds should have complete root penetration throughout the joint and be subject to the fault limitations of BS 2633: 1973*.

(m) Weld procedure and welder qualification tests should include impact testing of both weld and heat affected zone in their requirements and these should be in

accordance with the latest edition of the design code.

(n) All piping should be thermal stress relieved. (see footnote to para 63).

Piping: materials of construction

71 (a) Materials used for pipelines and fittings should be resistant to brittle fracture at the sub-zero temperatures encountered. (see para 80).

(b) Valves should normally be flanged and made of carbon steel which has been normalised as part of the manufacturing process. If welded-in valves are used, they should be made of impact-tested carbon steel.

(c) No copper or copper alloys should be used in valves or piping systems. (see para 7 (c)).

(d) Welding electrodes should be selected for low temperature duty. In order to minimise the risk of stress corrosion cracking the welding, consumables should overmatch the tensile properties of the piping systems by the smallest practicable amount.

Piping: fabrication and erection

72 (a) In general, forged butt welding fittings should be used for bends, tees, reducers and end caps.

(b) Socket-weld fittings and connections should be limited to 40 NS.

(c) Screwed fittings should be used only when no alternative is available and limited to small bore proprietary connections, eg pressure gauges.

(d) If the line is to be 'pigged', long radius wrought bends are preferred.

(e) Mitred elbows, lobster back bends and set-in branches should not be used at sub-zero temperatures.

(f) Set-on branches should have full penetration welds.

(g) Wrought bends and any fabricated fittings should be thermally stress relieved.

(h) All butt welds should be 100% radiographed and all fillet welds crack detected.

---

* BS 2633: 1973 *Class 1 Arc welding of ferritic steel pipework for carrying fluids.* British Standards Institution.

Piping: testing

73 Piping systems should be pressure tested before commissioning. This would preferably be an hydraulic test followed by drying, but in cases where hydraulic testing is not practicable, a pneumatic test using air or nitrogen may be used, provided that precautions are taken against the dangers inherent in this method of testing*.

Electrical equipment

74 Attention is drawn to the properties of ammonia and, in particular, to para 7(e).

75 Buildings such as compressor houses, in which electrical equipment might be subjected to an escape of ammonia, should be provided with through ventilation direct to atmosphere. Guidance on the provision of ventilation is given in BS 4434: Part 1, para 14.3†.

76 Electrical equipment in such buildings should be classified as Zone 2 to BS 4683: Part 3‡ or provided with circuit breakers controlled by detector devices, as described in BS 4434: Part 1 para 13.2.1.2.

77 Only motors which have no exposed copper parts should be used.

78 Switchgear should, wherever possible, be housed in dry, warm, enclosed buildings, to exclude ammonia vapour.

79 Ammonia should not be piped into control rooms or switch rooms.

Materials of construction (for ancilliary items)

80 Materials of construction should be in accordance with the latest edition of the relevant recommended design code, with due regard to sub-zero temperatures where applicable.

81 Austenitic steels are not prone to brittle failure at low temperatures.

* HSE Guidance Note GS4 Safety in pressure testing HMSO.

† BS 4434: 1969 Part 1 Requirements for refrigeration safety. British Standards Institution.

‡ BS 4683: 1972 Part 3 Electrical apparatus for explosive atmospheres. British Standards Institution.

Insulation

General

82 The need for insulation will depend on the conditions under which the vessel is to operate. Frequently, the operating temperature is such that there would be heat gain from the atmosphere and then, unless there is a process use for the vapour, it is necessary either to minimise the heat gain by insulation or to increase the capacity of the refrigeration plant. If insulation is to be applied, then the recommendations given in BS 5970* should be followed, together with the additional requirements given in this guidance.

Materials

83 *Insulating materials* As far as possible, all insulation materials should be highly fire resistant, for example foamed glass, foamed isocyanurate or fire retardant polyurethane. Finishing materials should be chosen with their fire-retardant properties as well as their resistance to atmospheric and environmental corrosive effects in mind.

84 *Vapour sealing* Attention is drawn to the importance of a vapour barrier*.

85 *Cladding* If metallic cladding is used, blind rivets which are electrolytically compatible with the cladding material should be employed.

86 *Securing insulation* The insulation may require metal support rings, which should be so designed that they can be fixed to the shell at the crown plates and at plates carrying the leg supports only. Any cleats required to locate and secure the rings should be welded to the appropriate plate in accordance with the requirements of BS 5500. This should be done by the manufacturer before the plates are thermally stress relieved. The insulating contractor should not be allowed to weld fittings to shell plates either before or after fabrication in any circumstances. Fixing studs by explosion welding is not permitted.

* BS 5970: 1981 Code of Practice for thermal insulation of pipework and equipment (in the temperature range -100°C to +870°C.

87 *Insulation at legs* When a sphere is supported on legs, the legs should be insulated for a sufficient distance to reduce heat gain in those areas.

Site safety facilities

88 In addition to the ancillary equipment and safety fittings, the following features should be incorporated to ensure safe operation of the storage installation.

(a) The area of the sphere and its associated equipment should be clearly marked to indicate potential hazard and to warn against unauthorised entry. Demarcation will vary from site to site; simple notices may suffice in some plant areas, while fencing may be necessary at an isolated location.

(b) Where access is limited, by fencing for example, two diagonally opposite gates should be provided so that in an emergency vehicles can get in whatever the direction of the wind. Emergency exits should be provided at each corner of the compound. For security reasons, these exits should be designed to restrict unauthorised access.

(c) Fire hydrants should be located around the area, about 25 metres from the sphere itself, so that access to a supply of water would always be available irrespective of the wind direction. Water curtains are effective in reducing the spread of an ammonia cloud. Care should be taken when setting up such a curtain to ensure that water does not come into contact with a pool of liquid ammonia because this would cause a large increase in the evolution of gaseous ammonia. In addition water should be available throughout the site for dealing with small spills and leaks.

(d) The storage area should be well lit at night.

(e) One or more wind socks should be provided in a prominent position so that they can be easily seen by personnel in the area.

(f) An emergency power supply or a flare stack should be provided where a power failure to the refrigerating compressors (resulting in a discharge of ammonia from the relief valves) could not be tolerated.

(g) Suitable crash barriers should be provided to protect vulnerable sections of pipeline and other equipment containing ammonia from vehicle collisions etc. (see also para 15).

(h) There should be emergency push-buttons at each exit, and any other locations deemed necessary. These should sound an alarm and shut the plant down in a safe condition. Where appropriate, the alarm should be incorporated into an existing factory or public warning system.

(j) Key instrument readings on which plant safety depends should be under constant surveillance, if necessary by remote reading. As a minimum, these should include the pressure in the vapour space of the sphere and the level of the liquid*.

(k) Personnel water drench facilities should be provided so that any one who may be sprayed with liquid ammonia will have immediate access to an adequate water supply. These facilities should preferably be located in at least two positions and, if possible, close to points where connections and disconnections are frequent.

(l) There should be an adequate supply of fire extinguishers of the CO_2 or BCF vapour type at strategic points in the area.

(m) The following safety equipment should be readily available:

(i) Suitable respiratory protective equipment for escape purposes for all personnel entering the storage area.

---

* *Pressure* Under normal operating conditions the pressure in the sphere will automatically start and stop the refrigeration compressors. If the start/stop mechanism fails to operate, the pressure in the sphere may become excessively high or low. The ultimate safeguards are the pressure relief valves, but, before these valves operate, the attendant should be given sufficient warning of the malfunction to take corrective action. Pressure values should be transmitted to a recorder sited in a manned control room and the recorder be fitted with low and high pressure audible alarms.

Liquid level Readings of sphere liquid levels should be transmitted to a manned control room. Since levels change slowly, level indication only is required. In addition, the sphere should be fitted with an independent high level device which will give an audible alarm in the control room, when it is activated (see also para 34)

(ii) Two longer duration sets of breathing apparatus for rescue purposes.

(iii) Two full protective suits for rescue and emergency purposes.

(iv) Plastic or rubber gloves and boots.

(v) Goggles.

(vi) First aid cabinets.

(vii) A number of eye-wash bottles, situated at several points in the area.

Employee training and safety

89 Although ammonia is a hazardous chemical, it can be safely handled by competent and fully trained personnel using the correct equipment and procedures.

Training

90 In addition to normal process training, all employees responsible for the operation of the plant should receive instruction in the following.

(a) The properties of ammonia and the behaviour of liquefied gas.

(b) The consequences of improper handling of equipment and the hazards that may result from a leakage of either liquid or gaseous ammonia.

(c) The action to be taken in the event of a spillage of ammonia.

(d) The correct use of all types of protective equipment, fire extinguishers and breathing apparatus.

Employee safety

91 The management should regularly satisfy themselves that safe working practices are constantly adopted.

92 All employees should be regularly involved in practice drills covering the action to be taken in the event of an emergency.

93 There should be at least an annual refresher programme for employees in the correct use of fire extinguishers, breathing apparatus and protective equipment.

94 Drench showers, eye-wash bottles and protective equipment should be regularly inspected to ensure continued availability and good condition. Precautions should be taken to prevent freezing.

95 All employees or other personnel entering the storage area should carry suitable respiratory protection equipment at the ready.

96 Smoking should be prohibited in the storage area and notices to this effect should be posted at several strategic points.

97 Appropriate protective equipment should be worn for the specific job being carried out.

Commissioning, operation and decommissioning

98 This section recommends procedures to be adopted in bringing an ammonia sphere into service and in taking it out of service for inspection. It is not concerned with commissioning procedures for the refrigeration and other ancillary plant which are outside the scope of this guidance. During commissioning the most important task is to remove impurities which, if left, might later promote stress corrosion cracking in the sphere. Since oxygen dissolved in the liquid ammonia is thought to be the major factor in causing such cracking, care should be taken to purge as much of the air as possible from the sphere before liquid ammonia is added.

99 Although stress corrosion cracking may be prevented by a well controlled thermal stress relief of the sphere before its first use with ammonia, the maintenance of a low oxygen content is recommended both as an additional safeguard and to minimise the risk of stress corrosion cracking elsewhere.

100 Two methods of purging air from the sphere are outlined, each of which is intended to reduce the average oxygen content of the gas in the sphere to less than 0.025% v/v prior to the introduction of liquid ammonia. This concentration of oxygen in the gas in the sphere will ensure that the concentration of oxygen in the liquid ammonia during and after filling will not exceed 2.5 ppm by weight which is considered to be the safe upper limit when

the water content it about 100 ppm*. To combine maximum oxygen removal with minimal ammonia loss to atmosphere, the air should be displaced by water followed by nitrogen or by nitrogen alone.

101 All methods described for commissioning and decommissioning involve venting gaseous ammonia to atmosphere. If this procedure is likely to give rise to environmental problems, the venting gas should be absorbed in water by using a suitable scrubber, which will not permit water to be sucked back into the sphere, especially during commissioning.

Commissioning

102 *Pre-commissioning* The following pre-commissioning activities and checks should be made that

(a) the sphere is clean and dry;

(b) all the refrigeration equipment is in working order;

(c) the instrument system and alarms are working;

(d) the float gauges are free to move and are transmitting correctly;

(e) the relief valves are correctly installed and have been set to the required pressure; and

(f) manhole covers are fitted and all pipe connections have been made.

103 *Leak testing and oxygen removal* The sphere is now ready for leak testing and for purging to remove oxygen. Of the various

possible purge procedures water and/or nitrogen displacement is preferred.

(a) *The water and nitrogen displacement method* The sphere is filled with clean water as full as possible, provided the engineering and civil design considerations permit this and provided the residual film of water and any dissolved solids can be tolerated in the ammonia. The water is then displaced with nitrogen gas which is introduced at the top of the sphere. This usually results in an oxygen level below 2%. If this is not achieved, pressurising and depressurising cycles can be used to bring the oxygen content to an acceptable level. Checks for leaks should be made at this stage.

A variant of this method is sometimes used where air is likely to be trapped in branches and manholes at the top. Water is filled to the top and its level is then dropped by about 2 ft or so by displacing it with nitrogen gas. The gas in this space is pressurised and depressurised until the oxygen content comes down to an acceptable level. The remaining water is then displaced with nitrogen gas. Any released nitrogen can be used to purge ancillary equipment.

A positive pressure must be maintained at all times to prevent any ingress of air.

(b) *The nitrogen alone displacement method.** The sphere is pressurised with nitrogen gas up to its working pressure and a check is made for leaks. It is then slowly depressurised; it is good practice to use the released nitrogen to purge ancillary equipment. The nitrogen pressurising and depressurising cycles are repeated until the oxygen content of the gas is reduced to 2% or less.

104 *Ammonia gas purge* Once the oxygen concentration in the sphere is below 2% then

---

* To minimise the possibility of stress corrosion cracking it is desirable that all traces of oxygen are removed from the system as quickly as possible after commissioning the sphere. Although completely reliable data are not available on the maximum levels of oxygen below which stress corrosion cracking will not occur, it is considered that the oxygen level should not exceed 2.5 ppm by weight when the water content is as low as 100 ppm. As a guide, every 1% oxygen left in the sphere after nitrogen purging will result in about 1 ppm in the liquid ammonia provided the subsequent ammonia purge is done carefully and as described in para 100. The situation can be further improved by filling the sphere as quickly as possible after commissioning and paying particular attention to purging non-condensibles from the system. Thereafter every effort should be made to ensure that the oxygen content is kept as low as possible.

---

* For very low pressure spheres the nitrogen method is not a practicable means of purging. In such cases either the water and nitrogen displacement method outlined in para 103(a) or the procedure used for atmospheric tanks is appropriate (See Code of Practice for the Large Scale Storage of Fully Refrigerated Anhydrous Ammonia in the United Kingdom. Chemical Industries Association, May 1985).

ammonia gas can be admitted to complete the purge.*

105 Ammonia gas is admitted at the top of the sphere and the effluent gas taken from its base but piped to a high level. The gas is introduced slowly initially, to achieve 'plug flow' condition in the sphere. In this way a stable cloud of ammonia vapour is established in the top few feet of the sphere with minimum mixing at the ammonia/nitrogen interface. The ammonia gas input rate can then be increased. Once the purge has started it should not be interrupted, otherwise undesirable mixing will take place.

106 After traces of ammonia are detected in the exit gas the concentration rises rapidly. The purging can be stopped by shutting the exit valve when an exit concentration of at least 90% is achieved.†

107 The ammonia can be used to purge the ancillary equipment. Gaseous ammonia is used to build up pressure in the sphere before admitting liquid ammonia to avoid local chilling of the sphere.

Operation

108 Although pure anhydrous ammonia is not in itself thought to be a medium liable to cause stress corrosion cracking of carbon steel, contamination of the ammonia with oxygen does appear to promote stress corrosion cracking.

109 A considerable degree of stress corrosion cracking has been found in some ammonia containers. High strength steels are more susceptible to cracking than low strength steels and the impurity which promotes cracking has been identified as oxygen. Ammonia as produced contains no oxygen, but contamination

can clearly occur when it is being transferred from manufacturer to user.

110 The following guidelines should be followed:

(a) Every effort should be made to keep the oxygen content of the ammonia as low as possible.

(b) Serious consideration should be given to raising the water content of the ammonia to 0.2% w/w as the presence of water at or above this concentration appears to provide protection in the liquid phase. When water is added, it should either be distilled water or plant condensate of equivalent quality.

(c) The oxygen content of the liquid ammonia should be checked at least once a month. With carefully controlled operation the oxygen content should not exceed 2.5 ppm w/w. If a significantly higher value is obtained additional measurements will be necessary to determine whether it is due to the very real difficulty of excluding extraneous oxygen from the analyser or to a departure from good operating practice which will need to be identified and corrected. With careful exclusion of extraneous oxygen from the sample and analyser, gas chromatography can be used to determine these low levels of oxygen.

Decommissioning

111 This section is concerned with safe procedures for removing liquid and gaseous ammonia from the storage sphere so that it can be entered for examination.

112 Remove as much liquid ammonia as possible by using the normal product pumps. There may be some residual liquid left in the sphere. Any remaining liquid will have to be removed by differential pressure transfer to an adjacent vessel, or to a road or rail tanker. It is important that all the liquid is drained from the sphere before the pressure is reduced to atmospheric otherwise more vapour will be evolved than necessary and, more important, the temperature in at least a part of the sphere will fall to minus 33°C. Some spheres are not designed for this temperature.

---

* A supply of gaseous ammonia is required to purge nitrogen from the sphere during commissioning. The source of gas will depend on the installation. Provision should be made for about 1 tonne of gas for each 1000 cubic metres of sphere volume.

† High concentration of ammonia is necessary otherwise the compressors will overheat due to an excess of non-condensable gases. A figure of not less that 90% ammonia is desirable.

113 Reduce the sphere pressure to the minimum possible, consistent with safe operation of the refrigerant compressor.

114 Isolate the compressor and reduce the sphere pressure to zero gauge by controlled venting to atmosphere.

115 Introduce air to the lowest point (eg the largest available bottom nozzle) on the sphere, venting from the highest point of the sphere to atmosphere. The air should be introduced slowly to maintain a good ammonia/air interface. Since ammonia gas is much less dense than air, displacement of ammonia will take place naturally due to the chimney effect. Once natural flow has stopped, extractor fans may be used to increase the air flow as in para 116. During the purge there will be a narrow band of mixed gas at the ammonia/air interface which lies in the ignitable range. It is generally considered that the risk of ignition is low. However, if it is decided that even a slight risk is unacceptable, a nitrogen purge may precede the air purge. The ammonia/air purge should not take place if thunderstorms threaten.

116 Open the largest available bottom nozzle(s), disconnect the nitrogen supply, if used, fit suitable extractor fans to the nozzles in the top of the sphere, and draw air through the sphere until the atmosphere is sweet enough for entry, in accordance with the requirements of Chemical Works Regulations - Regulation 7.

117 It should be noted that this method of decommissioning avoids the use of water altogether, but is likely to be slow, dependent upon atmospheric ammonia content at the venting point. Also conditions in the sphere may be unpleasant. A chemical wash may still be necessary to clean the inside of the sphere before unprotected entry can take place. Where disposal of ammoniacal water is practicable, an alternative method is to introduce water to absorb the residual ammonia once pressure has been reduced to atmospheric. Care should be taken to ensure that enough purge gas (air or nitrogen) can get in to prevent the creation of a vacuum.

Inspection and maintenance

General

118 The first in-service thorough examination by a competent person should take place after not more than two years service followed by periodic thorough examinations at intervals determined by the competent person. Subject to satisfactory results from the examination the intervals may be increased by steps of not more than two years to a maximum of not more than six years. Evidence of significant stress corrosion cracking should be taken to mean that the results of the examination were not satisfactory.

119 Subsequent examinations may not necessarily require a hydraulic test unless repairs have been carried out which affect the integrity of the vessel.

Internal

120 Existing spheres which have not been subjected to a 100% magnetic particle inspection of internal welds should be so examined at the next thorough examination.

121 Ammonia spheres which are to be returned to service after being out of use for a period, other than for examination or repair, should be recertified by a competent person as fit for continued use with ammonia. The scope of any examination necessary should be determined by the competent person with due regard to the vessel history, previous use and previous examinations. An in-service thorough examination should take place after not more than two years service and subsequent examinations should be determined as for new vessels (see para 118).

122 Existing spheres which are to be transferred to ammonia service should be fully stress relieved before being recertified by a competent person as fit for use for ammonia. The scope of any examination necessary should be determined by the competent person but this should include 100% magnetic particle crack detection of all internal welds and at the location of removed toggle cleats, temporary attachments and scars. An in-service thorough examination should take place after not more than two years service and subsequent examinations should be determined as for new vessels. (see para 118).

123 The examination referred to in para 118 and 122 should include the requirements in paras 124 to 139.

Internal

124 The examination should consist of visual inspection and internal magnetic particle crack detection of the welded seams in accordance with British Standard 6072 as a minimum requirement*. Techniques and flux density should be to the satisfaction of the competent person.

125 The induced magnetic field should be applied by electro-magnetic coils (not open circuit prods or probes) to produce a flux density of sufficient strength to reveal the presence of significant cracks†.

126 The extent of the magnetic particle crack detection examination should include 100% of all the internal welds and cleat areas. If significant defects are found, the next inspection should be within two years and should again include 100% magnetic particle inspection of the welds and cleat areas. Subject to no significant defects being found, any subsequent inspection should include at least:

(a) all the plate tee junctions in the lower half of the sphere.

(b) 25% of the bottom and second strake circumferential seams, and

(c) the top crown plate, first and second strake tee welds plus 25% of the joining circumferential weld seams.

Ultrasonic inspection

127 The wall thickness of the shell and nozzles should be measured ultrasonically and ultrasonic flaw detection of shell to nozzle welds shall be applied (see para 50).

128 Where practicable this examination should be made from the internal surface.

* BS 6072: Method for magnetic particle flow detection. British Standards Institution.

† Care must be taken to use a technique that is sufficiently sensitive to reveal very fine cracks. The technique used should have a sensitivity not less than that provided by the AC magnetic yoke. The use of fluorescent inks can improve definition.

Acoustic emission testing

129 Acoustic emission testing may be used to assist in determining the integrity of the sphere.

External

130 There should be a once-off assessment of the external surface. In the case of an existing uninsulated sphere the examination should consist of full visual inspection and magnetic particle crack detection examination along at least 10% of each butt weld. In the case of an existing insulated sphere, ultrasonic flaw detection testing from within the sphere of at least 10% of each external butt weld may be used in place of the external examination. If any significant defect is found the extent of the examination should be increased at the competent person's discretion.

131 In addition, at each subsequent examination where significant internal defects are detected, ultrasonic testing should be used from within the sphere to check the integrity of the external surface opposite the internal defect prior to the assessment called for in para 142.

132 Shell nozzles whose wall thickness cannot be measured ultrasonically from the nozzle bore should be delagged locally and exposed for examination.

133 The external support structure should be inspected for deterioration of the protective coating and resultant metal wastage. The attachment welds should be magnetic particle crack detected and breather holes (if any) checked.

134 All lines from the sphere to their first isolation should be inspected for support and securement. The butt welds of these lines should be delagged, 100% radiographed, and examined for external corrosion.

135 All in-line valves, such as isolation valves, excess flow and remote control valves should be removed and overhauled.

136 All instrumentation and alarms should be overhauled and re-calibrated.

137 Relief valves should be overhauled and tested at least every two years and the interlocking isolation thoroughly checked as far as its construction permits.

138 External insulation should be examined for damage and breakdown of insulating properties. The shell, where insulation is suspect, should be exposed to facilitate inspection of the metal surface prior to insulation repairs, particularly if the sphere is situated in an aggressive atmospheric environment.

139 All closure and mounting studs or stud bolts on the sphere should be renewed. All flange gaskets should be renewed. The flange gaskets and stud bolts should be renewed on the piping between the sphere and first isolation.

Thorough examination report

140 Any significant deterioration found should be recorded on the examination report with particulars of the inspection techniques used. The vessel should be reassessed for continued use with ammonia and the safe working limits confirmed or revised. Any significant weld or material defects found should be critically examined with regard to effect on vessel integrity, origin and likelihood of recurrence. Where defects are ground out or rewelded the effect on safe working pressure should be carefully analysed. Stress analysis should pay due regard to residual and operational stresses with appropriate stress intensification factors where they apply. Where defects are left their significance should be assessed by a fracture mechanics analysis and be suitably monitored when the vessel is returned to use. Where propagating defects are foreseeable a similar analysis should be made in helping to determine the date of the next examination. Where any metal has been removed or thinning has occurred, due consideration should be given to safe working pressure limits based on the remaining metal thickness. Certification should be provided specifying:

(a) maximum safe working pressure;

(b) minimum safe working pressure;

(c) maximum safe working temperature;

(d) minimum safe working temperature;

(e) maximum permissible ammonia fill;

(f) maximum permitted weight of contents;

(g) date of next thorough examination.

Competent person

141 A 'competent person' should have the knowledge, experience and resources to search for, detect and assess particular defects associated with vessels containing ammonia, eg stress corrosion cracks. They should have access to appropriate NDT and laboratory facilities and the professional technical ability to relate inspection findings to appraisals of vessel integrity safe working parameters and future use.

Routine inspection

142 In addition to the periodic throrough examination the following discipline checks should be carried out routinely.

(a) All automatic valves, alarms and trip systems should be checked periodically to ensure their satisfactory operation.

(b) In the case of spheres surrounded by a wall or bund, attention should be paid to surface water drainage. The general good housekeeping in the area should include maintaining it free of debris and undergrowth.

(c) Fire hydrants should be regularly serviced and maintained.

(d) External insulation should be maintained in good order.

(e) Personnel safety equipment points should be checked daily and the items (eg, respirators, goggles, gloves, safety showers, etc) kept serviceable.

(f) Instruction notices, sphere identity number and valve nomenclature should be clearly displayed and maintained legible by day and by night.

(g) Site illumination should be regularly maintained and serviced, (ie, kept clean and in working order).

Emergency plan

143 It is essential that the possibility, however remote, of a major escape of ammonia should be considered, and a plan of action worked out to deal with such an emergency. The plan will cover emergencies which can be brought under control by the works, possibly with the assistance of the local police and fire services. These authorities should be fully consulted, and the works plan should identify how works action would be integrated with that taken under the overall direction of the local police in the event of a major emergency involving the surrounding area. The police should also be consulted on the information to be given to the occupiers of neighbouring premises to prepare them adequately for the action to be taken in an emergency.

144 At premises which are subject to the Control of Industrial Major Accident Hazards Regulations 1984*.

(a) the occupier must prepare an on-site emergency plan;

(b) the local authority must prepare an off-site emergency plan;

(c) arrangements must be made to give information to the public who may be affected by a major accident at the premises.

Further guidance is given in The HSE booklet HS(R)21†.

145 The local police and fire services should know the location of the installation and the means of access to it. They should be informed of the consequences of a major escape, advised as to the protective equipment they should carry, and agreement should be reached on the action they would take if involved in an emergency. In particular, the fire services must fully understand the measures to be adopted in dealing with an escape of ammonia.

146 A written works plan should be drawn up and circulated covering the following points.

(a) the immediate action to be taken by operating personnel, including the procedure to be adopted to alert the works and summon the local police and fire services, should they be required;

(b) the nomination of a specific person to be present at the site of the incident and responsible for coordinating the activities of plant personnel and external bodies in dealing with the escape itself;

(c) the nomination of a senior manager as the controller of the whole incident, his role being to ensure that all possible action is being taken in both works and public sectors, and all necessary communication links are handled correctly (a written check-list should be drawn up and available for his guidance);

(d) the choice of suitable locations from which to control the emergency (two locations, situated in different wind direction sectors, should be available for this purpose), and

(e) where the storage installation forms part of a factory, a warning system and plan of action for the remainder of the site making all employees aware of the steps to take in the event of an emergency involving their particular work area.

147 There should be occasional practises of the works plan, coordinated with the local police and fire services.

148 Detailed guidance on the preparation of emergency plans is given in an HSE guidance note on the preparation of emergency plans* and two Chemicals Industries Association publications†.

* Regulation 6 of Control of Industrial Major Accident Hazards Regulations 1984, HMSO.

† *A Guide to the Control of Industrial Major Accident Hazards Regulations 1984*, ISBN 011 883762.

* HSE *The Control of Industrial Major Accident Hazards Regulations 1984 (CIMAH): Further Guidance on Emergency Plans*, (HS(G)25), HMSO ISBN 0 11 883831 8.

† Recommended Procedures for Handling Major Emergencies 2nd ed Chemicals Industries Association 1976.

Guidelines for Chemical Sites on off site aspects of Emergency Procedures Chemicals Industries Association 1985.

Cylindrical vessels

Introduction

149 Vessels for storing liquid ammonia at full pressure are usually cylindrical in shape with formed ends and may be installed with the axis either vertical or horizontal. It is customary, however, to mount these vessels in the horizontal position, particularly when the ammonia is removed by conventional pumping.

150 Vessels of this type are usually shop built and this, combined with regulations which impose limitations on the dimensions of loads transported by road, means that there is a limit to the size of vessel. There may be a further limitation on size governed by the capacity of the stress-relieving furnace available to the manufacturer.

151 In industry many processes require small quantities of ammonia and storage as pressure is the only means of serving this small but very important sector. Most deliveries to these users are made by road.

152 It is recommended in all cases that the amount of ammonia stored at pressure is as small as reasonably practicable consistent with the commercial operation.

153 A typical simplified line diagram of a pressure storage installation is shown in Fig 2.

154 The reader is referred to the general information given in the general information of this guidance and will readily recognise when it is applicable to ambient temperature storage in cylindrical vessels. Many of the recommendations for the safe storage of ammonia in spheres are applicable to storage in cylindrical vessels. Where identical or near identical recommendations apply, an appropriate reference is made to the preceding part of this guidance.

Physical properties and health hazards of ammonia

Refer to the general information given in paras 1 to 11.

Siting

155 The following are the minimum standards recommended for siting vessels which receive tanker delivery. They in no way override further requirements which may be imposed by the local authority or HSE.

156 Ammonia storage installations should be sited within a secure factory boundary, as far away as possible from residential areas and public buildings. The following distances should be regarded as minima.

Capacity	Distance
Up to 100 tonnes	250 metres
Over 100 tonnes	500 metres

157 Installations should preferably be sited outdoors, but if indoors, the building containing the vessel should be so constructed that any leak from the vessel will pass only to open air and not directly into occupied work spaces.

158 The off-loading area should be outdoors and in an area closed to other traffic movements while tankers are discharging. Road tankers should not, in any circumstances, stand on a public highway while off-loading.

159 The site should be selected to minimise the risk of damage from fire or explosion in surrounding plant or storage areas and should be so arranged that the pressure vessel and all equipment immediately associated with it is protected from possible damage resulting from any foreseeable accident.

160 The choice of site should take into account existing plans for future development in the area.

Vessel design

Design code

161 The vessel should be designed, fabricated, erected, inspected and tested in accordance with at least the equivalent standard to BS 5500 Category 1 with due regard to Appendix D. There should be 100% radiography of all butt welds and ultrasonic and/or magnetic particle inspection of all other welds. In addition, it is

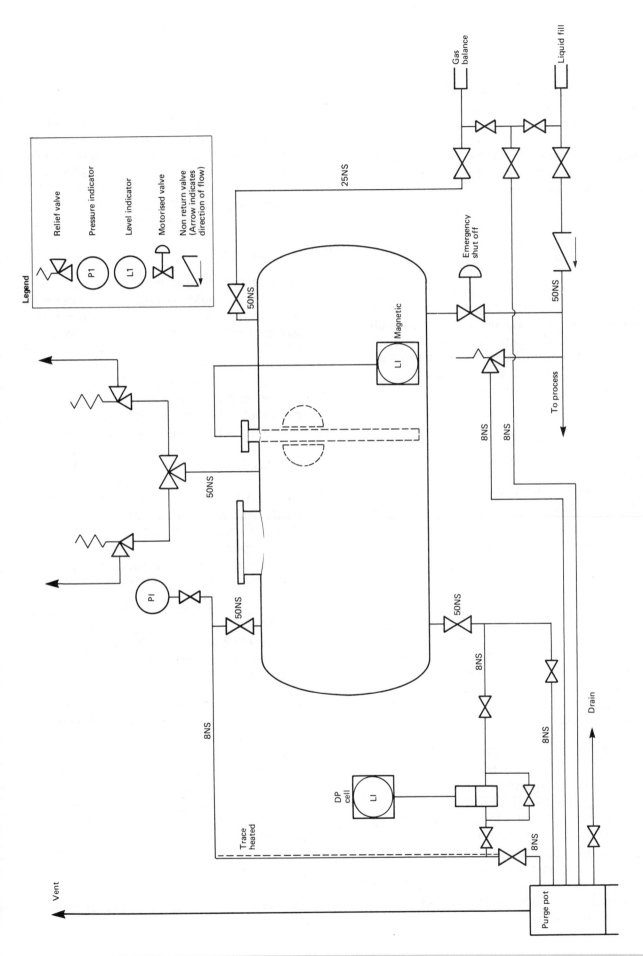

Line diagram of typical small pressure storage installation

recommended that all internal welds are subject to 100% magnetic particle inspection in order to provide a record against which all future inspections of the vessel can be assessed. Once fabricated, the vessel should be thermally stress relieved and thereafter no further welding should be undertaken unless the design code requirements for local stress relief are carried out.

Design conditions

162 *Design pressure* Any vessel used for ambient temperature storage should be designed for a pressure of not less than 15.5 bar absolute. However, if a vessel is not primarily a storage vessel and forms part of an integrated process it may be designed for a lower duty provided it is adequately protected from being overpressurised.

163 *Design temperature* The minimum design temperature should be the lowest temperature the vessel can achieve in service. Preferably this should be taken as minus 33°C but in no case should it be taken as warmer than minus 10°C.

Materials of construction

164 (a) *Metallic materials* The steels used should be limited at least to those permitted by BS 5500, Section 2. Also refer to paras 23 to 25 of this guidance for additional requirements. Alternative steels, having the same limitations in carbon content and maximum tensile strength and with the same impact properties, may be substituted. Copper and copper bearing alloys should *not* be used.

165 (a) *Non-metallic materials* The most suitable rubbers are nitrile and neoprene within their temperature limitations. Butyl and ethylene propylene rubbers are less permeable but, since they are affected by oil, they should only be used in ammonia gas systems. PTFE, polypropylene, polyethylene and nylon are relatively unaffected. Most other rubbers and plastics are unsuitable with fluoroelastomers being particularly badly affected.

Vessel supports

166 Horizontal vessels should be supported on steel saddles. Where these are welded to the vessel, the welding should be continuous so that corrosion cannot occur between the saddles and the shell. Vertical vessels should be provided with a welded-on skirt. The direct mounting of the vessel in a concrete saddle is not acceptable.

Vessel mountings

167 (a) *General* The number of openings in to the vessel should be kept to a minimum. In the interests of safety all nozzles and first isolation valves should preferably be at least 50 NS, but in no case should be less than 25 NS. Any branches, including dip pipes, entering the vessel below the normal maximum liquid level should be protected by remote operated emergency shut off valves, except in the case of small bore pipes to contents, gauges etc, within the protected area of the vessel site. These shut-off valves should preferably be mounted directly on to the appropriate nozzle with no intermediate pipework. However, where this is impractical, the outlet pipework should be kept as short as possible and the pipework and valve constructed in an austenitic stainless steel.

(b) *Access opening* The access opening should be provided on top of the vessel. The opening should preferably be 600 mm diameter, but in no case should it be less than 460 mm internal diameter*.

(c) *Relief valves* Relief valves should be fitted in accordance with BS 6759: Part 3: 1984 and the tail pipes should be arranged to vent harmlessly above the highest point on any adjacent structure. As a minimum they should vent not less than five metres above the highest point of the vessel. Over-pressure protection of vessels is discussed in more detail in paras 30 to 32.

* Factories Act 1961, and Regulation 7 Chemicals Work Regulations.

(d) *Level indicators* Every vessel should be equipped with at least one level indicator. Level indicators of the 'sight glass' type where the glass is exposed to ammonia vapour pressure should not be used.

(e) *Earthing bosses* Where earthing is required, vessels should be provided with two earthing bosses in accordance with Figure 22 of BS 4741* except that austenitic steel should be used instead of brass for the studs and washers and any copper conductor should be used instead of brass for the studs and washers and any copper conductor should be wrapped to prevent contact with ammonia.

(f) *Access stairs* If stairways and platforms are fixed to the shell of the vessel they should be bolted to cleats which have been attached to the shell with full penetration welds prior to its final thermal stress relief. The stairway should be at least 750 mm wide complete with handrails and toe boards. Ladders on existing vessels should be hooped and sufficiently robust to accommodate a person wearing breathing apparatus. Consideration should be given to alternative means of escape from long gantries.

Nozzle welding details

Refer to para 43.

Vessel testing and examination

168 The testing of the vessel should include filling with water and testing in accordance with Clause 5.8.3 of BS 5500†.

169 All vessels should be thoroughly inspected during construction in accordance with the fabrication code requirements. In addition, a full visual inspection and magnetic particle crack detection examination along at least 10% of each

---

butt weld should be carried out on the external surface of the vessel.

Foundations

170 The principles set out in paras 51 to 53 should be taken as a general guide on the design of foundations.

Bunding

171 As discussed in the Introduction there will be little or no collection of liquid from an escape caused by the rupture of a vessel working at ambient temperature. Even a very small hole would let the ammonia escape as a gas/liquid aerosol. The only exception may be when a minor leak occurs from a valve gland. The leak path is usually sufficiently long for the gas and liquid to separate causing wisps of ammonia gas and drips of liquid ammonia to form.

172 The local water authority may insist on a separately drained catchment area but this is usually a matter for drainage rather than bunding.

173 It is recommended that the area under the storage tank should be surfaced with smooth concrete arranged to slope to a drain, and the area delineated with a small kerb which should extend at least one metre beyond the tank or protruding piping.

174 The entire storage area should be protected from vehicle impact.

Ancillary equipment

175 Reference should be made to paras 57 to 82 noting that refrigeration equipment is not required with ambient temperature storage.

Insulation

176 It is not normally necessary to insulate ambient storage tanks, but if insulation is applied for particular process requirements reference should be made to paras 83 to 87.

Site safety facilities

177 Reference should be made to para 88, noting that the provisions of 88(f) and 88(j) will not apply.

---

* BS 4741: 1971. *Vertical cylindrical welded steel storage tanks for low temperature service - single well tanks for temperatures down to 50°C* British Standards Institution.

† BS 5500: *Specifications for unified fusion welded pressure vessels.* British Standard Institution.

178 In addition it is considered that chemical absorption type respirators are adequate for escape and lightweight protective suits are suitable for rescue and emergency purposes.

Employee training and safety

See paras 89 to 97.

Commissioning and decommissioning

179 The principles set out in paragraphs 98 to 117 should be taken as a general guide. With these relatively small vessels it is common practice to purge air from the system directly with ammonia gas. This is an acceptable practice because the risk of stress corrosion cracking has been minimised by the selection of appropriate steels and thermal stress-relief of the vessel.

180 Although it is still advisable to purge oxygen from the vessel as far as is practicable, a higher concentration of oxygen can be tolerated. Nevertheless it is considered desirable to continue the purge until a minimum concentration of 90% ammonia in air is measured in the discharge.

Inspection and maintenance

General

181 The following only applies to fully stress-relieved vessels. For any existing non-stress-relieved vessel being used for the storage of ammonia under pressure the inspection/examination procedures given in paras 118 to 142 to this guidance should apply. All vessels should be thoroughly inspected by a competent person during construction in accordance with the fabrication code requirement (see para 161) and again after not more than three years service*. Subsequent periodic examination should take place at intervals determined by the appropriate inspection authority, depending on the results of the first and each subsequent examination service examination. In no case should the second examination interval exceed six years

* The vessels covered by this part of the guidance are shop fabricated and thermally stress relieved, therefore the interval between inspections has been increased beyond the requirement for spheres.

and subsequent ones exceed twelve years.

Internal

182 Following a full visual examination for any obvious signs of deterioration, a magnetic particle examination should be carried out. The extent of the first in-service examination should include 100% of all the internal butt welds.

183 If significant defects are found, the next inspection should be within two years and should again include 100% magnetic particle inspection of the welds.

184 Subject to no significant defects being found, any subsequent inspection should include at least all the tee junctions and 10% of the total length of the butt welds selected at random (for details of magnetic particle techniques see paras 125 to 128).

185 A hydraulic test is not required under this guidance but may be called for by the competent person. It will normally only be required if welding repairs have been found necessary (see para 120).

186 The nozzle-to-shell attachment welds should be crack-detected by magnetic particle inspection methods, and if defects are found, the inspection requirements imposed in para 119 should apply.

187 When corrosion is evident or suspected ultrasonic thickness measurements should be taken.

External examination

188 If the internal examination exposes a significant defect there should be a one-off assessment of the external surface. In the case of an existing uninsulated vessel the examination should consist of full visual inspection and magnetic particle crack detection examination along at least 10% of each butt weld and opposite the defect. In the case of an existing insulated vessel ultrasonic flaw detection testing from within the vessel of at least 10% of each external butt weld and opposite defect may be used in place of the external examination. If any significant external defect is found the extent of the examination should be increased at the competent person's discretion.

189 In addition at each subsequent examination where significant internal defects are detected, external magnetic particle crack detection or ultrasonic flaw detection testing from within the vessel should be used to check the integrity of the external surface opposite the internal defects.

190 The shell and nozzles should be examined for external corrosion and a proportion of the welds crack-detected. Where corrosion is evident ultrasonic thickness measurements should be taken.

191 The external supports should be inspected and particular attention paid to any zone between the vessel and the support which is not readily accessible and where hidden corrosion may be taking place.

192 All lines connected with the installation including valves and other ancillary equipment should be inspected for corrosion and support.

193 All in-line valves such as isolation valves and remote control valves should be removed and overhauled.

194 All instrumentation and alarms should be overhauled and re-calibrated.

195 Safety valves should be overhauled and tested at least every two years. If an interlocking system is installed to enable the relief valves to be examined without losing the service of the vessel, the interlocking system should be thoroughly checked.

196 All closure and mounting studs, bolts or stud bolts on the vessel should be renewed. All flange gaskets should be renewed. The flange gaskets and studs/bolts should be renewed on the piping between the vessel and the first isolation valve.

Thorough examination report

See para 140.

Emergency plan

See paras 143 to 148.

Routine inspection

197 In addition to the periodic and thorough examination, the following discipline checks should be carried out as a matter of routine.

(a) At least once a year there should be an assessment of the general serviceability of the installation. A careful external visual examination of the vessel and ancillary equipment should be made by a competent person, paying attention to local corrosion, particularly at nozzles.

(b) All automatic valves, alarms and trip systems should be checked periodically, eg monthly, to ensure their satisfactory operation.

(c) The general good housekeeping in the area should include maintaining it free from debris and undergrowth.

(d) Fire hydrants should be regularly serviced and maintained.

(e) A periodic check should be made that all site safety equipment is available and being maintained in accordance with manufacturer's instructions. In addition, process operators should check daily that their personal safety equipment such as protective suits, respirators, goggles and gloves, is available and serviceable.

(f) Instruction notices, vessel identity number and valve nomenclature should be clearly displayed at all times.

(g) Site illumination should be regularly maintained and serviced, ie, kept clean and in working order.

BIBLIOGRAPHY

Other relevant standards

BS 1515 : Fusion-welded pressure vessels for use in the chemical, petroleum and allied industries. (now withdrawn).

ASTM E208: Tentative method for conducting drop weight tests to determine nil ductility temperatures of ferritic steels, 1969. The American Society for Testing and Materials.

BS 3799: Steel pipe fittings, screwed and socket-welding for the petroleum industry, 1974. British Standards Institution.

ANSI B.16.11: Forged steel fittings, socket-welding and threaded, 1973. American National Standards Institute.

Basic information

'Chronic toxicity of NH_3, 'fumes by inhalation' - J H Weatherby - The proceedings of the Society for Experimental Biology in Medicine, October 1952, pages 300 and 301.

'Comparative life fire and explosion hazards of common refrigerants' - The Underwriters Laboratories, November 1933.

'Determination of the explosion limits of gases' - H A Pieters, J W J Hovers and B J Rietveld - Fuels in science and practice, Volume 26, No 3, 1947, pages 80 and 81.

'Etude experimentale des proprietes de l'ammoniac' - Chimie et industrie genie chimique, Volume 102, No 6, October 1969.

'Limits of flammability of gases and vapors' - H F Coward and C W Jones - Bulletin 503, Bureau of Mines, 1952.

'Physiological response of man to ammonia in low concentrations' L Silverman and others - The Journal of Industrial Hygiene, March 1949, pages 74-78.

'Note on the Flammability of Ammonia' - APEA Technical Committee.

Flammability and Explosibility of Ammonia - I Chem. E Symposium Series No 49, pp 31-39 - GFP Harris & P E McDermott.

Regulations for the transportation of explosives and other dangerous articles by land and water, rail, freight express and baggage service and by motor vehicle (highway) and water, including specifications' - Department of Transportation USA.

'Tables of thermodynamic properties of ammonia' - Information circular No 142, US Bureau of Standards, April 1923.

'The total and partial pressure of aqueous ammonia solutions' - T A Wilson - Bulletin No 146, University of Illinois, 1925.

'The toxicity of ammonia' - E C King - Science, 21 July 1951, page 91.

Dangerous Substances (Conveyance by Road in Road Tankers and Tank Containers) Regulations 1981, and Approved Code of Practice on the operational provisions of the regulations, dealing with loading and delivery procedures and construction, maintenance and labelling of vehicles.

ADR, 'International Regulations Concerning the Carriage of Dangerous Goods by Road'.

'Dangerous goods by freight train and by passenger train or similar service. List of Dangerous Goods and Conditions of Acceptance (BR 22426 (Revised))' - British Railways Board.

'International Regulations concerning the carriage of dangerous goods by rail. (RID) - Her Majesty's Stationery Office.

Safe handling and storage

'Acids and caustics' - Safe practices pamphlet No 25 - National Safety Council, 1941.

'Ammonia' - Toxicological Review, September 1948 - American Petroleum Institute. 'Anhydrous Ammonia' - Chemical safety data sheet SD8 - Manufacturing Chemists' Association Inc. 1960..

'Anhydrous Ammonia' - Pamphlet G - 2 Compressed Gas Association Inc, New York, 1949.

'Anhydrous Ammonia, its storage, feeding and safe handling' - R J Quinn and Ralph L Carr - Water Works and Sewage, June 1941.

'Aqua-ammonia' - Chemical safety data sheet SD-13, Manufacturing Chemists' Association Inc, 1947.

'Handling ammonia for metal treatment' - L H Brandt - Metals and alloys, June 1942.

'New rules of ammonia highway tank transports' - CEP technical manual - Safety in air and ammonia plants, Volume 11, pages 46-49.

'Rupture of an ammonia road tanker at Lievin (France)' - CEP technical manual - Safety in ammonia plants and related facilities. Volume 12.

'Safe handling of ammonia solutions' - H R Kruger - Agricultural chemicals, November 1951, page 46 and following.

'Safe handling of compressed gases' - Compressed Gas Association Inc, New York.

'Safety in the use and handling of ammonia' - W L Nelson - Oil and Gas Journal, 16 September 1948, page 1053 and following.

'Safety recommendations for the construction of tank cars for the transport of ammonia by road.' - Association des Producteurs Europeens d'Azole (APEA).

'Storage and handling of anhydrous ammonia in tank car quantities' - L H Brandt, Chemical Industries, August 1943.

General information

'Anhydrous ammonia' - Chemical safety data sheet SE-8, revised - Manufacturing Chemists' Association Inc.

'Anhydrous ammonia' - Pamphlet G-2 - Compressed Gas Association Inc, New York.

Corrosion, Volume 18, page 229 - Loginow and Phelps, 1962.

'Rules and recommendations relating to the unloading of tank cars of ICC-105A and ICC-112A types containing anhydrous ammonia and the leasing of tracks or railroad property adjacent thereto for this purpose' - Bureau of Explosives circular No 17-F, 5 January 1962, Bureau of Explosives, Association of American Railroads.

Additional information

'Anydrous ammonia' - National Safety Council, Chicago, 1954.

'Recommendations for prevention of NH_3, contamination of LP-gas' - National LP-gas Association, Chicago.

References

Health and Safety at Work, etc, Act, 1974. HMSO.

BS 5500: *Specifications for unfired fusion welded pressure vessels,* (most recent addition). British Standards Institution.

BS 4741: *Vertical cylindrical welded steel storage tanks for low temperature service - single wall tanks for temperatures down to minus 50°C,* 1971. British Standards Institution.

CP 2004: *Foundations,* 1972. British Standard Code of Practice.

BS 3274: *Tubular heat exchanges for general purposes,* 1960. British Standards Institution.

Frost Heaves and Storage Vessel Foundation. CEP Technical Manual - Safety in ammonia plants and related facilities, Volume 12.

BS 3351: *Piping systems for petroleum refineries and petro-chemical plants,* 1971. British Standards Institution.

ANSI B31.3: American National Standard - *Code for pressure piping - Chemical plant and petroleum refinery piping,* 1976.

BS 2633: *Class 1 Arc Welding of Ferritic Steel Pipework for carrying fluids,* 1973. British Standards Institution.

BS 4434: *Requirements for Refrigeration Safety Part 1,* 1969. British Standards Institution.

BS 4683: *Electrical apparatus for explosive atmospheres, Part 3,* 1972. British Standards Institution.

BS 5970 *Code of Practice for thermal insulation of pipework and equipment (in the temperature range of -100°C to +870°C.*

Code of Practice for the Large Scale Storage of Fully Refrigerated Anhydrous Ammonia in the United Kingdom. Chemical Industries Association, May 1975.

Factories Act 1961, Section 30 and Chemical Works Regulations 1922, Regulation 7. See

Redgrave's *Health and Safety in Factories*
Second Edition Butterworth Shaw & Sons 1982 for
discussion of these requirements.

Note   ABCM Safety and Management: A guide
for the Chemical Industry, re-issued April
1972 by the Chemical Industries
Association. Chapter 7 interprets the
Factories Act in detail and is helpful as a
supplementary reference work).

Health and Safety Executive Guidance Note GS14
- *Safety in Pressure Testing,* HMSO.

BS 6072 - *Method for magnetic particle flow
detection.* British Standards institution.

*Control of Industrial Major Accident Hazards
(CIMAH) Regulations 1984* SO 1984 No 1902
HMSO.

HSE Booklet HS(R) - *A Guide to the Control of
Industrial Major Accident Hazard Regulations
1984.* HMSO.

HSE Guidance Note on the Preparation of
Emergency Plans (to be published shortly).

Recommended Procedures for Handling Major
Emergencies, 2nd Edition, 1976 published by the
Chemical Industries Association.

BS 6759: Part 3: 1984 *Specification for Safety
Valves for Process Fluids.*

Appendix 6

Example of a safety report

This is an example of a safety report which is required for all major hazard works coming under the EC "Seveso Directive". It has been produced for an existing plant in the Federal Republic of Germany by the plant management, and is reproduced by permission of Umweltbundesamt, Fachgebiet "Aufklärung der Öffentlichkeit in Umweltfragen", Bismarckplatz 1, 1000 Berlin (West) 33.

This manual is intended for countries which have well-developed major hazard control systems, and others which are considering such a system for the first time. A report of this complexity would probably be more appropriate to the first category of countries, but all countries which do not have a reporting system should consider which elements of a safety report would be appropriate to their own needs and practices.

*Safety report
pursuant to Article 7
of the Ordinance on
Major Hazard Control
of the Federal Republic
of Germany
(Störfallverordnung) for a
plant for the processing of
acrolein (Deka factory)*

**Safety report for an existing plant
Prepared in 1982**

Contents

The Deka factory is an existing plant for the production of organic intermediates. The individual processes for production of these intermediates are totally independent of one another and were also introduced at different times in the Deka factory.

The Deka factory is *one* plant in accordance with the Federal Law on Pollution Control *(BImSchG)*.

1. Description of the plant and the process

(Article 7 (1) 1)

1.1. Description of the plant

The Deka factory comprises the tank store G 404 with acrolein unloading station near building E 405 and the production building G 400 (open plant). To the south it is adjoined by the building containing the office, laboratory and control room.

1.1.1. Location

The Deka factory is located on the BASF site adjacent (see figure 6.1) to the other production plants (XXX to the north and east) and to storage and packing plants (XXX to the west). The distance from other plants is as follows: workshops 80-100 m, pool G 306 150 m, apprentice shop H 307 200 m, canteen H 421 200 m, site boundary 250 m.

The Deka factory is bordered by factory roads only in the south (west-east direction) and in the east (south-north direction). The building holding the offices and control room is located on the west-east road. The south-north road is closed to through traffic because of the railway tank-cars standing there.

The unloading station for acrolein tank-cars is located in the shut-off protective zones around tank stores F 405 and E 405 to the west of building E 405.

1.1.2. Protective zones

In accordance with the Explosion Protection Guide-lines (EX-RL) issued by BG Chemie, building G 400 is classified as a hazardous location, zone 1, for ignition temperatures >135° C (Ex T4). In compliance with VbF/TRbF, tank store G 404 is classified as a hazardous location, zones 1 and 2, for

ignition temperatures >135° C (Ex T4) within its protective zones according to TRbF 110 (see Ex-Notiz).[1]

1.1.3. Accessibility

The facilities of the Deka factory are accessible from several sides via passable roads (escape, rescue, fire-fighting routes). The escape routes in building G 400 meet the requirements of the Regulations for the Prevention of Accidents. They are apparent from figure 6.12.

1.2. Processes

The following processes are used in the Deka factory (basic diagrams in figures 6.3-6.7).

1. Conversion of aldehydes to the corresponding alkyl amines with ammonia,
e.g. $2\ CH_3-CH_2-CHO+NH_3 + 2\ H_2$
$$\rightarrow (CH_3-CH_2-CH_2)_2\ NH+2\ H_2O$$
Propionaldehyde+ammonia → Di-n-propyl-amine+water+hydrogen.

2. Conversion of alcohols to the corresponding alkyl amines with ammonia,
e.g. $CH_3-CH-CH_3+NH_3 \rightarrow CH_3-CH.CH_3+H_2O$
with OH below the first and NH_2 below the second
Isopropanol+ammonia → isopropylamine+water.

3. Conversion of aldehydes to the corresponding alkyl amines with amines, e.g. XXX.

4. Dehydrogenation of butane diol-1.4 to butyrolactone,
$HO-CH_2-CH_2-CH_2-CH_2-OH \rightarrow$ (ring structure) $+2\ H_2$
Butane diol-1.4 → r-butyrolactone+hydrogen.

5. Hydrogenation of unsaturates,
e.g. $CH_3\text{-}CH_2\text{-}CH = C\text{-}CHO+H_2 \rightarrow CH_3\text{-}CH_2\text{-}CH_2\text{-}CH\text{-}CHO$
with CH_3 below each
2-methylpentanal+hydrogen → 2-methylpentanal.

6. Synthesis of XXX from acrolein and reaction component B,
Substance $B+CH_2 = CH_2 \text{ - } CHO \rightarrow XXX$.

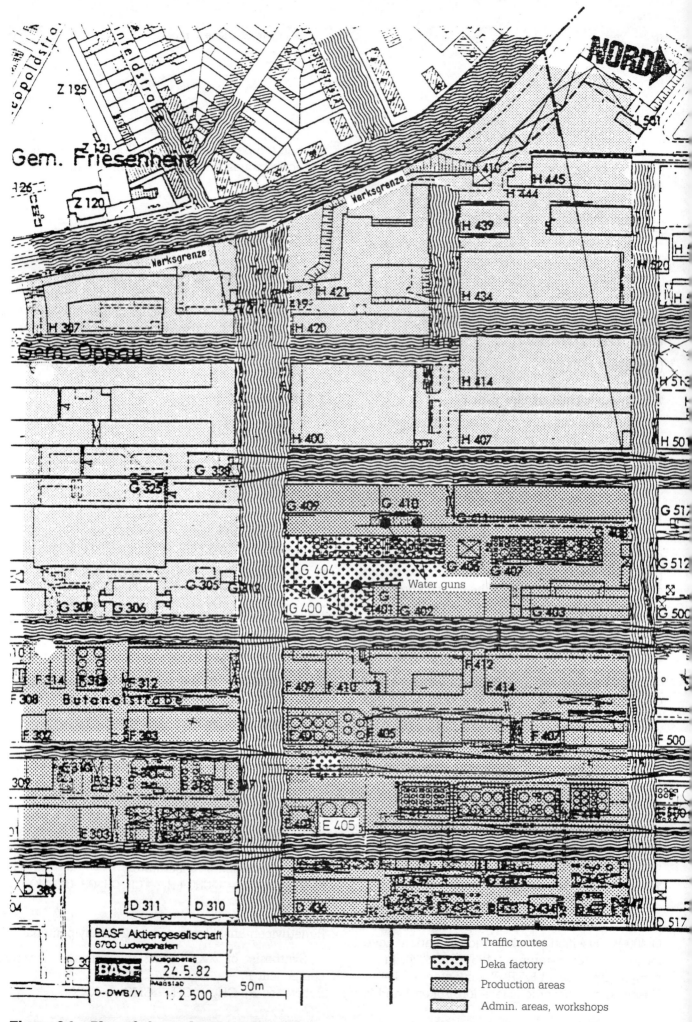

Figure 6.1. Plan of site and surrounding area

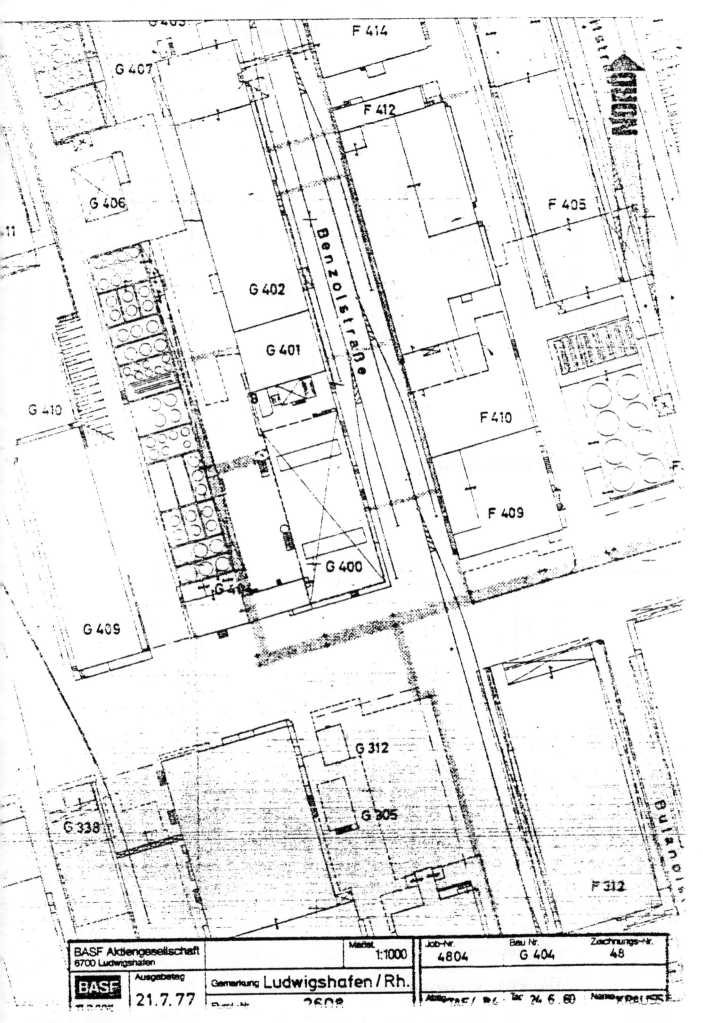

Figure 6.2.   Site plan

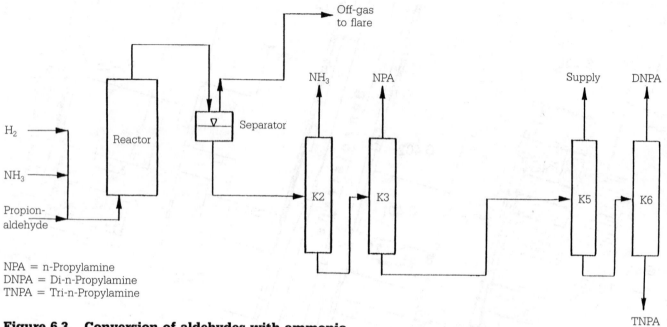

NPA = n-Propylamine
DNPA = Di-n-Propylamine
TNPA = Tri-n-Propylamine

Figure 6.3. Conversion of aldehydes with ammonia

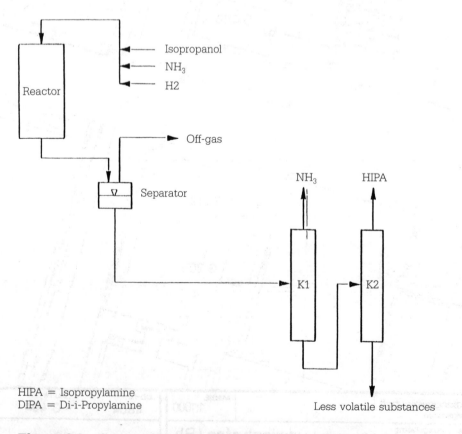

HIPA = Isopropylamine
DIPA = Di-i-Propylamine

Figure 6.4. Conversion of alcohols with ammonia

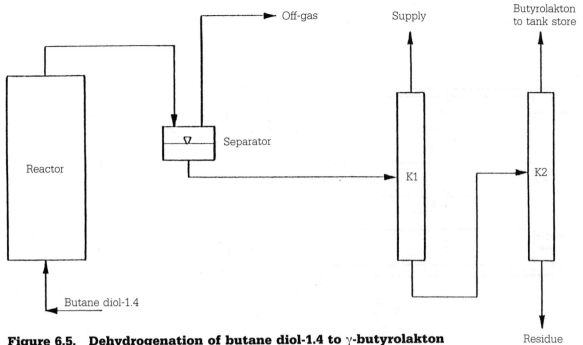

Figure 6.5. Dehydrogenation of butane diol-1.4 to γ-butyrolakton

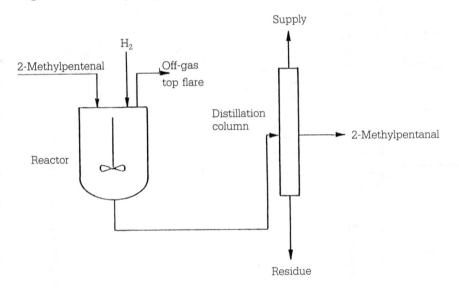

**Figure 6.6.
Hydrogenation of unsaturates**

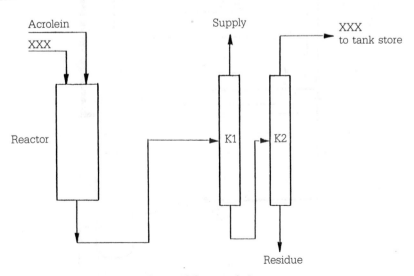

Figure 6.7. Conversion with acrolein

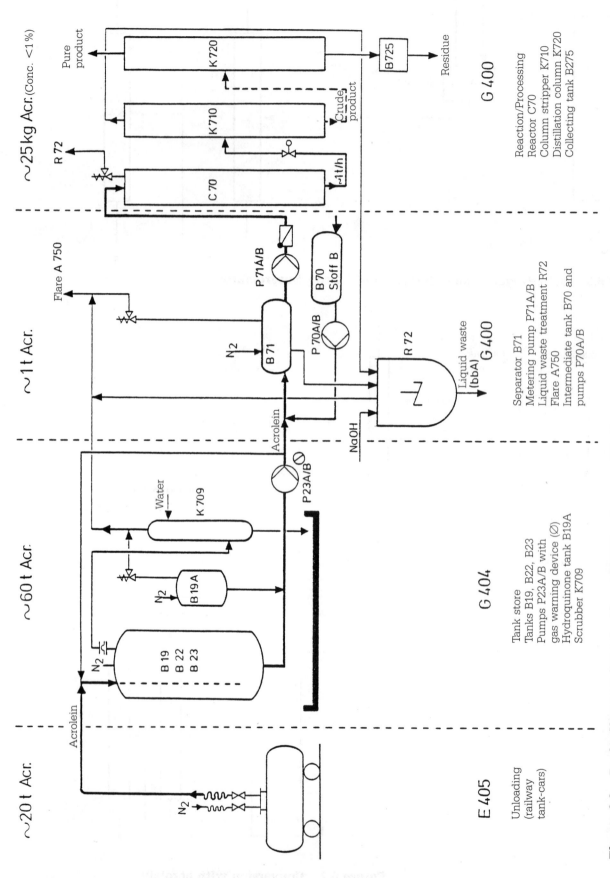

Figure 6.8. Basic diagram "Production of XXX using acrolein"

1.3. Reason for limiting the safety report to process No. 6 – conversion with acrolein

The plant units in which processes 1-5 are employed are integrated in the Deka factory. However, they are self-sufficient, independent plant units, which are not linked via the product chain.

Only process 6 uses a substance listed in Appendix II of the Ordinance on Major Hazard Control, namely acrolein (see basic diagram in figure 6.8).

When discussing the hazards, the possible hazards originating from plant units 1-5 are given special consideration (4.1.3).

1.4. Construction design

Product-carrying equipment, pipe-work and valves of the acrolein plant are manufactured from stainless steel (1.4541) and, in addition, in compliance with the Project Media Code.[2] The design data and constructive details of the equipment are documented in the equipment list (figure 6.9) and the technical data sheets.[3]

The design features of buildings G 400 and G 404 are apparent from the construction drawings/component arrangement drawings. Figure 6.12 is an extract from these drawings. The safety of the buildings was verified within the scope of the licensing procedure.

1.5. Description of the process

The complete description of the process – conversion of acrolein to XXX with substance B – is given in the licence application dated 15 June 1979 according to the Federal Law on Pollution Control of the Federal Republic of Germany.

1.5.1. Unloading and storage of acrolein (figures 6.8-6.11)

Acrolein is delivered in railway tank-cars and unloaded in front of E 405. N_2 pressure (approximately 1 bar overpressure) is used to empty the tank-cars into the acrolein tanks B 19, B 22 and B 23 in G 404.

Special safety measures are taken for storage of acrolein in tanks B 19, B 22 and B 23 because acrolein tends towards exothermal polymerisation

Figure 6.9. Equipment list with design data (see figure 6.8.) for process No. 6: Conversion with acrolein

Equipment				Design data		
Abbreviation	No.	Identification	Size	Temp. [°C]	Overpressure p_e [bar]	
B 19	1	Storage tank for acrolein	35 m³	50	3	
B 22	1	Storage tank for acrolein	30 m³	50	4	
B 23	1	Storage tank for acrolein	28 m³	50	2	
P 23	2	Centrifugal pump	3 m³/h	120	10	
B 19 A	1	Hydroquinone intermediate tank	1 m³	50	6	
K 709	1	Scrubber	0.4 × 5 m	50	0	
B 18	1	Storage tank for XXX (crude)	33 m³	50	0	
B 33	1	Storage tank for XXX (pure)	90 m³	50	0	
B 57	1	Storage tank for XXX (pure)	50 m³	50	0	
B 70	1	Intermediate tank	2 m³	200	2	
P 70	2	Pump	1 m³/h	200	10	
B 71	1	Separator	2.5 m³	200	6	
P 71	2	Metering pump	2 m³/h	200	130	
R 72	1	Tank with stirrer	4 m³	200	6	
C 70	1	Reactor	1 m³	300	80	
K 710	1	Column stripper	0.6 × 10 m	200	2	
K 720	1	Distillation column	0.8 × 24 m	200	0	
B 725	1	Collecting tank	6 m³	200	2	

Acrolein unloading in E405 side view
Top view see G400/257 b-8

① Folding stairs, four steps with safety hook

② Monitoring room with process
measuring and control systems

③ Suspension device for acrolein and N_2 hose

Acrolein to G404

N_2 from cold gasifier

Cable route process
measuring and control
lines

Concrete
paving stories

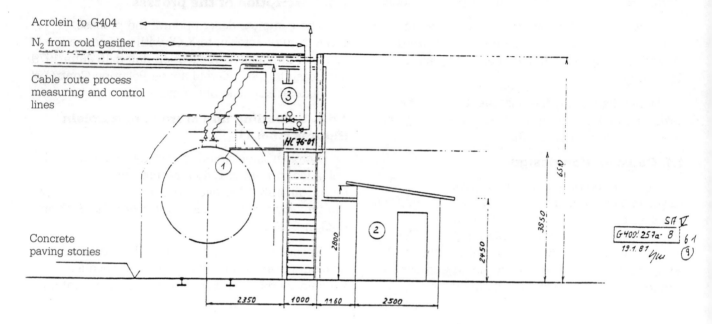

Acrolein unloading in E405 (top view)
Side view in G400/2570-B

① ② s. G400/257 a-8

③ Emergency and
eye shower

④ Hydrant

⑤ 4 rail dewatering
boxes 30 m in front
of and behind
filling point *

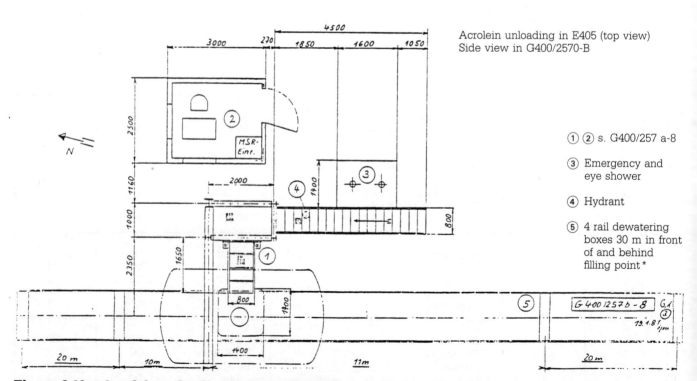

Figure 6.10. Acrolein unloading in front of building E 405

* (connected to b.b.A culvert)

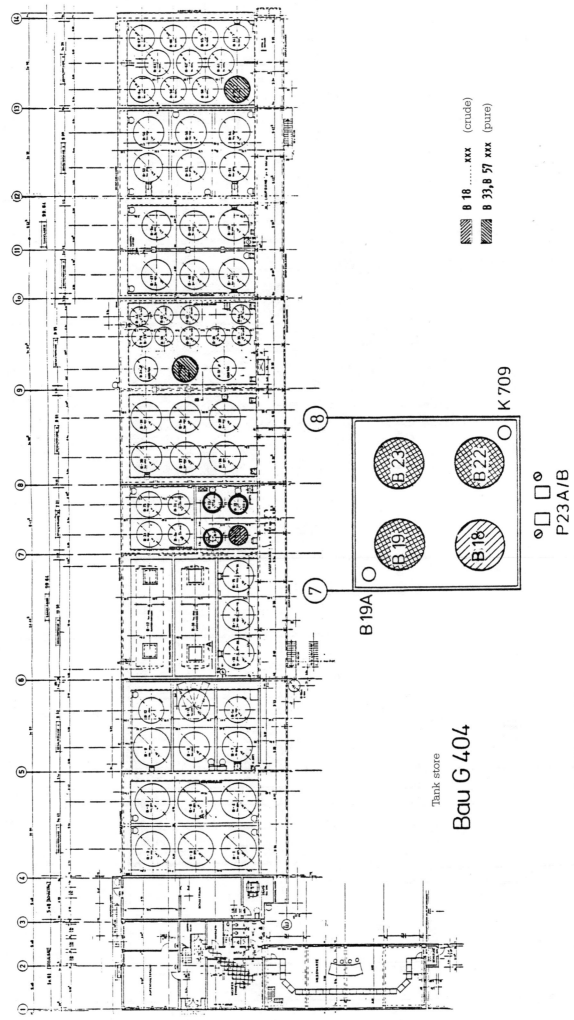

B 18 ......xxx (crude)

B 33, B 57 xxx (pure)

Tank store

Bau G 404

Figure 6.11. Plan of tank store, building G 404

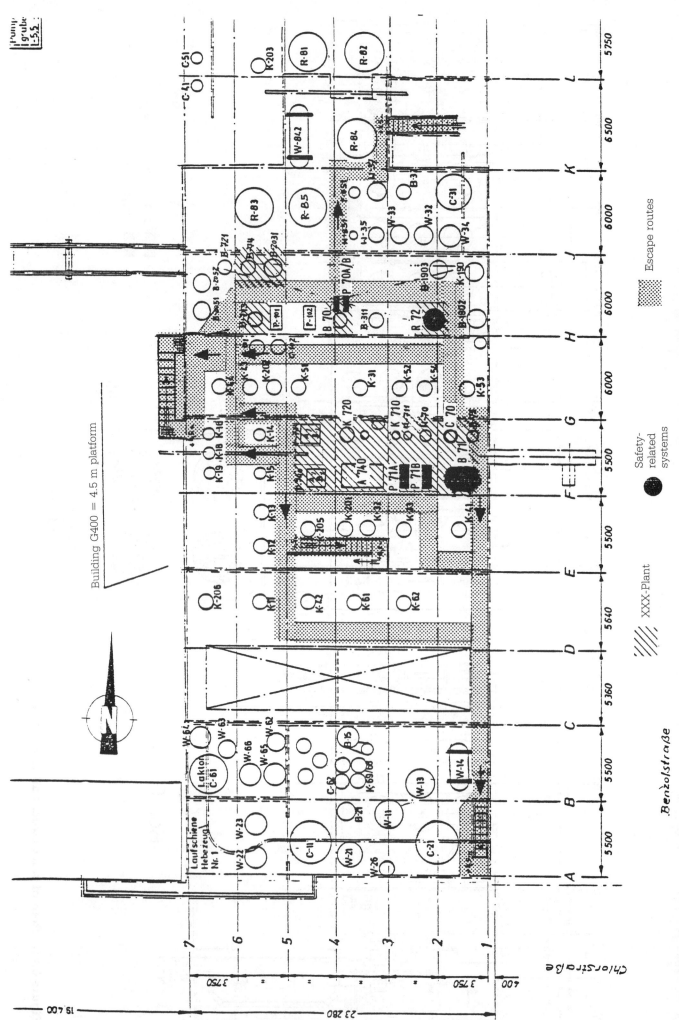

Figure 6.12. Plan of building G400, 4.5 m platform (extract from construction and component arrangement drawings)

Escape routes

Safety-related systems

XXX-Plant

Building G400 = 4.5 m platform

Benzolstraße

Chlorstraße

at higher temperatures and in the presence of substances which cause an alkaline reaction (see figure 6.13).

1. Each tank is vented with nitrogen (highly purified) to keep substances causing an alkaline reaction away from acrolein.

2. Each tank can be sprinkled with water for cooling purposes.

3. The acrolein is continuously circulated by pumps. Methanol containing approximately 5 per cent hydroquinone is automatically added into this acrolein loop from tank B 19A using a nitrogen overpressure of 2 bar if the temperature in one of the tanks exceeds 30° C.

4. Temperature and tank level are measured and recorded. Both measured values are linked to an optical and acoustic alarm.

5. Each tank is equipped with two rupture discs installed in series in a nozzle (set to 1.1 and 1.9 bar overpressure). In the event of a pressure increase in the tank, e.g. as a result of polymerisation of the acrolein, bursting of the first rupture disc automatically initiates the water sprinkling system of scrubber K 709 which is filled with Raschig rings. On bursting of the second rupture disc, the acrolein vapour produced in the tank is transferred to this scrubber and reacted there. The scrubber, and all other plant equipment from which acrolein vapour can escape, are connected to a header leading to flare A 750.

1.5.2. Production (figures 6.8, 6.9 and 6.12)

The reaction component B is supplied via pipework and input into the mixing tank B 71 via intermediate tank B 70 and pump B 70. Acrolein is also transferred from the tank store G 404 via pipework. In the mixing tank B 71 (overpressure approximately 4 bar, ambient temperature), a small quantity of the water present in the acrolein separates out and is transferred to tank R 72.

The premixed feedstocks are transported via the metering pump P 71 into the reactor C 70, which is operated at temperatures of 100-200° C and a pressure of 20-70 bar.

In the reactor C 70, acrolein reacts with component B to form XXX. The reaction product is transferred through a control valve to the non-

pressurised column stripper K 710, in which highly volatile substances (primarily non-converted feedstock) are distilled off and transferred to R 72.

The water in R 72 contains approximately 1 per cent acrolein. This is decomposed in an exothermal reaction by the continuous addition of caustic soda to form higher molecular products. The water discharged into the liquid waste network for liquid waste requiring treatment is free of acrolein; it contains organic materials, which can be biologically decomposed and contain neither metals nor halogens.

The XXX, from which most of the highly volatile fractions have been removed in column K 710, is transported to tank B 18 in the tank store G 404, where it is temporarily stored. The XXX is then transferred from this store to column K 720 for further purification.

In K 720, XXX is distilled at the top of the column and is then collected as XXX (pure) in tanks B 33 and B 57 of tank store G 404. The sump from K 720 is collected in B 725 and discharged to the residue incineration plant. The sump, which contains neither metals nor halogens, can be incinerated without any problems.

The synthesis section of the plant is operated and monitored from the main control room of the Deka factory. Systems for further processing are operated locally.

All off-gas displaced from acrolein tanks B 19, B 22, B 23 and the production plant is burned in flare A 750 (figures 6.8 and 6.16).

1.5.3. Energy supply

For its energy supply, the Deka factory is connected to the respective BASF network for electricity, cooling water, steam, nitrogen, compressed air and natural gas. Emergency energy supplies are not required (see 4.1.2.4 and 4.1.2.5).

Highly purified nitrogen: in order to assure the necessary purity, a separate nitrogen supply system which is independent of the nitrogen network is installed to provide nitrogen for operating systems containing acrolein (see figure 6.13). It consists of a nitrogen cold evaporator and an emergency supply from a battery of nitrogen steel cylinders.

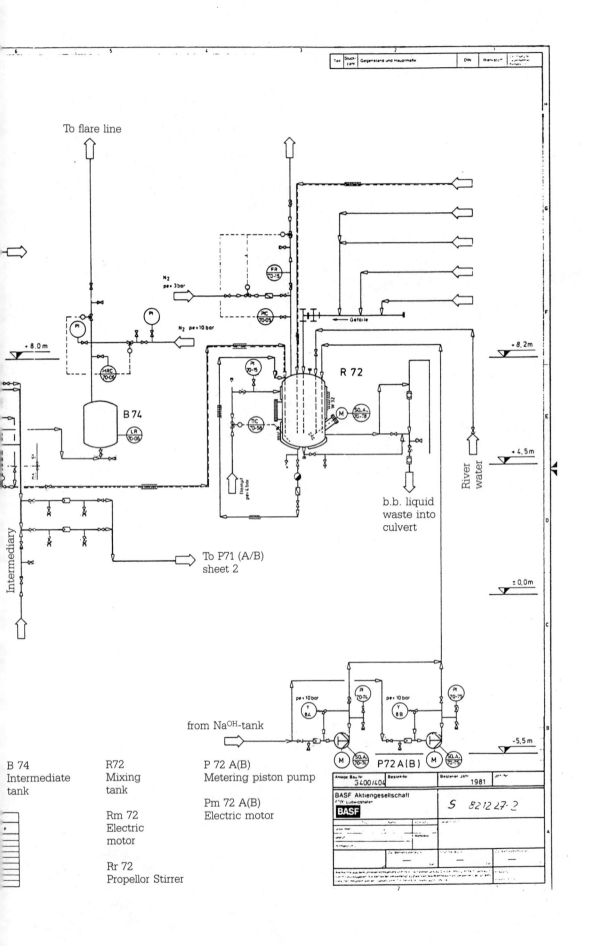

To flare line

N₂ pe = 3bar

N₂ pe = 10 bar

+ 8.0 m

B 74

R 72

+ 8,2m

Gefälle

+ 4,5m

River water

b.b. liquid waste into culvert

± 0,0m

Intermediary

To P71 (A/B) sheet 2

pe = 10 bar

pe = 10 bar

from Na^OH-tank

-5,5 m

P72 A(B)

B 74	R72	P 72 A(B)
Intermediate tank	Mixing tank	Metering piston pump
	Rm 72 Electric motor	Pm 72 A(B) Electric motor
	Rr 72 Propellor Stirrer	

Anlage Bau Nr
3400/404
Besteller JAhr
1981

BASF Aktiengesellschaft
BASF
S 821227-2

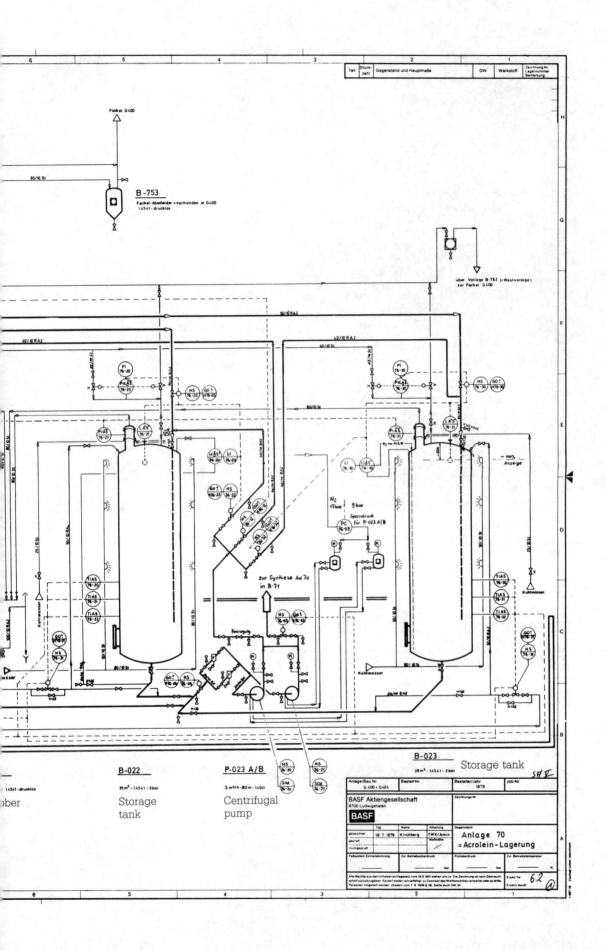

Fackel G 400

65/10 St

B -753
Fackel-Abscheider = vorhanden in G 400
1.4541 - drucklos

über Vorlage B-752 (=Westvorlage)
zur Fackel G 400

zur Synthese Anl 70
in B-71

N₂
17bar   9bar
Sperrdruck
für P-023 A|B

Kuhlwasser

Kuhlwasser

Kuhlwasser

Anzeige

B-022
35 m³ - 1.4541 - 3bar

Storage tank

B-023
28 m³ - 1.4541 - 2bar   Storage tank

P-023 A/B
3 m³/h - 80 m - 1.4541

Centrifugal pump

SH Ⅴ

Anlage/Bau Nr. G 400 + G404	Bestell-Nr.	Besteller/Jahr 1979	Job-Nr.

BASF Aktiengesellschaft
6700 Ludwigshafen

BASF

	Tag	Name	Abteilung	Gegenstand
gezeichnet	18. 7. 1979	Kirchberg	TWX/Amin	
geprüft			Maßstäbe	**Anlage 70**
normgeprüft				**= Acrolein-Lagerung**

Ersatz für 6.2
Ersatz durch

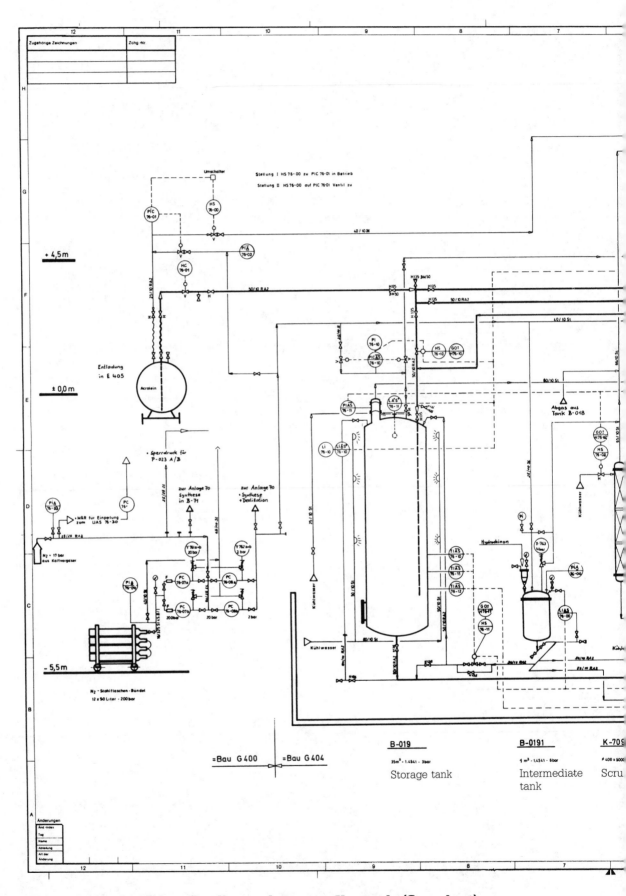

Figure 6.13. Acrolein unloading and storage, N₂ supply (flow chart)

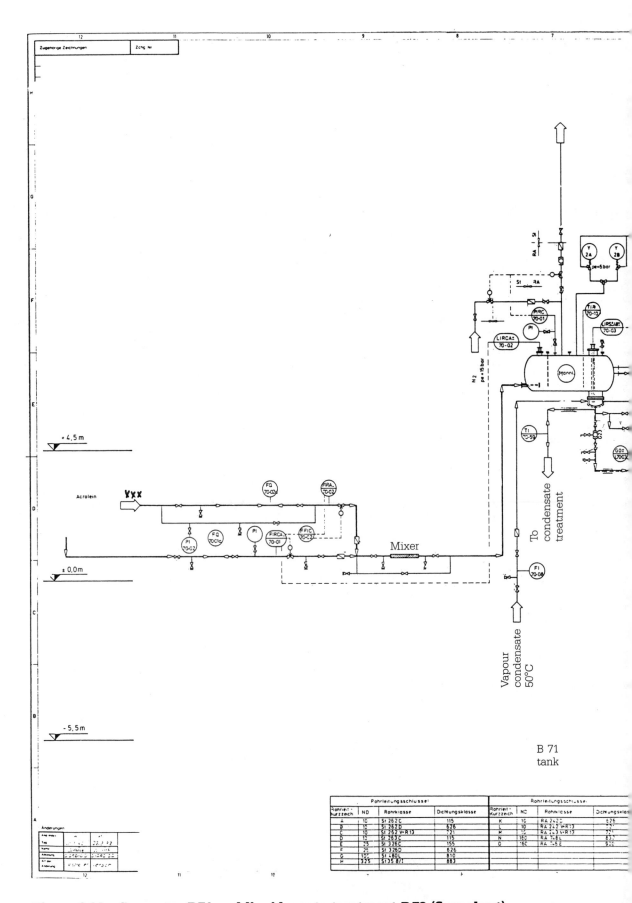

Figure 6.14. Separator B 71 and liquid waste treatment R 72 (flow chart)

The safety lighting for control room and escape routes is assured by lamps equipped with individual batteries.

2. Description of the safety-related systems, the hazards and the preconditions for the occurrence of an accident

(Article 7 (1) 2)

2.1. Safety-related systems

The safety-related systems are established through systematic consideration of the flow charts of the overall plant. First of all, the overall plant is divided into technical units (systems) which either (i) can be operated independently, or (ii) are of great importance for the overall plant, or (iii) are necessary as auxiliary systems for plant operation (e.g. cooling system, off-gas system).

A system is safety related if:

- substances listed in Appendix II are present or can form in quantities of significance for safety;

- the system is required for safe operation of the plant because it prevents accidents or limits consequences (protective systems and other systems required for operating safety).

The following safety-related systems are established on the basis of these considerations (figures 6.8, 6.10-6.12; flow charts, figures 6.13-6.16).

2.1.1. Acrolein unloading in front of building E 405 (figures 6.10 and 6.13)

- Railway tank-cars containing 20 t of acrolein, normal tank-cars with riser pipe without floor drain, design in compliance with GGVE (Ordinance on Rail Transportation of Hazardous Materials), Appendix XI (4 bar), unloading equipment with hose connection, manual valves, pipeline via pipe bridge to tank store, building G 404.

- Unloading and transport of acrolein using nitrogen at 1 bar overpressure (highly purified N_2 from cold gasifier or compressed nitrogen cylinder battery), controlled by PIC 76-01. Maximum overpressure from reducing station

PC 76-08 a/b: 2 bar, protected by safety valve Y 762 a/b. In addition, the operation is carried out in compliance with the operating and safety instructions.

2.1.2. Acrolein storage 3 x 20 t, building G 404 (figure 6.13)

- Storage tanks B 19, B 22, B 23 with level, pressure and temperature safety devices and circuits:

  $LIA^{\pm}S^+$ 76 – 10, 20, 30; LA^+S^+ 76-11, 21, 31; $PICA^{\pm}S^+$ 76 – 10, 20, 30; PIA^+S^+ 76-11, 21, 31; TIA^+S^+ 76 – 10/11/12, –20/21/22, –30/31/32 (in each case 2 out of 3).

- Centrifugal pumps P 23 A/B for the transport and circulation of acrolein (see 1.5.1 (3)) with double rotating mechanical seal and sealing liquid (methanol) at an N_2 overpressure of 9 bar.

- Protective and safety equipment:

  - hydroquinone tank B 19A (see 1.5.1 (3)): this is at an N_2 overpressure of 2 bar and is protected by safety valve Y 763 which is set at 4 bar; further alarms and switching by PIA- 76-00 and LIA-S-76-00 respectively;

  - scrubber K 709 (see 1.5.1 (5)): liquid waste is collected in tank tub;

  - water sprinkling system for storage tanks (see 1.5.1 (2));

  - collecting tank (tank tub): dimensioned in compliance with TRbF 110 (can hold contents of largest tank); collected liquid can only be pumped into the liquid waste requiring treatment if the sump pump is started up;

  - gas warning system at pumps P 23 A/B:

  - Sieger remote gas sensor at each pump, alarm threshold in ppm range.

Further inspection and safety measures are specified in the operating and safety instructions.

2.1.3. Water separator B 71 and tank R 72 with stirrer (liquid waste treatment) (figure 6.14) description in 1.5.2

- B 71 is operated at an N_2 overpressure of 4 bar (PIRC 70-01) and is protected by two safety valves set at 6 bar overpressure. The off-gas from the pressure control system and the safety valves is transferred to flare A 750 via a liquid separator.

– R 72 is operated unpressurised. In addition, the operating and safety instructions are observed.

2.1.4. Injection pump P 71 A/B, which feeds against overpressure in reactor C 70 (figure 6.15), see 1.5.2

Check valves in the line to the reactor C 70; safety valves as overflow valves Y 3 A/B, response overpressure 80 bar.

2.1.5. Flare for off-gas A 750 (figure 6.16)

Off-gas collection system; safety system TIA- 75-00.

In addition, the flare is operated and regularly inspected in compliance with the operating and safety instructions.

2.1.6. Pipe-work and valves

Materials and construction of piping, seals and valves in compliance with Project Media Code.[2]

The pipe from the acrolein unloading station from E 405 to G 404 is continuously welded and insulated. Flanges are sealed with special seals, type Spiroflex. All pipes carrying acrolein are designed for a nominal pressure of at least 10 bar.

The reactor C 70 and the downstream columns are non-safety-related (see figure 6.8).

The reactor C 70 and the downstream columns contain a maximum total of 25 kg of acrolein with a concentration of <1 per cent by volume (established by means of analyses). The reaction in the reactor C 70 is exothermal. The contents of the reactor exhibit practically ideal mixing: the acrolein

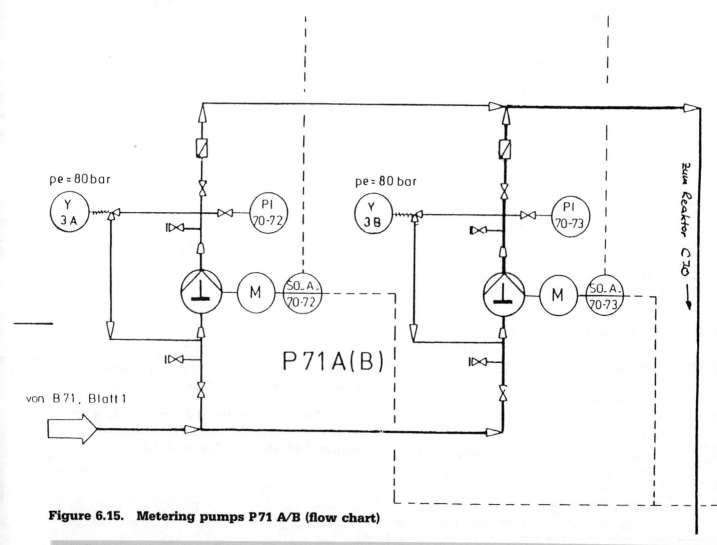

Figure 6.15.   Metering pumps P71 A/B (flow chart)

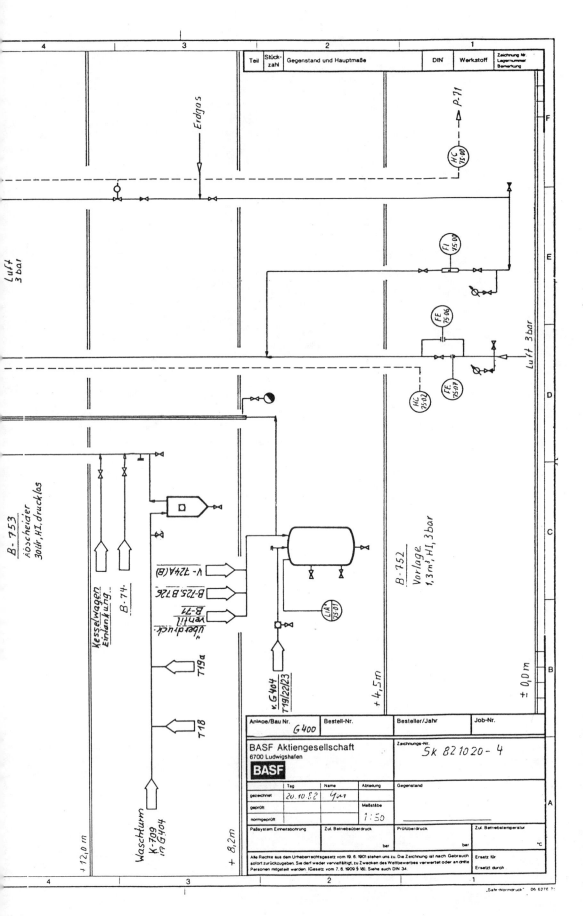

Figure 6.16. Flare (A 750) (flow chart)

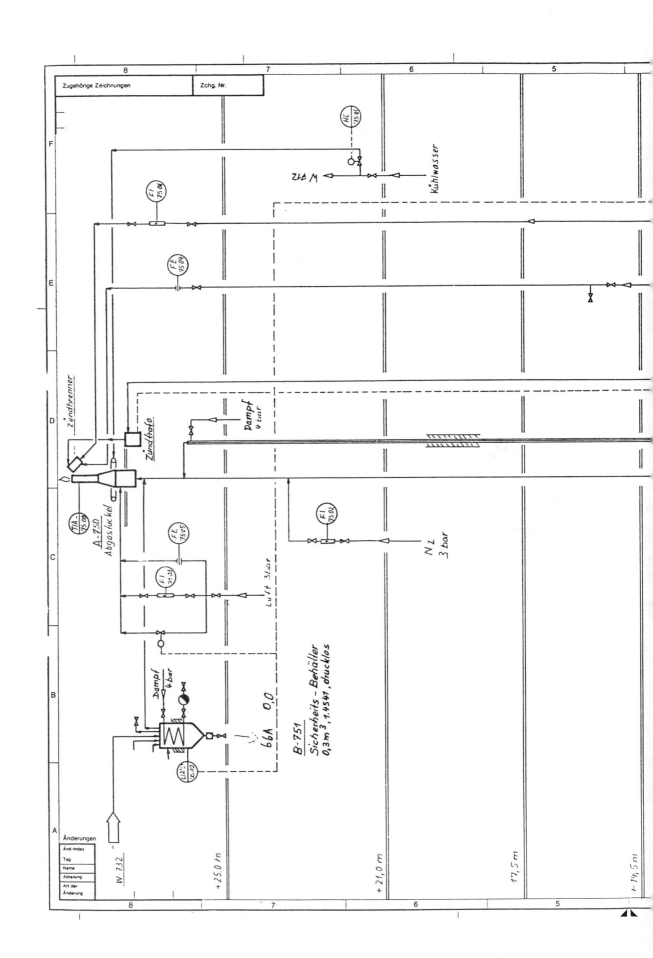

concentration is therefore the same at all points of the reactor. The reaction is controlled in such a way that it takes place very quickly. For this reason, the acrolein concentration is less than 1 per cent by volume. Although the reaction in C 70 is exothermal, there are no conceivable events at which temperatures and pressures could occur which would be unacceptable from a safety-related viewpoint.

Even failure of reactor cooling (without simultaneous failure of the injection pump) does not lead to a hazardous condition: at a peak of 250° C the injection pump P 71 is shut down by the "temperature high" alarm and the subsequent reaction only causes a slight temperature and pressure rise. This shut-down, however, is not a safety measure in the sense of accident prevention: if shut-down is not effected and P 71 continues feeding, (undesirable) high-molecular products form with increasing temperature. However, their vapour pressure is so low that there is no further pressure increase. The solids which have formed in the reactor must then be removed mechanically. Shut-down does not cause conditions which would endanger safety, but rather conditions which are operationally undesirable.

Feedback from the reactor C 70 to upstream systems as a result of a backflow of material is ruled out by the check valves between P 71 A/B and C 70 and by the diaphragm pumps P 71 A/B themselves (see figure 6.15). Similarly, the downstream columns contain only very slight quantities of acrolein; no reactions at all take place there either.

2.2. Hazards and preconditions for an accident

There is the possibility of an accident occurring if large quantities of acrolein are released. In principle, acrolein can be released as a result of:

- overfilling of the storage tanks caused by operating errors when handling the unloading equipment and failure of the level safety systems;
- damage to/leakage from the acrolein tank-car and the acrolein storage tanks because of failure of the pressure safety systems;
- rupture of the hose connections of the unloading system;

- polymerisation of acrolein in the acrolein storage tanks because of impurities in the acrolein or filling of the acrolein storage tanks with other products;
- leakage from the centrifugal pumps P 23 A/B;
- damage to/leakage from B 71 because of failure of the pressure control system;
- exothermal reaction in R 72 because of failure of the level safety system and operating errors when discharging water;
- leakage from the diaphragm pumps P 71 A/B;
- failure of flare A 750 because of operating errors or loss of natural gas supply.

Leakages from pipes (4.1.1.6), use of unsuitable material (4.1.2.2), sampling (4.1.2.3), loss of energy (4.1.2.4), machine failure (4.1.2.5), hazards from other units of the Deka factory (4.1.3), environmentally incurred hazards (4.1.4) and sabotage (4.1.5) can be ruled out as hazards leading to a major accident.

3. Chemical identification of substances; condition and quantity of substances in accordance with Appendix II

(Article 7 (1) 3)

Quantity of acrolein handled:

(a) tank store: maximum 60 t;

(b) B 71: approximately 1 t;

(c) acrolein tank-car: 20 t.

Temperature: ambient temperature.

Material data: safety-related and toxicological data are apparent from figure 6.17. Safety-related side reactions are not known.

4. Description of fulfilment of the requirements imposed in Articles 3 to 6

(Article 7 (1) 4)

4.1. Measures for the prevention of accidents

4.1.1. Special operational hazards

4.1.1.1/2. Acrolein unloading and storage (figure 6.13)

Operating errors and failure of the level safety system (LIA±S+76-10, 20, 30 and LA+S+ 76-11, 21,

Figure 6.17.   Material and reaction data– acrolein (2-propenal, acrylaldehyde)

Acrolein is a colourless, very reactive, toxic liquid with a penetrating smell. Irritation of skin, eyes and mucous membranes. Inhalation causes burning of the respiratory tract and lungs, oral intake leads to irritation, vomiting, diarrhoea.

(a) General material data

Formula	$CH_2 = CH - CHO$
Molecular weight	56.06
Melting point	−88°C
Boiling point at 1013 mbar	53° C
Vapour pressure at 20° C	286 mbar
Density at 20° C	0.84 g/cm³
Rel. vapour density (air = 1)	1.94
Solubility in water at 20° C	26.7 g/100 cm³
Soluble in many organic solvents	

(b) Safety-related material and reaction data

Flash point	−29° C
Danger class acc. to VbF	AI
Ignition temperature	280° C
Ignition temperature (stabilised)	210° C
Temperature class	T 3
Explosion limits in air	2.8 – 31 vol. per cent

Stabilised with hydroquinone (tendency to polymerisation)
Violent reaction with alkalis and oxidising substances

(c) Health effects

Acute toxicity :
man : inhalation, LCLo = 153 ppm/10 min. ;
animal : rat, oral, LD_{50} = 46 mg/kg ;
mouse, oral, LD_{50} = 40 mg/kg ;
odour level : = 0.2-0.4 pm.

(d) Maximum workplace conc. 0.1 ppm ≙ 0.25 mg/m³

References :
C. W. Smith :	"Acrolein", Hüthig Verlag, 1975.
Hommel :	"Handbuch der gefährlichen Güter", Merkblatt 218.
Kühn-Birett :	"Merkblätter gefährliche Arbeitsstoffe", No. A 09.
DEGUSSA :	Merkblatt Acrolein.
NIOSH :	"Registry of toxic effects of chemical substance", 1980.

31) can cause *overfilling of storage tanks* B 19, 22 and 23.

On the whole, operating errors are ruled out by the operating instructions for unloading of the tank-cars and for acrolein storage. If overfilling, nevertheless, becomes a threat because of operating errors or carelessness, the level safety system issues an alarm and closes supply valves HS 76-10, 20, 30 (shut-down). Both alarm and shut-down have redundant back-up support (LIA±S±and LA±S±). Consequently an alarm will always be signalled and shut-down always effected even in the case of failure of a process measuring and control safety system.

These measures practically rule out overfilling of the acrolein storage tanks.

Damage to/leakage from the tank-car, as a result of too high internal pressure, can only be caused by simultaneous failure of the nitrogen reducing station PC 76-08a/b, the related safety valves and the pressure control system PIC 76-01.

Damage to/leakage from the acrolein storage tanks as a result of too high internal pressure, can only be caused by simultaneous failure of the nitrogen reducing station PC 76-08a/b, the related safety valves and the "pressure high" safety system PICA±S+ with simultaneous non-bursting of one of the rupture discs. PICA±S+ closes the ball valves in the acrolein supply line HS 76-10, 20, 30 and the nitrogen supply valve at "pressure high" in the nitrogen line.

These safety measures practically rule out the occurrence of a leakage from the acrolein storage tanks and the tank-car.

The following measures rule out *rupture of the hose connection of the unloading equipment* and release of acrolein :

(a) there is no motor vehicle traffic at the unloading station (see site plant, figure 1) ;

(b) the acrolein tank-cars cannot be moved inadvertently because of the use of stop blocks ;

(c) the only track to the unloading station is blocked by a shunt which is locked in the opposite direction and a double red lamp to prevent the approach of other railway cars during the unloading process ;

(d) the hose of the unloading equipment is always visually checked for defects before use;

(e) during unloading, the operator supervises the unloading process continuously. If leakages occur, the following measures are taken on the spot: acrolein is blown down into the flare via the emergency blow-down system (HS 76-00 open), and the acrolein line is closed (HC 76-01 closed).

Filling of the acrolein tanks with a different product can lead to polymerisation of acrolein, which in turn can cause bursting of the rupture discs (see 1.5.1 (5)) and, finally, the ingress of acrolein into the collecting tank. The following measures can almost certainly rule out this hazard:

(a) only acrolein tank-cars are unloaded at the unloading station. As no other product is unloaded there, the acrolein tanks cannot be filled with a different product even if operating errors are made by the personnel (mixing up of valves or unloading couplings);

(b) before an acrolein tank-car is unloaded, an analysis must be carried out to confirm that it contains acrolein of the specified purity;

(c) the acrolein storage tanks are only connected by piping to the unloading station E 405 and the acrolein plant. There are absolutely no gas or liquid-carrying pipe connections to other operating systems (except for the nitrogen supply lines).

Even slight impurities in the acrolein can lead to polymerisation. This hazard is ruled out by the fact that highly purified nitrogen is used to expel the acrolein from the tank-car and to cover the tank contents. This nitrogen is not withdrawn from the nitrogen network, but rather is highly purified nitrogen supplied by a cold gasifier.

In the event of *loss of the nitrogen supply* from the cold gasifier, an emergency supply of highly purified nitrogen is available from steel cylinder batteries. Declining nitrogen stocks are signalled by PIA- 76-03 and 76-04 in the control room.

Polymerisation of the acrolein in the storage tanks is not to be expected in view of the existing organisational and technical measures. If, contrary to expectations, polymerisation nevertheless occurs, the following measures are provided for this extremely unlikely case.

Starting polymerisation is initially detected by a temperature increase. The temperature is always kept below 20° C with the aid of the water sprinkling system. Temperature safety systems TIA$^+$S$^+$ 76-10/11/12, -20/21/22, -30/31/32 are designed redundantly (two out of three) because of their importance. This practically rules out non-detection of a temperature increase. If two of three measuring points detect a temperature in excess of 30° C, an alarm is signalled in the control room and the safety system automatically initiates the following measures:

(a) hydroquinone from the hydroquinone tank B 19A is injected into the acrolein loop by opening the respective valves HS 76-11, 21, 31;

(b) ball valve HS 70-03 is closed. This stops the product flow from the tank store to the production plant;

(c) pump P 71 is shut down.

Polymerisation of acrolein is a reaction via radicals. Hydroquinone captures radicals. Hydroquinone radicals would react with the radicals of the polymerisation reaction and therefore stop the reaction.

The quantity of hydroquinone – dissolved in methanol – which is stored in tank B 19A amounts to approximately 40 kg. This is approximately 0.2 per cent of the maximum quantity of acrolein stored in one tank (the quantity of hydroquinone used for stabilisation of commercially available monomers is in the order of 100 ppm).

As a first approximation, this quantity of hydroquinone amounting to approximately 40 kg could react with the same quantity of a radical starter (with the same molecular weight). It is not conceivable that such a quantity could enter an acrolein tank as an impurity. This therefore ensures that even the starting of polymerisation can be prevented.

Nevertheless, additional protective systems are provided: the collecting tank for acrolein, the water jets which can also cool the ouside of the storage tanks and the scrubber K 709.

The pressure between the two series-connected bursting discs of the storage tank is measured, PIA$^+$S$^+$ 76-11, 21, 31. On bursting of the first disc, the water valve HS 76-02 for scrubber

K 709 is opened automatically. On bursting of the second disc, acrolein enters the scrubber. The scrubber is loaded with approximately 2.5 m³/h of water. A rough estimate shows that if acrolein enters the scrubber in gaseous form, the scrubber can condense up to 1 t/h, while if acrolein enters the scrubber in liquid form, it can remove up to 3 t/min.

An evaluation of the planned measures leads to the conclusion that a hazard resulting from any polymerisation of acrolein can be ruled out under realistic assumptions.

A leakage of acrolein from the centrifugal pumps P 23 A/B is prevented by equipping both pumps with double rotating mechanical seals (see 2.1.2). As additional protection, a gas warning device is installed with two remote gas sensors directly at the two pumps (see 2.1.2) (primary explosion protection measure in compliance with E 1.4.1 EX-RL).

4.1.1.3. Water separator B 71 and tank R 72 (figure 6.14)

Failure of the pressure control PIRC 70-01 in water separator B 71 can lead to dangerous overpressure. The tank is therefore equipped with two safety valves (shuttle valves), thus ruling out this hazard.

Exothermal reaction acrolein – caustic soda in R 72. The water settling as the lower phase in B 71 is locally discharged by hand into mixing tank R 72 to prevent an unnecessary release of acrolein. At the same time, this discharge is monitored in the control room via LIRCA±70-02 and LIRS±A±70-03. The level process measuring and control system LIRS±A±70-03, which measures the level of the acrolein-water interface and closes valve 70-03 at level "low", is used only for additional safety.

In the event of failure of LIRS±A±70-03 and simultaneous operating errors during discharge, large quantities of acrolein can enter tank R 72 and cause a significant temperature increase as a result of the exothermal reaction with the caustic soda present in the tank. If this occurs, the contents of the tank can be directly cooled and diluted with water via an additional water inlet. A pressure increase is not possible as R 72 is freely vented to the atmosphere.

This effectively prevents a hazardous reaction between acrolein and caustic soda.

4.1.1.4. Injection pump P 71 A/B (figure 6.15)

A hazard as a result of leakages at this pump is not to be expected. This is a diaphragm pump which does not present any problems to the outside arising from the sealing of rotating or moving parts.

Hazardous overpressure, which could form on closure of the pressure side of the pump, is prevented by an overflow valve between pressure side and suction side (see 2.1.4).

4.1.1.5. Flare for off-gas A 750 (figure 6.16)

Failure of the flare can be caused by *operating errors* or by *loss of natural gas supply.* Failure is detected by a decrease in temperature at the tip of the flare and is signalled in the control room by TIA- 75-00. On failure, the entire acrolein plant is shut down in compliance with the operating and safety instructions.

Until the plant has come to a complete standstill there is an emission of non-burned acrolein via the failed flare. The quantity emitted is low: assuming 50 per cent saturation (the thermodynamically possible saturation) of acrolein, one obtains a value of approximately 0.3 kg/h of acrolein for approximately 1 m³/h of off-gas from the pressure and level control systems. The gas leaves the flare at a height of about 28 m.

Therefore failure of the flare does not present any hazard.

4.1.1.6. Pipe-work, valves

Leakages at pipes and valves are unlikely as the pipes are continuously welded wherever possible and the flanges are equipped with special seals (type Spiroflex). Possible leakages are at most slight inconveniences which can be quickly eliminated. The detection and localisation of leakages is considerably simplified by the typical smell of acrolein and the very low odour level. Inspection tours of the plant are made every hour (4.3.1).

Mechanical rupture of a pipe carrying acrolein is not classified as a hazard. The pipes are laid with maximum protection. Furthermore, the fact that the pipes are designed for a nominal pressure of at least 10 bar (which is not necessitated by the process) ensures that they can withstand possible external mechanical loading.

In order to avoid any *error,* e.g. during repairs, the pipes are marked at intervals of approximately 5 m.

4.1.2. General operational hazards

4.1.2.1. Corrosion

All plant equipment and pipe-work coming into contact with the product is manufactured from stainless steel (1.4541). According to the state of the art (e.g. Ullmann), stainless steel is completely resistant to acrolein. This is confirmed by the existing plant, in which no corrosion has been detected in the course of a 15-year period.

4.1.2.2. Use of unsuitable material

The plant is designed and erected in compliance with the Project Media Code, which is also adhered to for repairs and alterations. Since commissioning of the plant, there has been no indication of the fact that a material other than that specified has been used at any point as a result of error.

4.1.2.3. Sampling

Prior to unloading of the acrolein tank-car, a small vessel installed in the pipe between the tank-car and the storage tank is first filled. The operator then takes a sample by hand from this vessel which is isolated by valves. He only starts the unloading operation after analysis. This basically rules out any danger in connection with the sampling process.

4.1.2.4. Loss of energy

In the event of loss of steam, cooling water, compressed air, natural gas or electricity, the plant is shut down in compliance with the operating and safety instructions. As none of the safety-related systems has to be heated or cooled, loss of steam or cooling water cannot cause a hazard.

The heating (TIC 70-58) at R 72 is used only for heating at very low outside temperatures and to protect the plant from freezing during shut-down. The reaction in R 72 takes place at ambient temperature.

However, sprinkling of the acrolein tanks would also fail in the event of loss of cooling water. A very slow temperature increase in the acrolein tanks

would result over a period of several days during hot weather.

Such a slow temperature increase would, however, also indicate the absence of impurities in the acrolein, i.e. that there is no danger of polymerisation. Simultaneous occurrence of polymerisation of acrolein as a result of impurities and loss of cooling water is considered to be so unlikely that this possibility is ruled out. Note: acrolein without any impurities is transported in railway tank-cars without cooling. The redundant temperature safety systems of the acrolein tanks (and the related safety measures) are provided to prevent any polymerisation from starting with rapid temperature increase.

In the event of loss of compressed air or electricity, the process measuring and control systems, the electrical circuits fail-safe and the plant can be shut down without any danger.

If the natural gas supply is cut off, there is a slight emission of acrolein (see 4.1.1.5). The highly purified nitrogen supply for coverage of all systems containing acrolein is assured (see 2.1.1, 4.1.1.1/2).

Loss of energy therefore does not cause a hazardous operational condition. For this reason, the plant is not equipped with independent energy inputs nor with an emergency supply (except for highly purified nitrogen). The safety lighting is described in 1.5.3.

4.1.2.5. Machine failure

If the energy supply is cut off, all machines stop. No further product is transported (P 23 A/B, P 71 A/B). Failure of pumps P 23 and P 71 is not of relevance for safety; it is only of importance for product quality and plant reliability.

On shut-down of P 23 A/B, acrolein is no longer circulated in the tank store. Hydroquinone cannot be mixed in. Simultaneous occurrence of loss of energy with a demand for hydroquinone to the hydroquinone tank B 19A because of a temperature increase in an acrolein tank is considered as being so unlikely that an additional safety measure is not taken. (Long-term experience has shown that the energy supply fails for one-half to two hours every few years; it has not been necessary to mix in hydroquinone since acrolein storage commenced in 1969.)

If the stirrer in R 72 fails, the reaction between acrolein and caustic soda does not take place completely. There is an unpleasant odour because of traces of acrolein.

4.1.2.6. Fire and explosion protection

All installations in the Deka factory are in compliance with the primary explosion protection measures as stated in E 1.3.1, E 1.3.2 and E 1.3.3 EX-RL.

In hazardous locations (see 1.1.2), ignition sources such as hot surfaces, flames and hot gases, mechanically generated sparks, electrical installations, electrical compensating currents, static electricity and lightning stroke are prevented or rendered ineffective by protective measures in compliance with E 2 EX-RL (secondary explosion protection measures).

An explosion cannot occur inside the equipment and pipe-work because all systems containing flammable liquids and vapours are covered with nitrogen (primary explosion protection measures in accordance with E 1.2.2 EX-RL). All flammable off-gases are conveyed to the flare A 750, the ignition and combustion flame of which is outside hazardous locations.

All work with an open flame must be approved in writing in advance.

It is clearly shown that the plant can also withstand the loadings in the case of malfunction, and that it is adequately equipped with warning, alarm and safety systems as well as with sufficient redundant process measuring and control systems with proven equipment design. The plant is designed in compliance with state-of-the-art safety engineering; in particular it complies with the Regulations for the Prevention of Accidents, the Pressure Vessel Code, the AD specifications, the TRbF specifications, DIN/VDE standards and the EX-RL of the Union of Industrial Mutual Indemnity Associations.

The reliability of each individual installed process measuring and control system is assured by pertinent operating experience and special tests. Abnormal operating conditions are signalled optically and acoustically in the control room. All safety-related process measuring and control functions, e.g. level, pressure and temperature in the storage tanks, are designed redundantly.

4.1.3. Hazards from other operational units of the Deka factory

The adjacent operational units of the Deka factory contain flammable and toxic substances. In principle, hazards for the acrolein plant are, therefore, (i) toxic emission, (ii) fire, and (iii) explosion. Emission without ignition does not endanger the acrolein plant. The operating personnel is provided with the necessary personal protective equipment and can shut down the acrolein plant at any time and without any problems to the control room. In order to prevent fire or explosion, all equipment in the Deka factory is in compliance with explosion protection guide-lines (see 1.1.2). The acrolein plant has the same safety standard as the other operational units. All operational units can be shut down at any time.

Fires in the direct proximity of the acrolein storage tanks and the acrolein plant can be fought effectively (see 4.2.2).

A further hazard is the release of pressurised hydrogen with self-ignition from pieces of equipment located at a distance of about 30 m. The distance is too great for a hydrogen flame to come into direct contact with components containing acrolein (according to a flame length estimate based on the jet theory assuming unfavourable conditions). The indirect effect of a hydrogen flame as a result of radiation is low since no soot particles can form. Furthermore, the plant can be shut down at any time without any risk. Therefore this hazard can be disregarded.

4.1.4. Environmentally incurred hazards

4.1.4.1. Adjacent plants (see site plan, figure 6.1 and section 1.1.1)

The Deka factory is surrounded on two sides – to the south and the west – by workshops, a pool, the canteen and office buildings, as well as storage and packing plants. These do not represent any hazard for the Deka factory.

Production plants are located to the north and the east. Only minor hazards are to be expected from these plants: the distances are too great. The statement given in 4.1.3 is valid for the emission of toxic substances. Fire and explosion are prevented in the surrounding plants, as in the Deka factory (see 4.1.2.6), by stringent explosion protection measures in compliance with EX-RL. The Deka factory and the surrounding plants all exhibit the same standard of safety.

The X factory presents a specific risk, namely the emission of flammable gases. The X factory is subject to the Ordinance on Major Hazard Control of the Federal Republic of Germany. The most important measure in this case is fast elimination of all ignition sources (extinguishing of the flare, cancellation of any permits which have been issued for work with open flame, see 4.1.2.6).

If the Deka factory is endangered by adjacent plants, the Deka factory is alerted via the block alarm. The block alarm and measures to be taken are discussed in 4.2.3.

4.1.4.2. Traffic

The distance to the Rhine is approximately 800 m; the distance to a public road approximately 250 m. The situation on the factory site is apparent from the site plan (figure 6.1) and section 1.1.1. The only factory road (east-west road) in the vicinity of the Deka factory which is open to traffic is provided with a 10 m broad safety zone. In addition, the Deka factory building containing offices and control room separates the acrolein plant from the road. The distance from the road to the acrolein plant is approximately 30 m. Traffic regulations on factory roads are as follows: 30 km/h. The plant is not in the vicinity of an airport or airfield.

Traffic-incurred hazards can therefore be ruled out.

4.1.4.3. Natural hazards

The plant is situated in an area with low seismic activity (DIN 4149 seismic zone 1). In compliance with the building regulations, stability is assured by the corresponding construction of the foundations and the design.

Danger as a result of flooding is not to be expected as the plant is located above the maximum high-water mark which has been established on the basis of many years' observation.

4.1.5. Sabotage

The plant is situated on a fenced-in site and access to the plant is only granted to authorised persons. The plant is illuminated at night and is checked by guards who make hourly inspection tours. Any persons not employed in the plant must register before entering the plant (registration card system). This satisfactorily rules out sabotage.

4.2. Measures to limit accident consequences

4.2.1. Foundations and supporting structures

Foundations and supporting structures were designed and constructed in compliance with the building regulations. Their stability, which was examined within the scope of the construction permit and the permit issued in compliance with the Federal Law on Pollution Control of the Federal Republic of Germany, is suitable for the anticipated loadings.

4.2.2. Protective measures and safety systems

The collecting tank for the acrolein storage tanks was planned and constructed in compliance with TRbF 110 (see 2.1.2).

The water sprinkling system for the storage tanks primarily serves to cool the tank contents.

Although the four stationary water jets are also used for cooling, they are primarily for fighting fires and for precipitating gases and vapours. They are positioned in such a way (see site plan, figure 6.1) that the acrolein tank store in particular can be easily reached with the water jet from all sides. In the event of a fire in the direct vicinity of the acrolein tanks, they could be cooled effectively. The water jets and related booster pump are dimensioned on the basis of pertinent experience collected by the plant fire brigade.

The two gas warning devices at pumps P 23 A/B enable fast detection of leakages (see 2.1.2 and 4.1.1.1/2).

The number of fire extinguishers specified by the plant fire brigade is available.

When working under difficult conditions, walkie-talkies are used to ensure communication between the plant and the control room.

In compliance with the operating and safety instructions, an adequate quantity of the necessary protective gear is available for the operating personnel. The control room is equipped with fresh air connections and with the necessary fresh air masks. An adequate number of emergency showers and fresh air connections is provided. The emergency plan for incidents including fire and acrolein emissions forms part of the operating and safety instructions.

The teams of the medical department and the plant fire brigade are on duty at all times. The plant is easily accessible to the emergency forces and the fire brigade (see 1.1.3).

The plant fire brigade is alerted by telephone. The south fire station is approximately 1 km away. A time of three minutes will elapse between sounding of the alarm and the arrival of the fire brigade. With the assistance of the plant personnel, it will immediately take measures to fight the accident and to avert danger.

4.2.3. Emergency plans

4.2.3.1. Emergencies initiated by events in the Deka factory

The operating personnel and, if necessary, the plant fire brigade are alerted in compliance with the Deka factory emergency plan. This differentiates between :

- operational emergencies :
  cause : slight to medium leakage at pumps, pipe-work or valves, which can presumably be corrected quickly and does not constitute a hazard for neighbouring plants ;
- small-scale emergency :
  cause : medium-sized product discharge, which cannot be eliminated immediately and which can endanger neighbouring plants ;
- large-scale emergency :
  cause : large product discharge which directly endangers neighbouring plants.

Measures

The fire brigade is responsible for alerting personnel and closing off the surrounding area, in particular the workshops, pool and canteen. The operating personnel follow instructions specified in the operating and safety instructions.

According to the Deka emergency plan, all employees must follow the general instructions listed below :

- close all doors and windows, switch off fans. Eliminate all ignition sources (cigarettes, electrical equipment, welding work and work with open flame) ;
- leave basements and rooms on lower levels ;
- follow the fire brigade's instructions ;
- leave the building if eyes start to water. Use escape routes ;
- do not use elevators ;
- proceed to known assembly points.

4.2.3.2. Emergencies initiated by events in neighbouring plants

Block alarm F 400/G 400 is valid in this case : the Deka factory is alerted :

- by the loud horn of the neighbouring plant ;
- via teleprinter from the central BASF warning system.

Measures in compliance with the emergency plan :

- erection of road blocks by the personnel until arrival of plant security ;
- in the Deka factory :
  - extinguish flare A 750 on building G 400 ;
  - no smoking in any room ;
  - cancellation of any permit for work with an open flame ;
  - close windows and doors, switch off ventilation and air conditioning systems to prevent the ingress of dangerous gases ;
  - leave rooms on lower levels ;
  - do not use elevators ;
  - in general, get away from glass windows. Never observe a fire or a gas release from behind window panes ;
  - stay at your work stations except for persons (e.g. in the laboratory or in offices) who work directly beside windows ;
  - wait to see if an alarm is signalled for your building ;
  - when told to proceed to known assembly points by the fire brigade, use escape routes.

The emergency plans have been agreed on with the competent authorities.

4.2.4. Responsibility

The management of the Environmental Protection and Occupational Health and Safety Division is responsible for the mitigation of accident consequences. Management can be reached at all times via the plant fire brigade, which is always on duty.

4.3. Supplementary measures

4.3.1. Monitoring, maintenance and repair activities

The plant is subject to continuous monitoring in the form of surveillance and checks in the control room and locally in the form of hourly inspection tours through the plant to check for normal operating conditions. Safety-related electrical, measuring and control systems are checked regularly according to the maintenance and inspection plan. Equipment, machines, pipe-work and valves are serviced and repaired as necesssary and on plant shut-down. The pressure vessels are inspected regularly in compliance with the Pressure Vessel Code.

Necessary maintenance and repair work is performed by well-trained specialists in accordance with the state of the art and observing relevant technical codes and standards.

4.3.2. Training of personnel, operating and safety instructions

In compliance with the BASF safety guide-lines, operating personnel must be briefed on the contents of all operating and safety instructions at least once per year. Such training and briefing is based on the operating and safety instructions. On-the-job instruction, which takes special consideration of the consequences of incorrect behaviour, can essentially prevent possible operating errors. The existing process measuring and control safety systems prevent consequences of any operating errors which might still occur.

4.3.3. Documentation

Inspection of the electrical, measuring and control equipment is documented on a special inspection sheet. Regular checking of the plant from the control room is documented in the plant operating log, and the hourly local inspection tour of the plant is documented in a special log.

5. Accident consequences

(Article 7 (1) 5)

The safety systems installed in the plant, which have been described in the course of this report, allow one to conclude that disturbances in the operating sequence can be controlled and that an accident is not to be expected. This is confirmed by experience which has been gained with the handling of acrolein in the Deka factory since 1969.

As a result of the safety measures, an acrolein fire is not to be expected. However, if a fire occurs the measures described in 4.2 are taken to limit its consequences. Furthermore, this is a normal fire of a liquid with relatively low boiling point. Danger and substantial irritation are not to be expected because of the strong thermal lift. An acrolein fire has not occurred to date, either in the plant or in the tank store.

Releases of small quantities of acrolein in the past have troubled employees because of the product's very intense smell and its tendency to cause eyes to water. This effect, however, is limited to a surrounding area amounting to 10-20 m and cannot be regarded as a major hazard. The very low stimulus threshold of the product acts as a built-in warning system. This makes people aware of the danger and rules out unnoticed impact.

Leakages at flanges, pumps, etc., are therefore detected very quickly during the inspection tours and are always restricted to small quantities.

If one nevertheless assumes quite a large leakage of approximately 1 l/h (1-5 drops per second), the affected area is 18 m for the following conditions: immediate evaporation, worst dispersion conditions according to the Air Pollution Control Code (dispersion category 1), limit concentration for effects 2 ppm.

There is good agreement with the above values derived from experience.

Despite implementation of the measures described in 4.1.1.1/2, the filling hose could burst while acrolein is being filled into the tanks. Approximately 5 l, i.e. the contents of the hose and pipe up to the highest point of the pipe (see figure 6.10) are released spontaneously and 1.7 kg evaporate within five minutes. An affected area of 250 m results for the conditions listed above.

Even the release of acrolein into the tank tub, which should not be realistically assumed, does not affect a larger area than rupture of the filling hose. This is because the escaping acrolein is diluted within seconds with water from the water jets which are directed on to the tub and are always ready for operation, thus drastically lowering the vapour pressure. When compared with rupture of the filling hose, the larger evaporation surface of the tub is compensated by the low effective vapour pressure, thus resulting in approximately the same evaporation rates and affected areas.

Precautions have been taken against all of these events: the fire brigade is alerted as scheduled, any plants which may be affected are warned in compliance with the emergency plan. The fire brigade implements on-site emergency measures after five minutes at most (confirmed by numerous drills). The point of leakage is flushed with water and/or covered with foam. This drastically lowers the quantities discharged to the atmosphere (by at least a factor of 10). Water screens are used if necessary.

The affected areas have been established on a purely theoretical basis and are maximum estimates: in each leakage case, the pollutant concentration builds up slowly over minutes and is reduced within minutes by the measures implemented. The worst dispersion condition is seldom encountered and, as has been shown by our experience, cannot occur at all in the factory because of the specific atmospheric (wind direction, wind velocity, thermal lift at sources) and topographical conditions.

One can therefore assume that even if a large quantity of acrolein was unexpectedly released, on-site emergency measures and round-the-clock readiness of the plant fire brigade would limit the disturbance to the plant itself, thus ruling out any effect on the surrounding area.

The Deka factory is situated within a large plant complex. An off-site emergency plan exists for all hazards which could in principle originate from this plant. This plan was drawn up by the competent authorities with the co-operation of plant management and is interlinked with the on-site emergency plans of the plant. If there is any danger from a dispersing pollutant cloud, all emergency plans for the municipal area and all measures to be taken by off-site emergency forces have been specified in advance. Precautions which should be taken by the population in the case of an alarm, and with which the population is familiarised by means of addressed circulars and newspaper articles, are always the same independent of the specific pollutant. No other measures are necessary. In principle, the municipal off-site emergency plan covers any hazards originating from the Deka factory.

Notes

[1] Record of explosion classification, i.e. establishing of hazardous locations.

[2] The Project Media Code contains specifications for the materials and the construction of piping, seals and valves for all media (substances) in the project, i.e. present in the plant, as a function of pressure, temperature and nominal diameter.

[3] Technical data sheets are used for technical descriptions in inquiries and orders for equipment, tanks, pumps, etc. They contain the design data as well as necessary data on materials, dimensions and type.

Appendix 7

Example of
accidents reporting form

(derived from Annex VI
to EC Directive (82/501/EEC))

Information to be supplied to the Commission by the Member States pursuant to Article 11

Report of major accident

Member State:

Authority responsible for report:

Address:

1. General data

   Date and time of the major accident:

   Country, administrative region, etc.:

   Address:

   Type of industrial activity:

2. Type of major accident

   Explosion ☐   Fire ☐   Emission of dangerous substances ☐

   Substance(s) emitted:

3. Description of the circumstances of the major accident

4. Emergency measures taken

5. Cause(s) of major accident

   Known:
   (to be specified)   ☐

   Not known: ☐

   Information will be supplied as soon as possible   ☐

6. Nature and extent of damage

   (a) **Within the establishment**

   – casualties   .... killed

                                                   .... injured

                                                   .... poisoned

   – persons exposed to the major accident   ....

   – material damage   ☐

   – the danger is still present   ☐

   – the danger no longer exists   ☐

(b) **Outside the establishment**

   – casualties   .... killed

                                                           .... injured

                                                           .... poisoned

   – persons exposed to the major accident   ....

   – material damage   ☐

   – damage to the environment   ☐

   – the danger is still present   ☐

   – the danger no longer exists   ☐

7. Medium- and long-term measures, particularly those aimed at preventing the recurrence of similar major accidents (to be submitted as the information becomes available).

—————

Annex VII

STATEMENT RE ARTICLE 8

The member States shall consult one another in the framework of their bilateral relations on the measures required to avert major accidents originating in a notified industrial activity within the meaning of Article 5 and to limit the consequences for man and the environment. In the case of new installations, this consultation shall take place within the time-limits laid down in Article 5(2).

Appendix 8

Land-use near to major hazard works

1. It is generally considered prudent to try to separate works storing and using significant qualities of hazardous materials from nearby centres of population including housing, shopping centres, schools, hospitals, etc.

2. Different countries pursue this objective using arrangements appropriate to their particular legislation. In the United Kingdom, for example, the use of land is controlled through land-use planning legislation where development normally requires specific planning permission from the local authority, which can take account of any adjacent major hazard works.

3. An important consideration is the degree of separation which is necessary. Ideally, one could calculate the worst-case accident occurring at the works and permit development only outside its hazard range. For most countries, and particularly for toxic hazards where the consequences could, at worst, extend for several kilometres, such a policy would blight large areas of land at considerable cost both to the area and the country.

4. An alternative approach is to use the techniques of quantified risk assessment (QRA) to predict the risk (or likelihood of harm) to an occupant of the proposed development, and then to decide whether such a risk is tolerable. This approach requires considerable sophistication in analysis and computation techniques and would be unlikely to be appropriate except where comprehensive major hazard control measures are already in operation.

5. A middle approach, which has been endorsed by the United Kingdom Advisory Committee on Major Hazards, is to try to arrange a separation of developments from major works. This will achieve almost complete protection from the more common but relatively minor accidents and, in addition, worth-while but not complete protection from the severe but very rare major events.

6. Based on this approach, table 8.1. gives suggested approximate separation distances for a range of major hazard works. These distances should be regarded as tentative and would need to be considered under local circumstances to decide on their applicability. Where these distances are considered to be unacceptably large, more detailed assessment work (paragraph 4) may be necessary.

7. *Categorisation of development*

7.1. In deciding on the separation required from a works, it can be helpful to categorise the proposed development. This will enable individual development decisions to be made within the framework of a consistent approach.

7.2. Categories of development can take account of a number of relevant factors in deciding on whether to permit development, e.g. amount of time individuals spend in the development, ease of implementing an emergency plan, vulnerability of occupants of the development (old people more vulnerable to thermal radiation).

One broad categorisation which has been widely used is based on three general categories:

Category A: Residential, including houses, hotels, flats;

Category B: Industrial, including factories (unless they have high-density employment), warehouses;

Category C: Special, including schools, hospitals, old peoples' homes.

Other types of developments can then be added to the most appropriate of these categories, e.g. theatres/cinemas and shopping centres could be included as Category A.

7.3. In table 8.1., *and as a first approximation*, the separation distances given should be considered as follows:

(a) within the separation distance – no Category C development;

(b) within about two-thirds of the distance – no Category A development;

(c) no restriction of Category B development.

Table 8.1.   Suggested approximate separation distances for major hazard works

Substance	Largest tank size (t)	Separation distance (para. 7.3.) (m)
Liquefied petroleum gas, such as propane and butane, held at a pressure greater than 1.4 bar absolute	25- 40	300
	41- 80	400
	81-120	500
	121-300	600
	More than 300	1 000
	25 or more, only in cylinders or small bulk tanks of up to 5 te capacity	100
Liquefied petroleum gas, such as propane and butane, held under refrigeration at a pressure of 1.4 bar absolute or less	50 or more	1 000
Phosgene	2 or more	1 000
Chlorine	10-100	1 000
	More than 100	1 500
Hydrogen fluoride	10 or more	1 000
Sulphur trioxide	15 or more	1 000
Acrylonitrile	20 or more	250
Hydrogen cyanide	20 or more	1 000
Carbon disulphide	20 or more	250
Ammonium nitrate and mixtures of ammonium nitrate where the nitrogen content derived from the ammonium nitrate exceeds 28 % of the mixture by weight	500 or more	See note [1]
Liquid oxygen	500 or more	500
Sulphur dioxide	20 or more	1 000
Bromine	40 or more	600
Ammonia (anhydrous or as solution containing more than 50 % by weight of ammonia)	More than 100	1 000
Hydrogen	2 or more	500
Ethylene oxide	5-25	500
	More than 25	1 000
Propylene oxide (atmospheric pressure storage) (stored under pressure)	5 or more	250
	5-25	500
	More than 25	1 000
Methyl isocyanate	1	1 000
Classes of substances not specifically named		
1. Gas or any mixture of gases which is flammable in air and is held in the installation as a gas (except low-pressure gasholders)	15 or more	500
2. A substance or any mixture of substances which is flammable in air and is normally held in the installation above its boiling point (measured at 1 bar absolute) as a liquid or as a mixture of liquid and gas at a pressure of more than 1.4 bar absolute	25- 40	300
	41- 80	400
	81-120	500
	121-300	600
	More than 300	1 000
	25 or more only in cylinder or small bulk tanks or up to 5 te capacity	1 000
3. A liquefied gas or any mixture of liquefied gases which is flammable in air, has a boiling point of less than 0°C (measured at 1 bar absolute) and is normally held in the installation under refrigeration or cooling at a pressure of 1.4 bar absolute or less	50 or more	1 000
4. A liquid or any mixture of liquids not included in items 1-3 above which has a flashpoint of less than 21°C	10 000 or more	250

[1] For bagged ammonium nitrate stored in stacks of 300 t (maximum) a separation distance of 600 m is appropriate. For loose ammonium nitrate, the separation distance is given by—

$$600 \left\{ \frac{\text{stack size (t)}}{300} \right\} 1/3.$$